365 BRAIN BUSTERS

First published by Parragon in 2010

Parragon
Queen Street House
4 Queen Street
Bath BA1 1HE, UK

Content and Design by quadrum
Quadrum Solutions, Mumbai, India
www.quadrumltd.com • Tel: 91-22-24968212

ISBN: 978-1-4454-0643-5

Printed in China

EXERCISE AND TRAIN YOUR MIND
WITH THIS FANTASTIC COLLECTION!

Bath • New York • Singapore • Hong Kong • Cologne • Delhi
Melbourne • Amsterdam • Johannesburg • Auckland • Shenzhen

INTRODUCTION

Challenge, stimulate, and exercise your brain with this brand new collection of puzzles. It's the perfect way to keep your mind in shape whilst having lots of fun too. Packed with puzzles including logic tests, number and letter games, picture puzzles, and many more! All 365 puzzles are in full-color, with mixed levels of difficulty. Some of the puzzles you will find easy to do, others you may find more of a challenge so may take you longer to complete. However much time you have to spare, you can choose to do a puzzle a day or pick a few to do at a time—the choice is yours!

Many of the puzzles entries are accompanied by fascinating facts, items of trivia, and interesting quotes from some of the greatest minds in history. So along with stimulating your brain and having fun, you may learn something new or be inspired by a quote.

365 Brain Busters is the ultimate way to put your brain through its paces in a fun and entertaining way. Take the challenge, boost your brain power, and enjoy the benefits of a mentally agile mind.

“*There is a foolish corner in the brain of the wisest man.*”
Aristotle

“Puzzles are like songs–a good puzzle can give you all the pleasure of being duped that a mystery story can. It has surface innocence, surprise, the revelation of a concealed meaning, and the catharsis of solution.”

Stephen Sondheim

HOW TO USE THIS BOOK

365 Brain Busters gives you a complete mental workout with lots of challenging puzzles, as well as fascinating facts and interesting quotes.

Puzzle number This book contains 365 puzzles designed to challenge your mind.

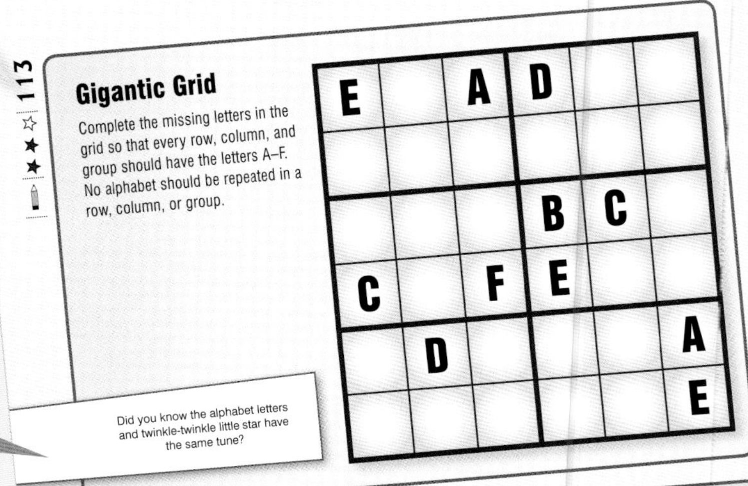

113
Gigantic Grid
Complete the missing letters in the grid so that every row, column, and group should have the letters A–F. No alphabet should be repeated in a row, column, or group.
Did you know the alphabet letters and twinkle-twinkle little star have the same tune?

Facts Many of the puzzles are accompanied by a fascinating fact or item of trivia to inform and entertain you.

Match the Bucket
There are buckets with different designs in a shop. You need to identify the bucket that matches the unfolded one.
68

Items you will need
Some puzzles may require some basic equipment and these are listed here.

 PEN

 PAPER

Difficulty Use this star guide to tell you the difficulty level of each puzzle. You may solve 'Easy' puzzles quite quickly but the 'Hard' puzzles may provide you with more of a challenge.

115

Identify the Pack of Cards

Each triangle has three playing cards placed in it. You can find pairs for triangles with similar placement of cards. However, one triangle does not have a pair. Find the odd triangle.

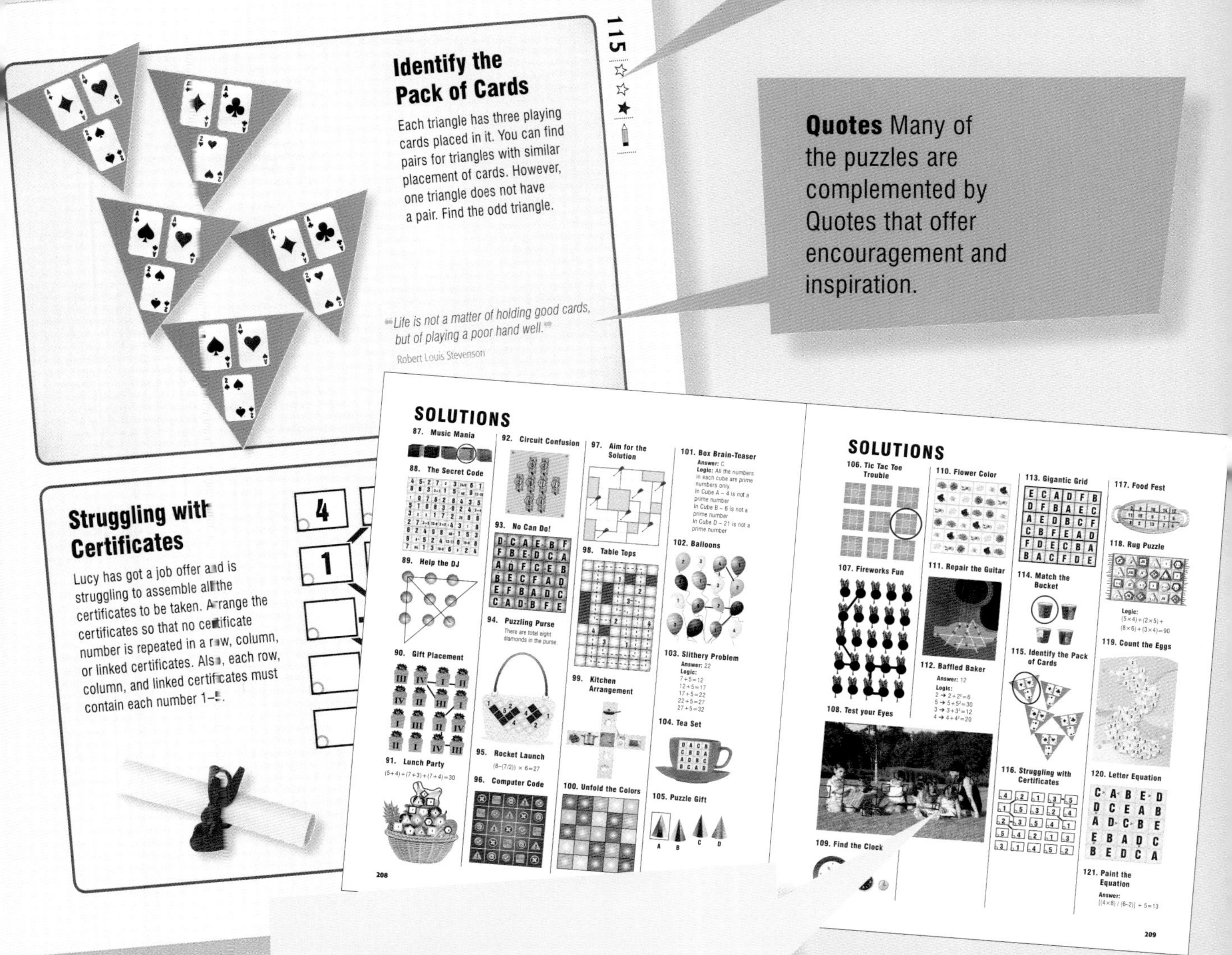

Quotes Many of the puzzles are complemented by Quotes that offer encouragement and inspiration.

"Life is not a matter of holding good cards, but of playing a poor hand well."

Robert Louis Stevenson

Struggling with Certificates

Lucy has got a job offer and is struggling to assemble all the certificates to be taken. Arrange the certificates so that no certificate number is repeated in a row, column, or linked certificates. Also, each row, column, and linked certificates must contain each number 1–5.

SOLUTIONS

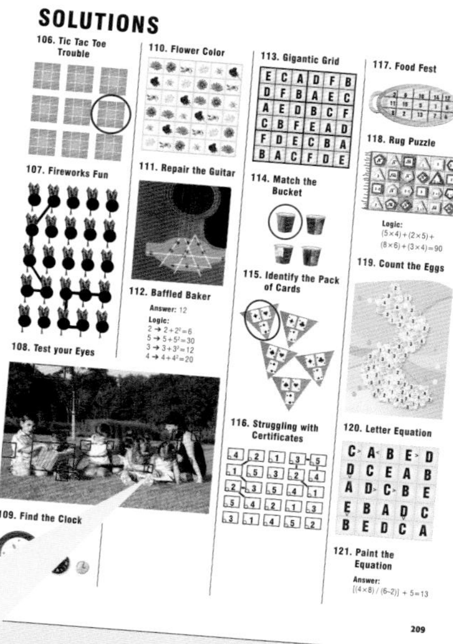

Solutions Full color solutions and explanations are found at the back of the book so that you can check that you've completed the puzzle correctly or get help if you're stuck! See pages 203–224.

1

Disco Light

You need to fill the white spaces and arrange the six colors in such a way that each row and column has all six of them. Take care that no color is repeated and also should not be repeated in the smaller groups of six squares.

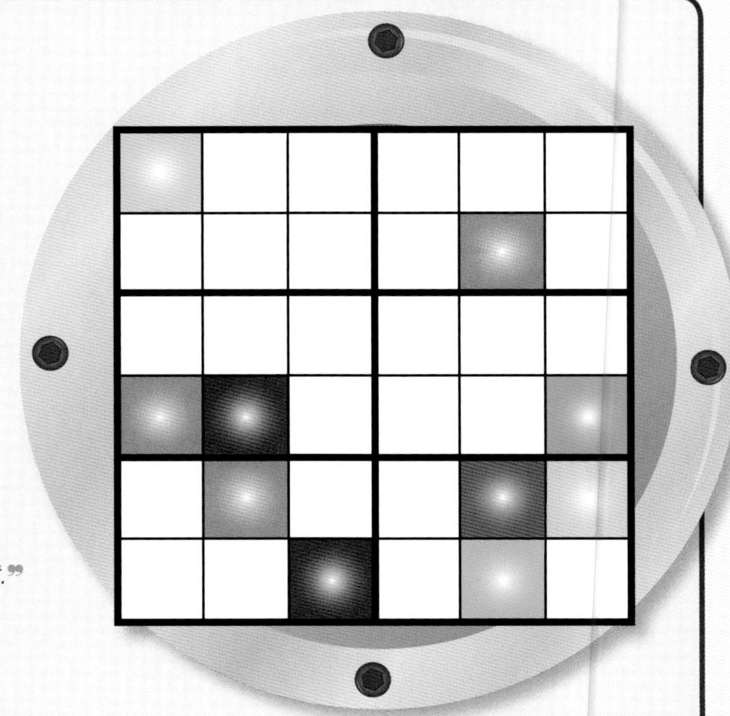

"We are each gifted in a unique and important way. It is our privilege and our adventure to discover our own special light."

Mary Dunbar

2

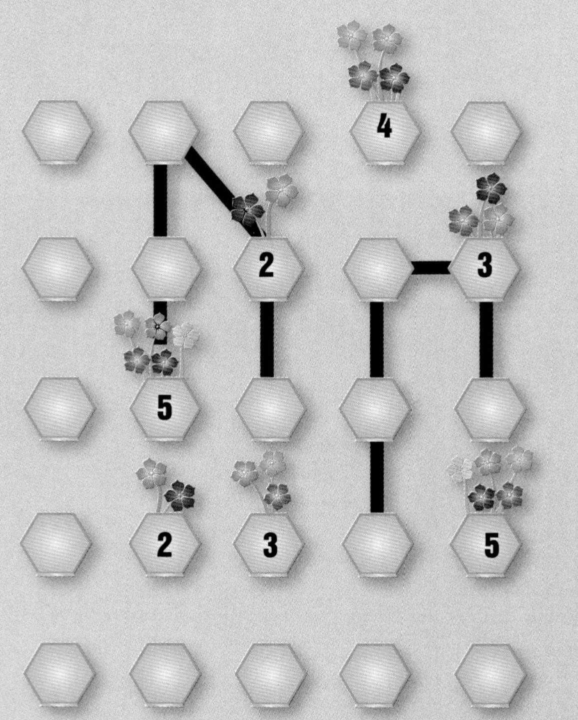

Flower Power

There are 25 vases and every vase has the numbers 1–5 written on it indicating the number of flowers in it. You have to arrange the vases so that every row and column has all five numbers. In addition to this, the vases that are joined with lines should not have any repeated numbers on them.

Did you know that there are over 15,000 species of roses cultivated across the world?

Find the Missing Block 3

Can you work out which cube from A, B, C and D will fill the empty box?

8	3	14
9	20	11
6	17	12

9	2	4
7	17	10
13	15	8

5	3	2
1	9	8
7	6	4

9	4	5
1	6	8
11	2	13

A

9	14	7
2	15	8
6	1	2

B

9	14	7
2	15	13
8	1	6

C

10	2	3
5	20	7
17	18	10

D

Odd Shape Out 4

Each shape appears only once apart from one which appears twice. Can you find the odd one?

"The soul never thinks without a picture."

Aristotle

5

Train Passkey

You're going on a holiday, and your friends have hidden gifts for you in two compartments. You need to find the passkey to get your gifts. Use the existing numbers on the compartments to find the missing numbers.

The world's busiest railway station is believed to be Shinjuke Station, Tokyo which is used by 3.22 million people everyday.

6

Score Card

Each square represents the points scored by a swimmer. The score card is currently incomplete. You need to fill up the score card by entering numbers in each empty cell with the help of the more or less signs specified. Every row and every column should have numbers 1–6. No number should be repeated in a row or column.

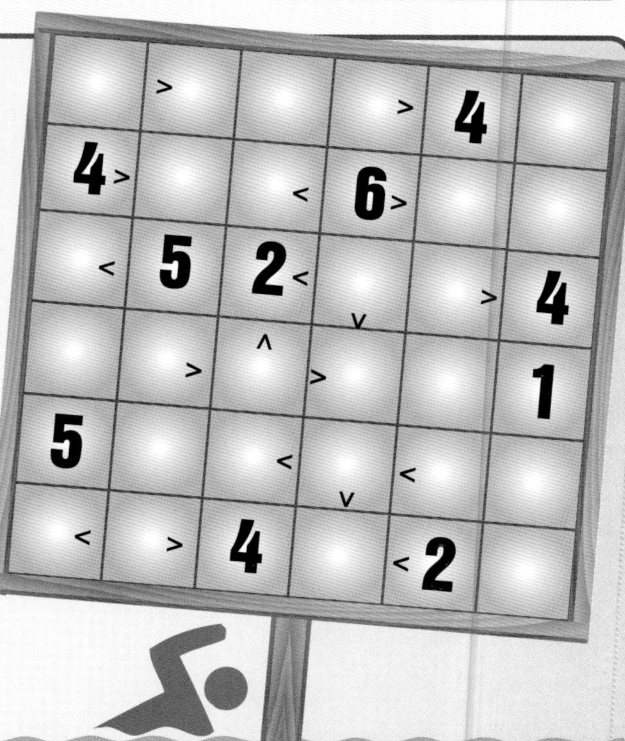

"If you want to learn to swim jump into the water. On dry land no frame of mind is ever going to help you."

Bruce Lee

Kite Flying

Here is a kite with a new design printed on it. Each block has different shapes and there are numbers inside each shape. Add the figure inside the shape to the number of edges the shape has. Find six adjacent blocks which total 58.

"Imagination is the highest kite that one can fly."
Lauren Bacall

7

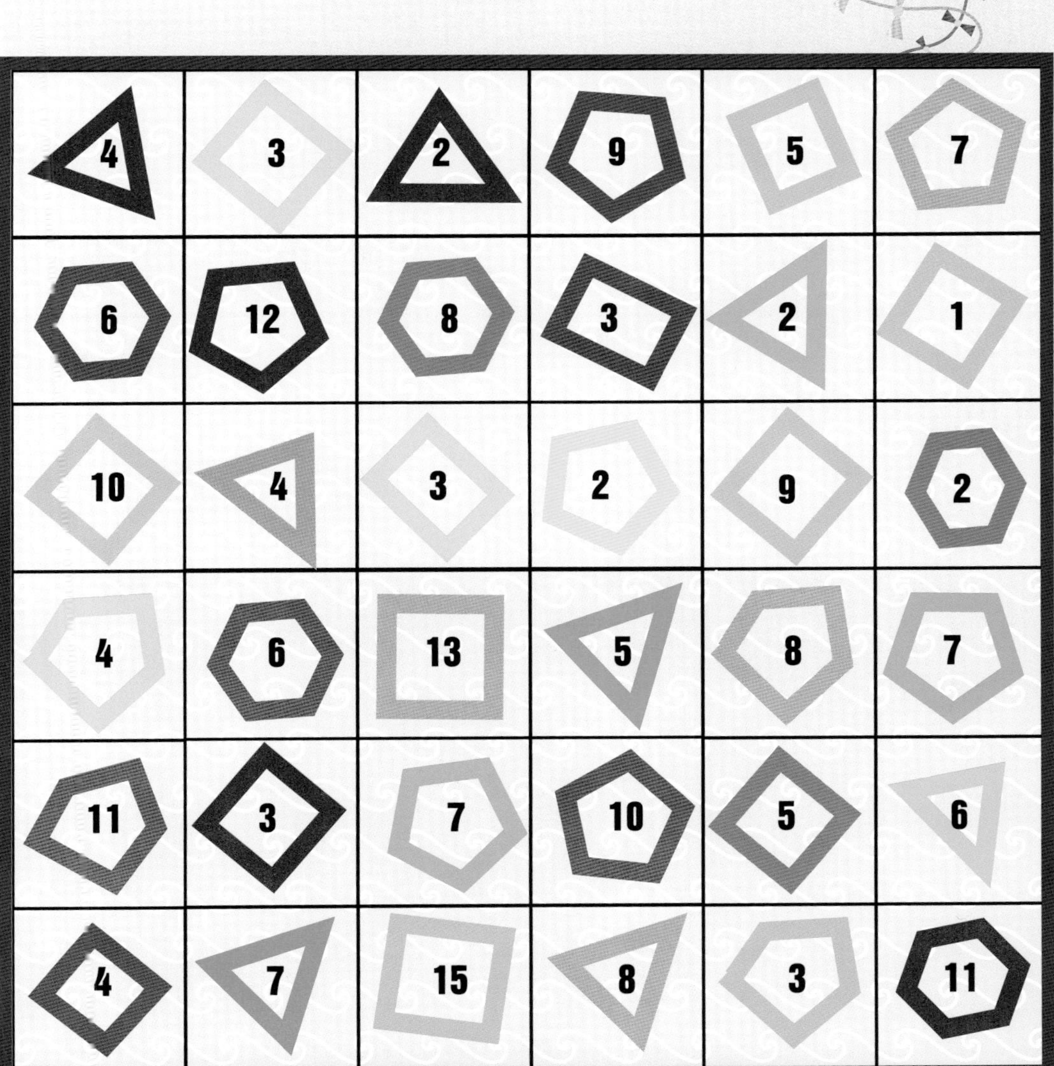

8

Alpha Add

Every row and every column in the puzzle should have the letters A–I. No letter should be repeated in a row or column.

	F			G	H		D	E
	D		F		I			
H			C					
G								
B	H			E				C
	C		B			H		D
		C					G	
					C			
A			I			D		

9

Tricky Triad

Find the missing numbers so that the numbers in each pair of triangles add up to the number in the triangle directly above them.

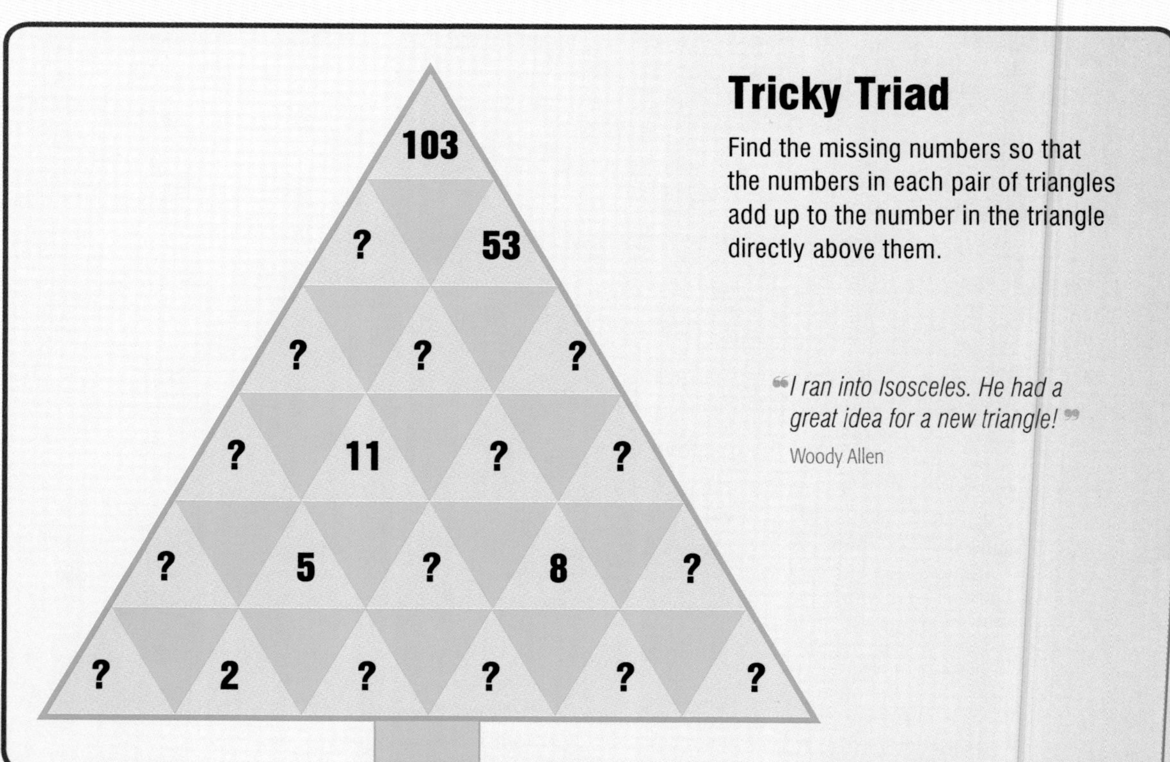

"I ran into Isosceles. He had a great idea for a new triangle!"

Woody Allen

10

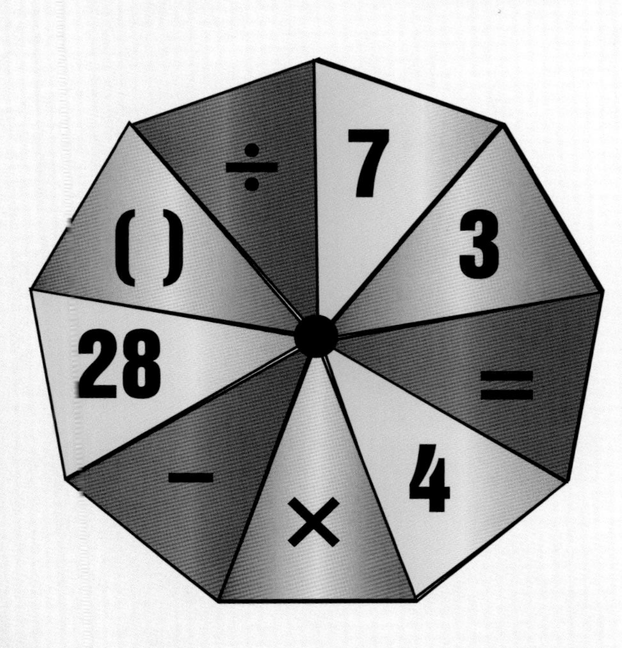

Aptitude Test

You need to create an equation using each number only once to get 14 as the result. You can use the mathematical signs in any combination and as many times as required.

"I didn't fail the test, I just found 100 ways to do it wrong."

Benjamin Franklin

11

Smile Please

The puzzle has equal number of rows and columns with some cells blocked. There are also groups of cells that have been highlighted. You need to insert smileys in such a way that each row, each column and each group of cells has only one smiley in it.

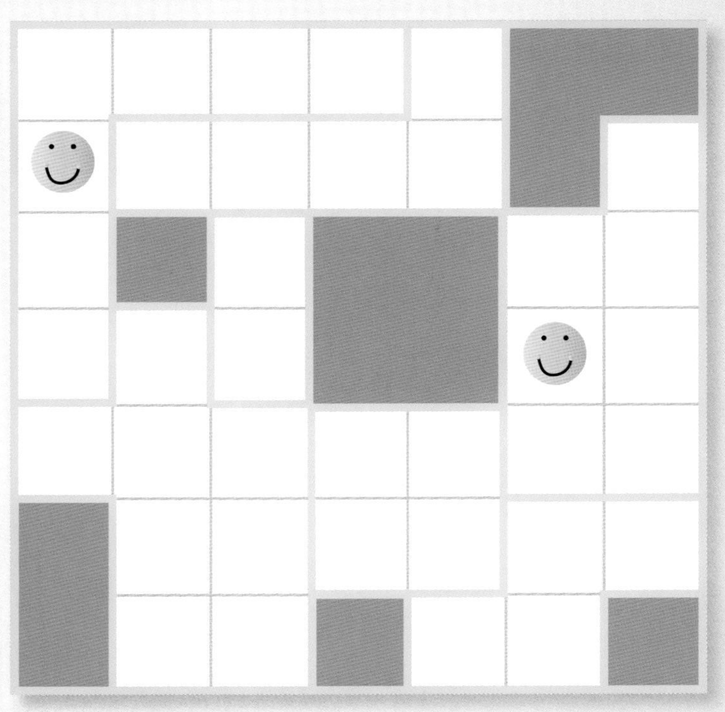

When you smile you use about 53 muscles and release endorphins, the chemical found in the brain that makes people happy.

12

Paired Patterns

The pentagons have five patterns in them. Each one has a pair, except for one. Find the odd one out.

13

Complete the Flower

Based on the two complete flowers, can you work out the number that the third flower should have in its center?

"The flowers of late winter and early spring occupy places in our hearts well out of proportion to their size."

Gertrude S. Wister

Number Connection

14

The puzzle has numbers in pairs. You need to join each pair with a line without crossing lines for any other connections. The lines you draw cannot pass through blocks grouped into one.

			4							
								5		
					3					
					1					
			3		2	4				
							1	2		
								5		

"If people do not believe that mathematics is simple, it is only because they do not realize how complicated life is."

John Louis

Egg Equation

15

A bird has laid eggs in its nest, of which all are broken apart from three. The number in each egg indicates the number of eggs that are broken around that particular egg. Shade the broken eggs to find the three that are not broken.

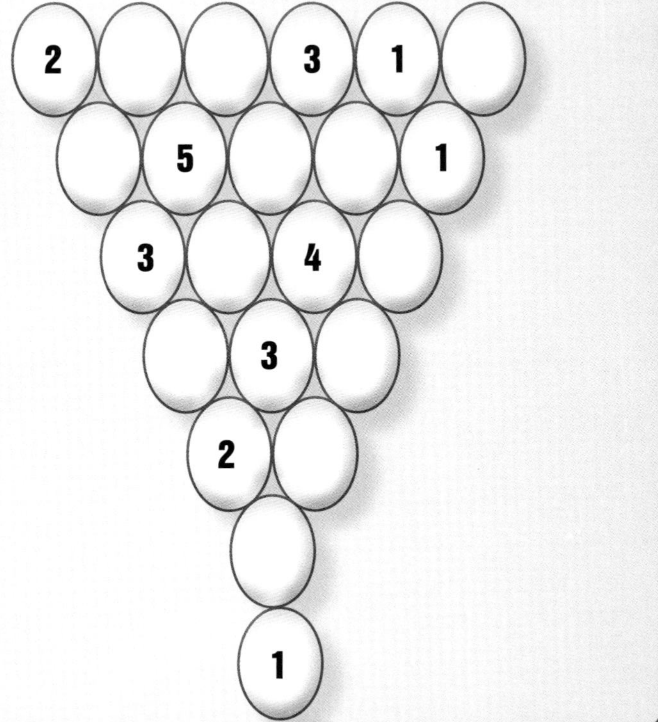

"The key to everything is patience. You get the chicken by hatching the egg, not by smashing it."

Arnold H. Glasgow

16 ☆☆★

Chain Relation

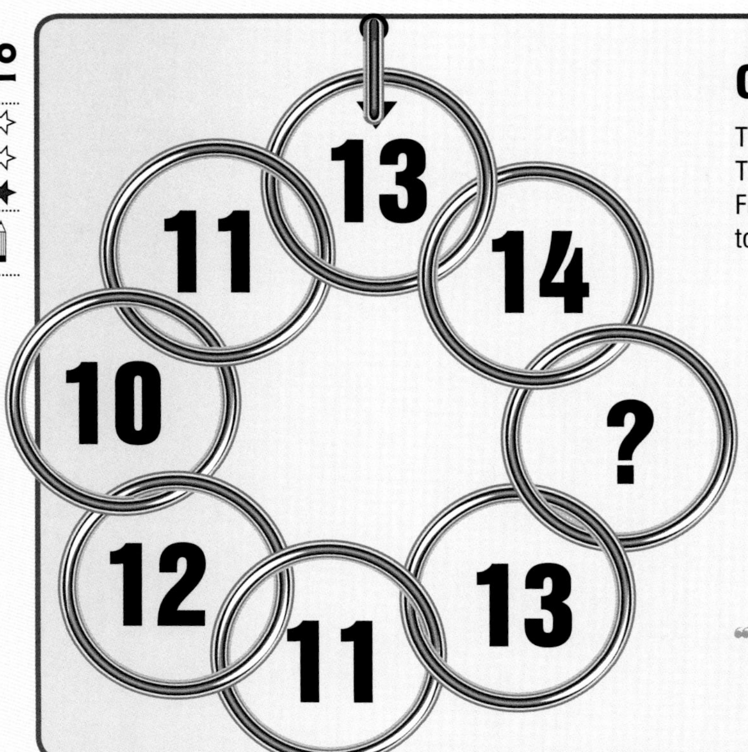

This bracelet has a chain of numbers. The arrow shows the starting number. Find the relation between the numbers to find the missing number.

"A chain is no stronger than its weakest link, and life is after all a chain."

William James

17 ☆☆★

Circuit Connection

The numbers on Granny's phone are lost. Arrange the numbers 1–9 in such a way that no consecutive number is together or in the same line.

Did you know that Alexander Graham Bell, the inventor of the telephone, also invented the metal detector and hydrofoils?

Number Connection

18 ☆☆★

While driving, your car breaks down. The connections between some parts of your car are lost. These disconnected parts are represented by numbers. Join each number with its pair to get the parts connected again. Your lines cannot pass through the shaded blocks.

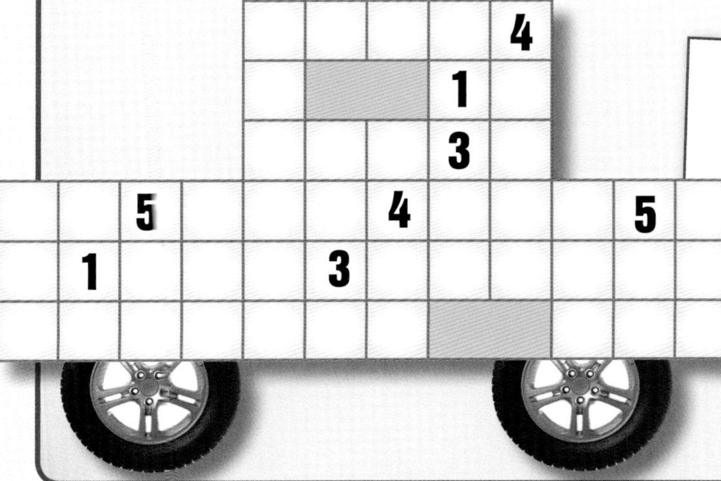

Did you know that the world's longest traffic hold-up was 110 miles long, between Paris and Lyon on the French Autoroute in 1980?

Shape and Color Shuffle

19 ★★★

This puzzle has five colors and five shapes. Every row and column should have each shape and each color in it. Insert the shapes in such a way that none are repeated in a row, column or diagonally. Each shape should also be represented in the five given colors.

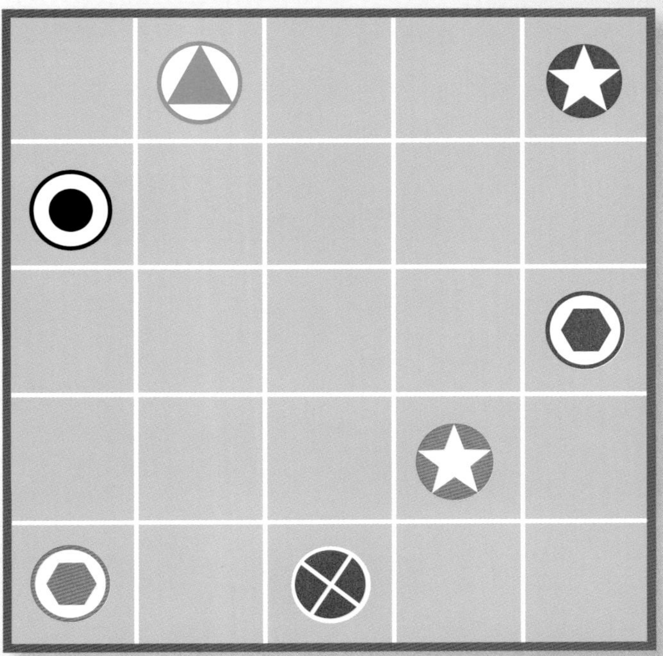

"Forming and breaking in the sky, I fancy all shapes are there; temple, mountain, monument, spire; ships rigged out with sails of fire, and blown by the evening air."

J.K. Hoyt

20 ★★★

Drawer Code

The drawer has confidential office documents that are required for a meeting. Open the third drawer by entering the missing code number. You can crack the code by using consecutive prime numbers.

"Far and away the best prize that life offers is the chance to work hard at work worth doing."

Theodore Roosevelt

21 ☆☆★

Photo Frame

You need to join these eight dots to draw a photo frame. However you cannot lift your pen. Can you do this by forming two squares and four triangles?

"Unlike any other visual image, a photograph is not a rendering, an imitation or an interpretation of its subject, but actually a trace of it."

John Berger

22

Charity Drive

A charity drive has been organized. Each envelope represents the amount of money donated by each person. Can you find a relation between the amounts of money to work out the amount in the last envelope?

$3 $11 $29 $67 $?

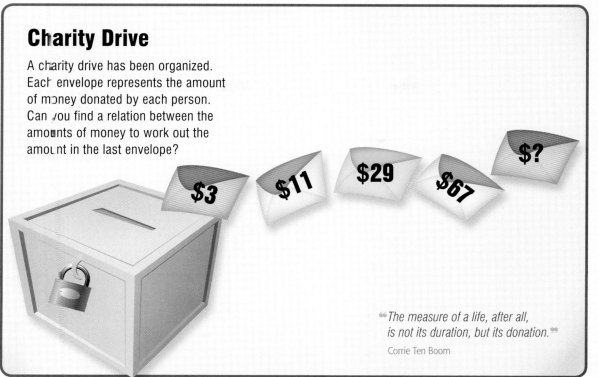

"The measure of a life, after all, is not its duration, but its donation."

Corrie Ten Boom

23

Find the Missing Fruits and Vegetables

This photograph is divided into eight parts. Some parts got lost and only four were found, can you identify which four parts are still missing.

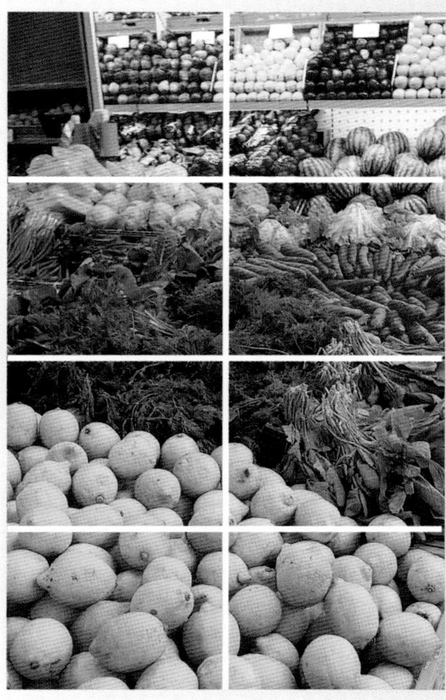

"An onion can make people cry but there's never been a vegetable that can make people laugh."

Will Rogers

24

Prism Pairs

Here is a handbag with a pattern of prisms on it. There is also an unfolded prism displaying its various sides. Identify the prism on the handbag that matches the unfolded one.

Prisms are named for the shape of their bases. A cuboid or rectangular prism has a rectangular base.

25

Secret Star

Find the secret number in the last star. Use the numbers at the corner of the stars to form the central number in the same way in all three cases.

"Aim for the moon. If you miss, you may hit a star."

W. Clement Stone

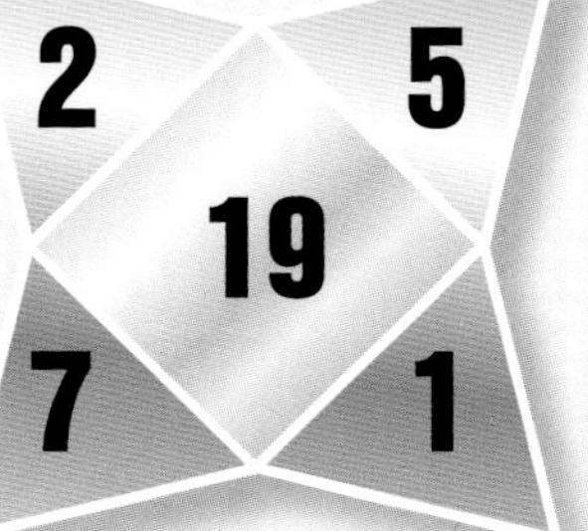

Bricks in their most primitive form were hardened by being dried in the sun.

26

Baffling Bricks

Find the missing numbers so that each pair of bricks totals to form the brick directly above them.

50

? 23

? ? ?

? 6 7 ?

? 2 ? ? ?

27

Dream Land

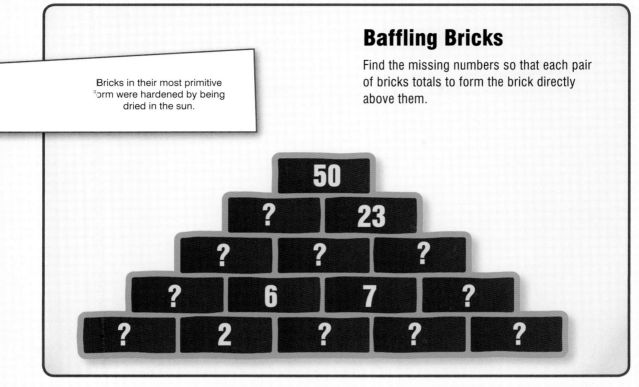

Insert the cloud icon in the chart so that each row, column, and group of cells has only one cloud icon in it.

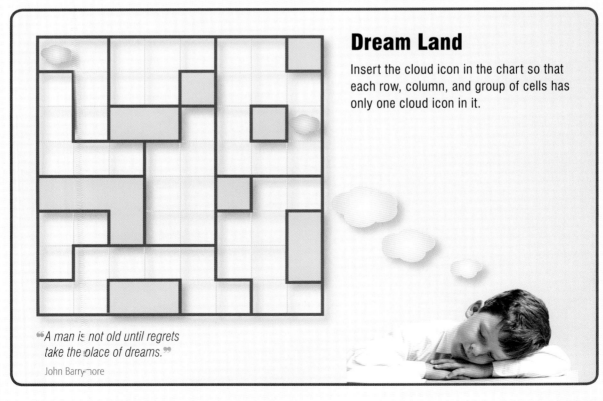

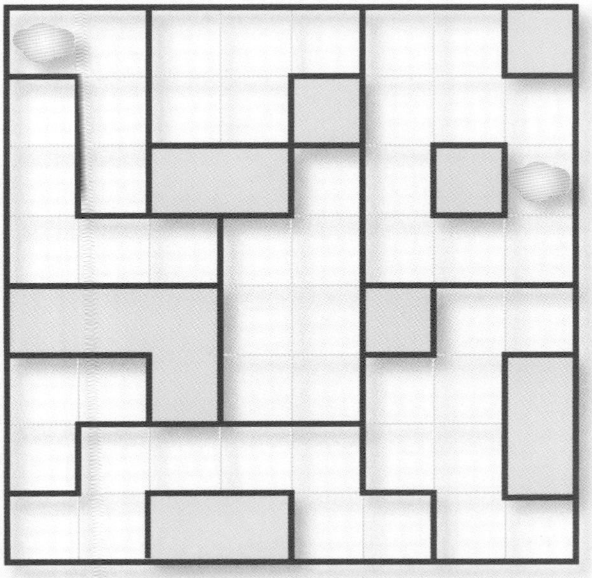

"A man is not old until regrets take the place of dreams."

John Barrymore

28

Match the Swimming Rings

Only one of the floats is unique.
All the others have an exact double.
Can you find the unique one?

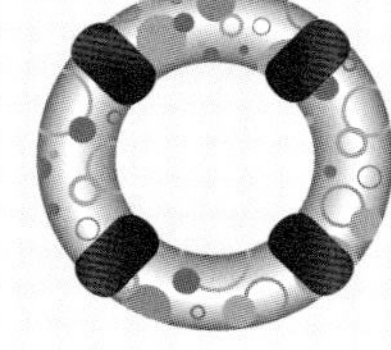

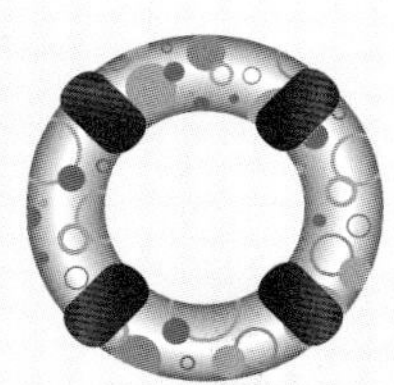

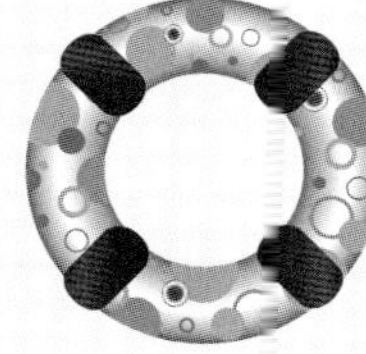

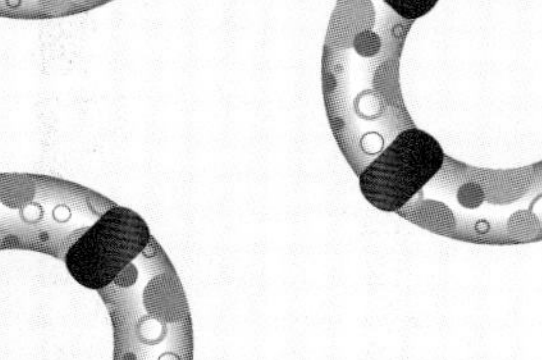

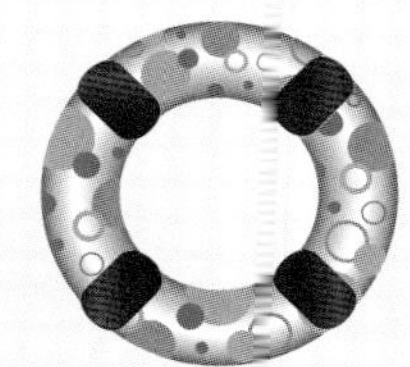

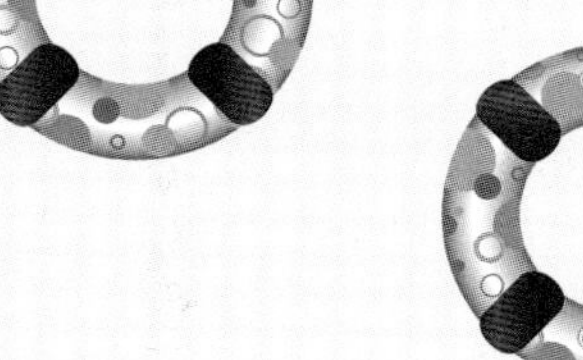

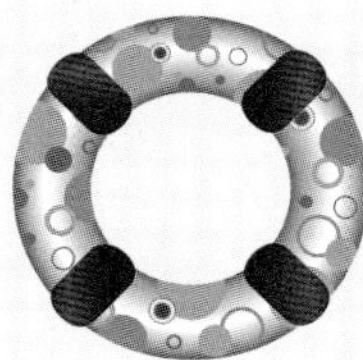

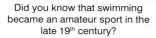

Did you know that swimming became an amateur sport in the late 19th century?

29

Candy Confusion

Find the missing numbers on the candy wrapper. Use the more or less signs to help you find the missing numbers. Every row and every column should have numbers 1–4. No number should be repeated in a row or column.

"Candy is dandy but liquor is quicker."
Ogden Nash

30 ★★★

Ice Cream Equations

Create an equation with the different numbers and mathematical signs given on the cone to get 10 as the result. Each number can be used only once. You can use the mathematical signs in any combination and as many times as required.

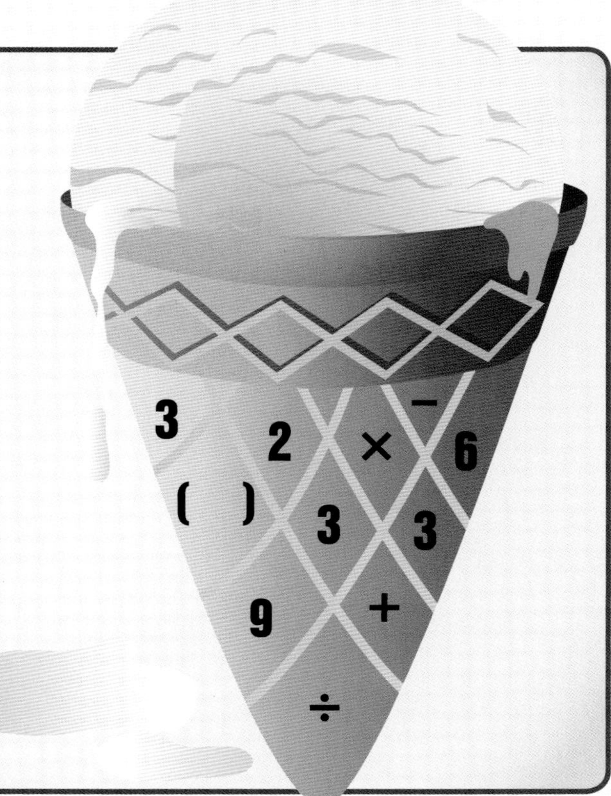

Did you know that the major ingredient in ice cream is air?

31 ☆★★

Ball Game

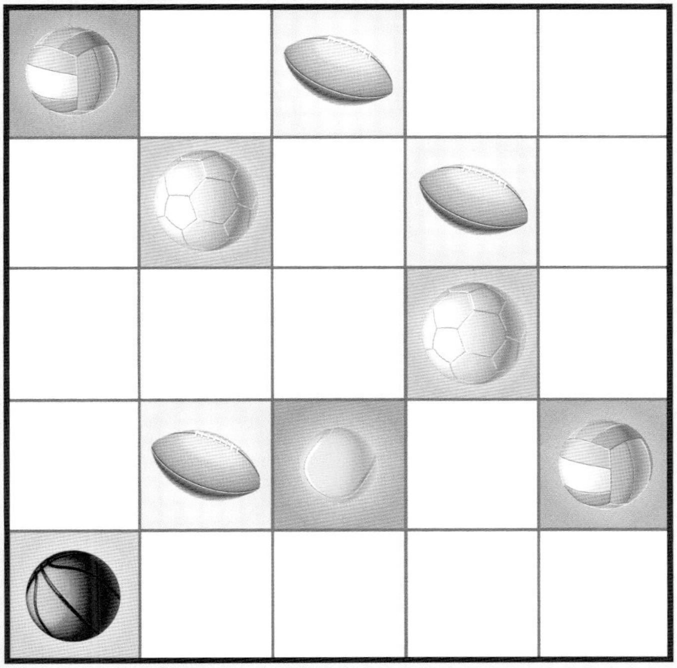

Place the sports items on the shelf in such a way that every row and column has each item and color in it. No item or color should be repeated.

"Competition is the spice of sports; but if you make spice the whole meal you'll be sick."

George Leonard

32

Birthday Buzz

These candles represent your friends' birthdays.
Can you work out the missing last two dates?

It is believed that the Greeks started the tradition of birthday candles.

33

Complete the Sequence

Can you work out which cube from A, B, C and D will fill the empty box?

3 is the only prime number followed by a square.

5	15	5
8	2	15
12	8	5

1	5	5
8	2	1
2	4	5

13	2	4
4	7	8
2	10	7

A

3	7	2
6	5	1
3	2	9

B

1	8	6
10	4	6
4	3	8

C

3	6	7
9	2	5
4	8	6

D

11	6	4
7	10	4
3	5	13

34

Unfold the Scroll

The scroll has multiple shapes with a letter in it. Each letter has a number in the alphabet, for eg. A=1, B=2. You have to multiply the number of the letter with the number of the edges of the shape the letter is in. Can you find the three adjacent boxes which adds up to 100?

Did you know that scrolls were the first form of editable record for keeping texts, used in Eastern Mediterranean and Ancient Egyptian Civilizations?

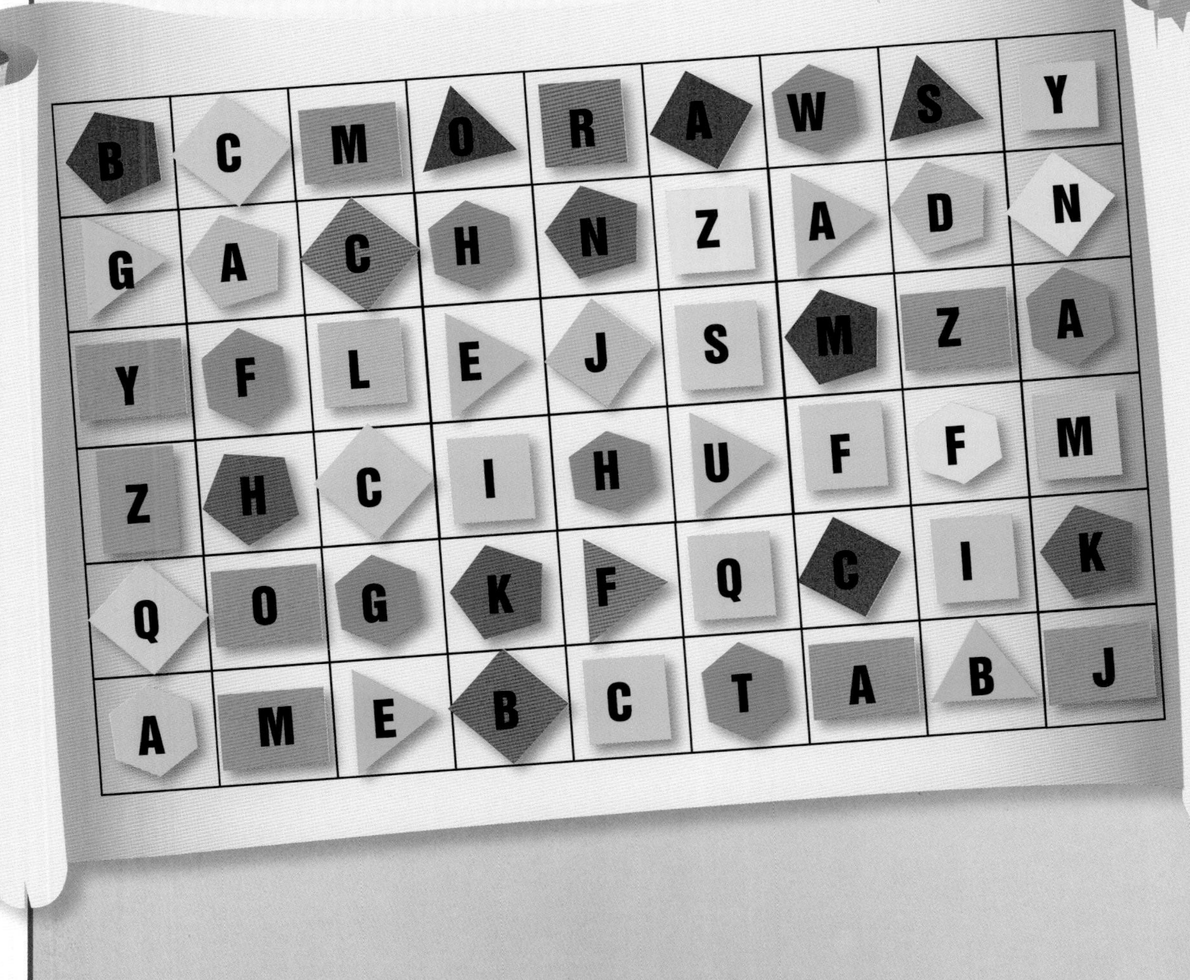

35 ★★★

Crack the Fireworks

Use the numbers at the corner of the fireworks to form the central number in the same way in all three cases. Find the number that should replace the question mark for the third item.

"I guess we all like to be recognized not for one piece of fireworks, but for the ledger of our daily work."

Neil Armstrong

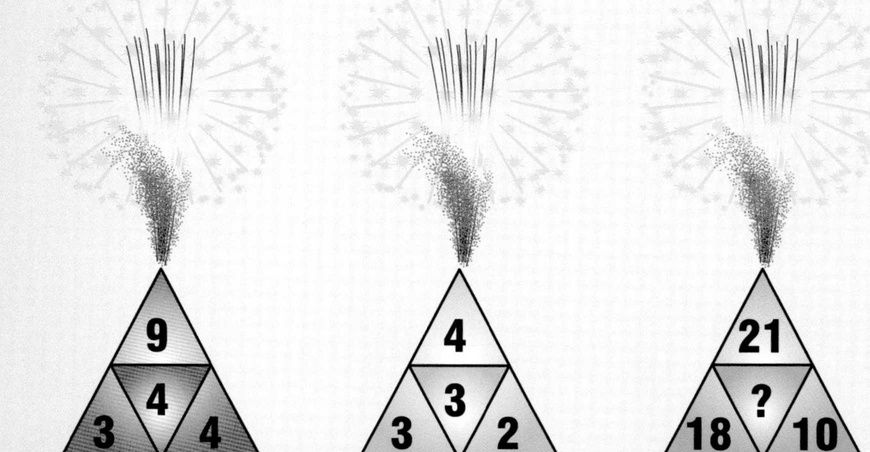

36 ★★★

Wrack your Brains!

Fill the missing numbers on the puzzle using the more or less signs. Every row, column and highlighted group should have the numbers 1–9, without any repetition.

3 <		^	7 <					1
	4					< 3	^ 5	
		> 5		4 >			<	
<		8 v		<	>			
7 v			1	6 v	9		^ 8	v 5
			< 5					9
>		9	3 <			v 2	v	
		<	4	5	1	9		<
^		< 4		2 <			<	

"Mathematics possesses not only truth, but also supreme beauty."

Bertrand Russell

37

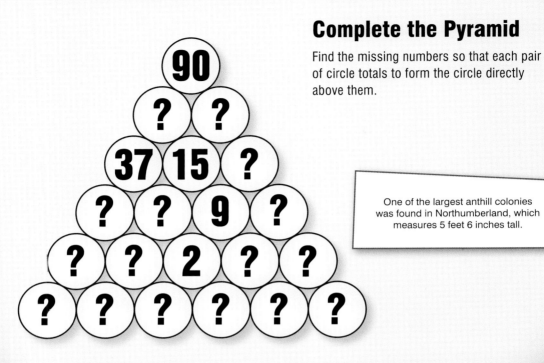

Complete the Pyramid

Find the missing numbers so that each pair of circle totals to form the circle directly above them.

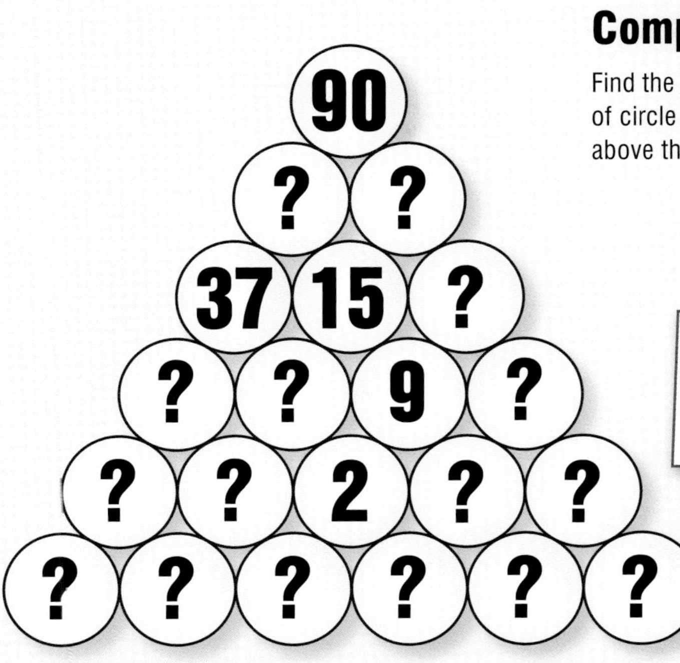

One of the largest anthill colonies was found in Northumberland, which measures 5 feet 6 inches tall.

38

Snowflakes

The puzzle has 12 dots arranged in 3 rows and 4 columns.
Join all the dots with five lines without lifting the pen or pencil.

"Every mile is two in winter."

George Herbert

39

Identify the Pen Stand

There are different pen stands kept on your office desk. Also, there is one unfolded pen stand. Identify which pen stand matches the unfolded one without turning the unfolded pen stand upside down.

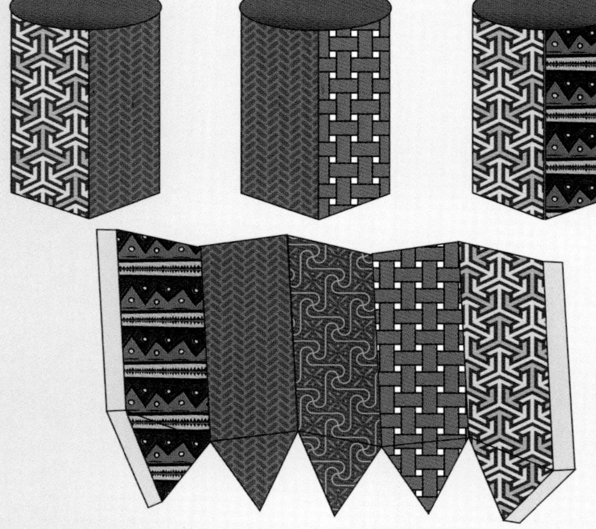

"Beneath the rule of men entirely great, the pen is mightier than the sword."

Robert Bulwer-Lytton

40

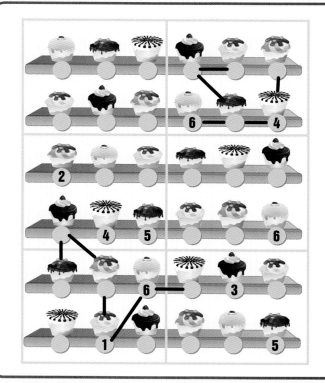

Number the Cup Cakes

Number the six types of cup cakes so that no same number is repeated in a row, column or group. Also, each row, column, group, and linked cup cakes should have each number 1–6.

"A compromise is the art of dividing a cake in such a way that everyone believes he has the biggest piece."

Ludwig Erhard

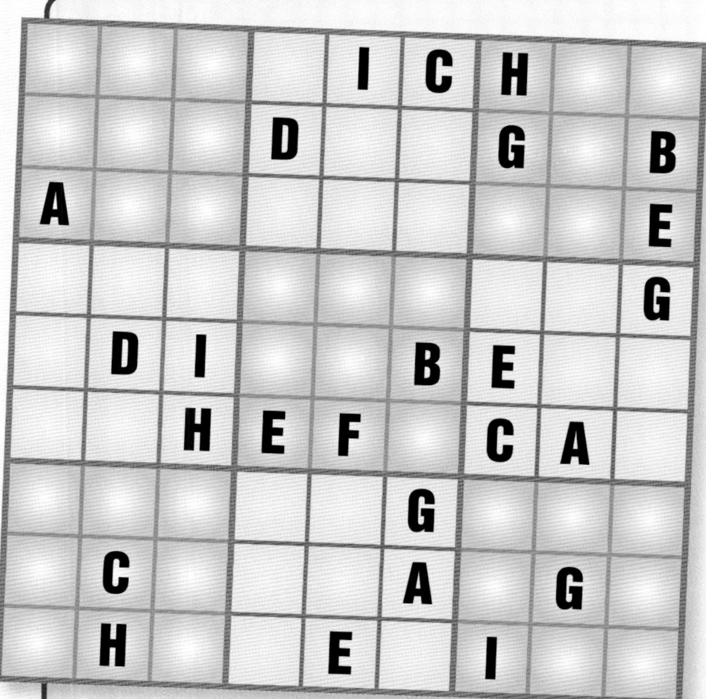

41

Alpha Addle

Find the missing letters in the box. Every row, column and group should have the letters A–I. No letter should be repeated in a row, column, or group.

> "Reading is a discount ticket to everywhere."
>
> Mary Schmich

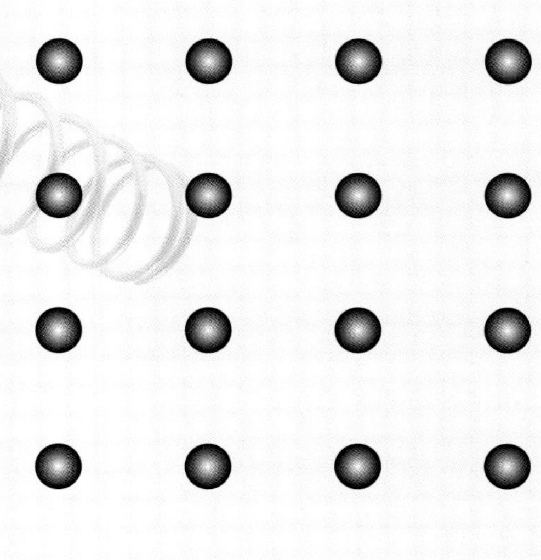

42

Create a Spring

Your friend has a wire that needs to be bent to form a spring. You have to join all 16 dots using 3 arcs without lifting your pen or pencil.

Did you know that a resilient tree branch can be used as a spring?

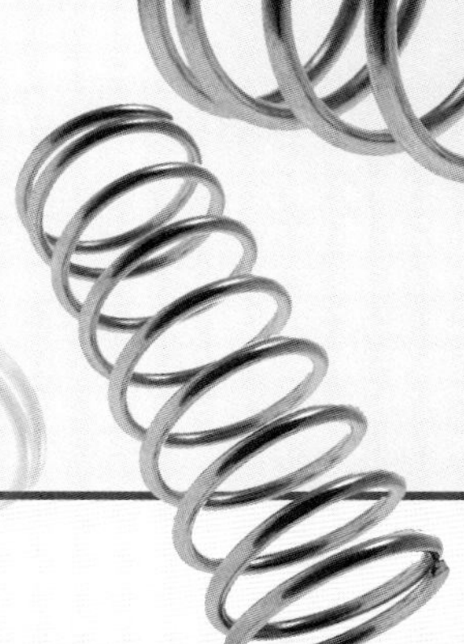

43

Book Management

The library has multiple books that need to be arranged on a shelf. Ensure that no books with consecutive numbers are placed next to each other. Also, books of the same color must not be placed next to another. Find the way to arrange the books.

"You know you've read a good book when you turn the last page and feel a little as if you have lost a friend."

Paul Sweeney

44

Colorful Cubes

In the sequence below, which of the numbered alternatives, A, B, C, or, D, should replace the question mark?

"We are like chameleons, we take our hue and the Color of our moral character, from those who are around us."

John Locke

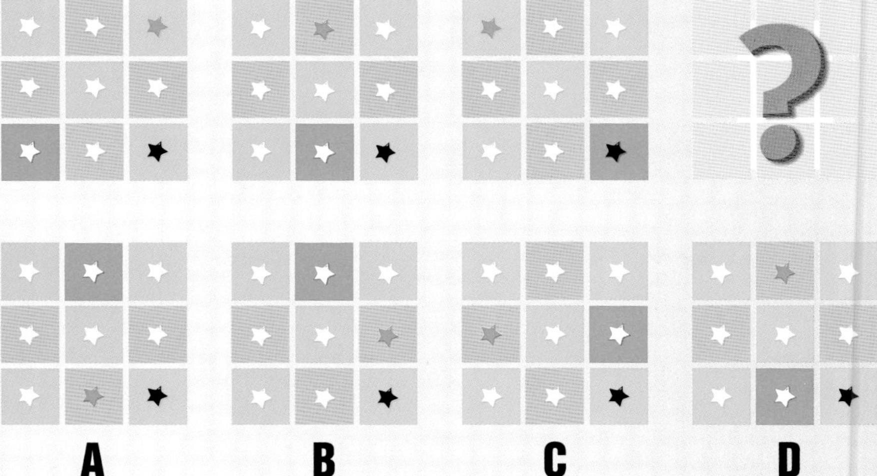

45

Puzzling Hot Air Balloon

The unique hot air balloon has multiple blocks. Each block has different shapes and numbers. Calculate the number inside each shape and add it with the number of edges around it. Find 3 adjacent blocks that add up to 30.

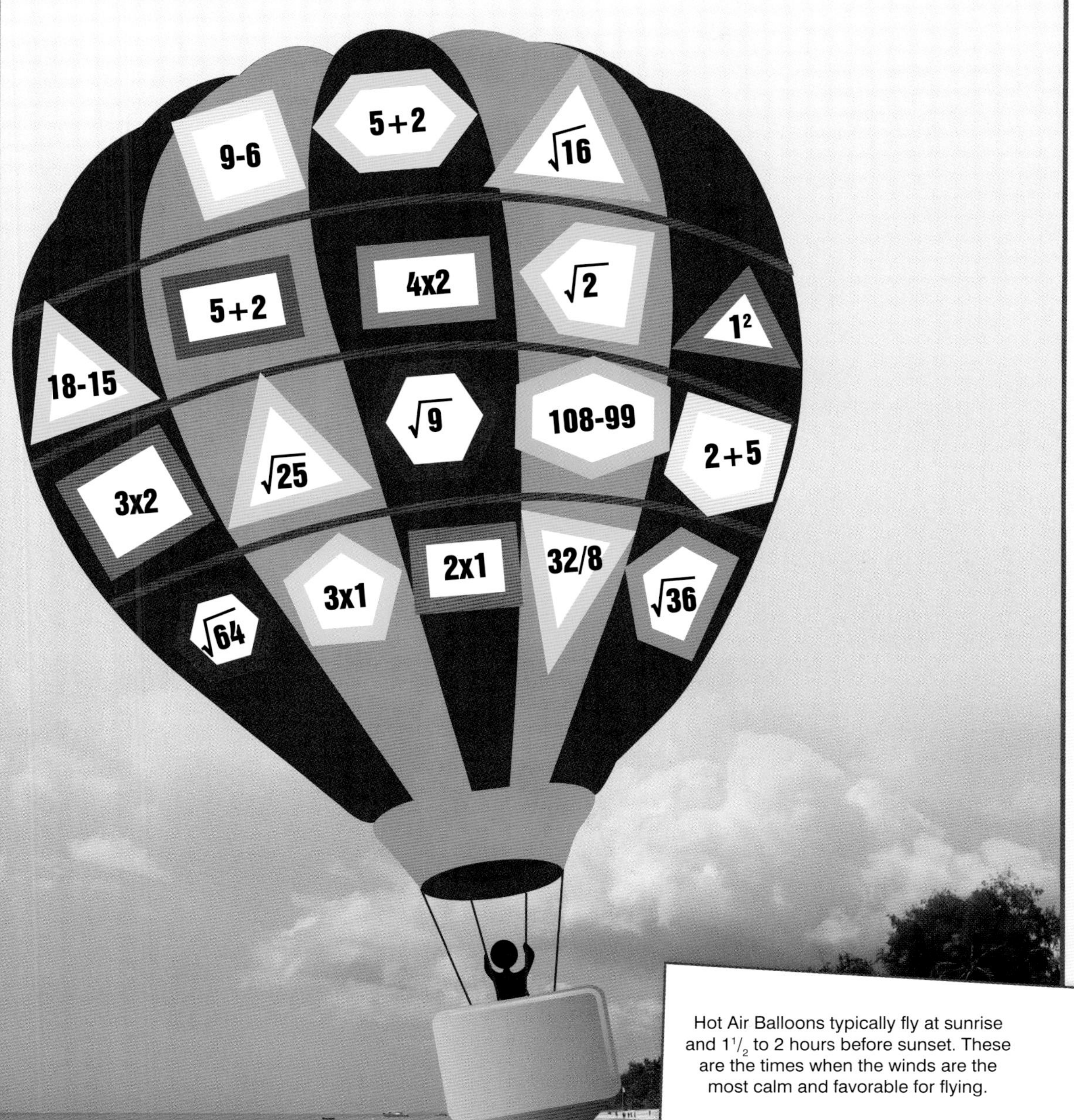

Hot Air Balloons typically fly at sunrise and $1^1/_2$ to 2 hours before sunset. These are the times when the winds are the most calm and favorable for flying.

46

Geometric Chart

Draw the missing geometrical shapes in the puzzle. Every row, column, and highlighted group should have each shape in it. No shape should be repeated in a row, column, or group.

"Geometry is the science of correct reasoning on incorrect figures."

George Polya

47

Power Failure

There is a power failure and you have lit the house with these candles that have numbers and mathematical signs on them. Create an equation using each number only once to get the result 42. Use the required mathematical signs in any combination and as many times as required.

"Anger is a wind which blows out the lamp of the mind."

Robert Green Ingersoll

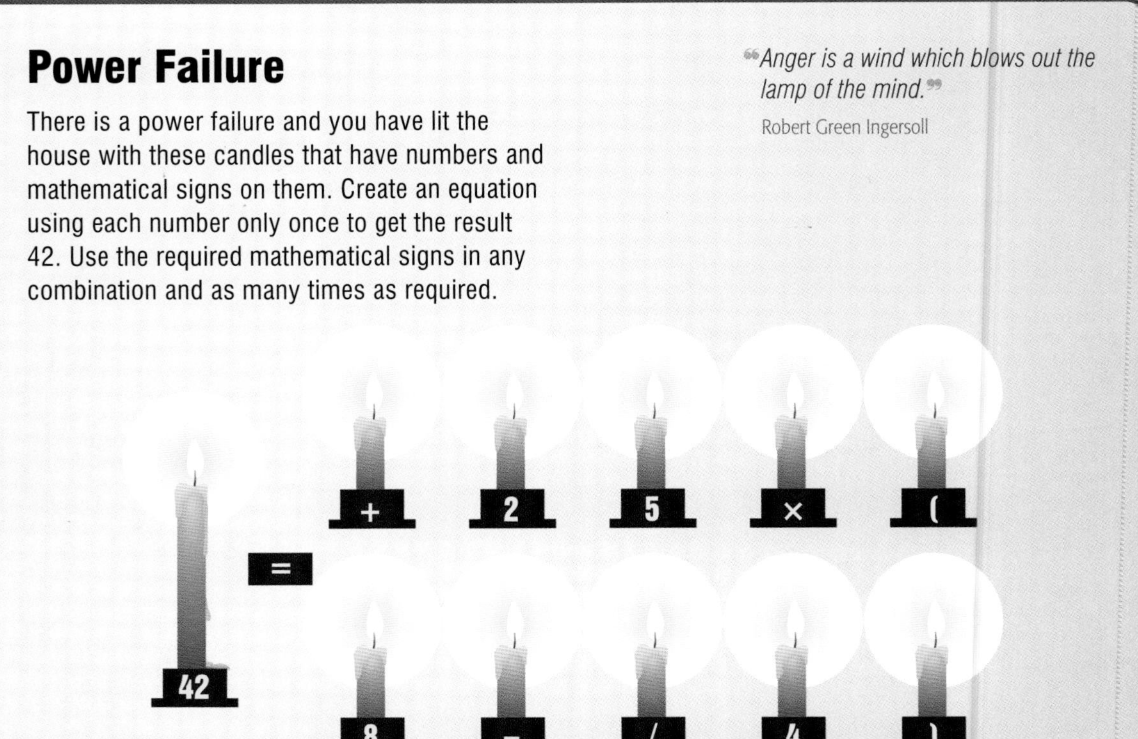

48

Music Maze

You need to insert musical notes into the maze so that each row, column, and group of cells has only one musical note in it.

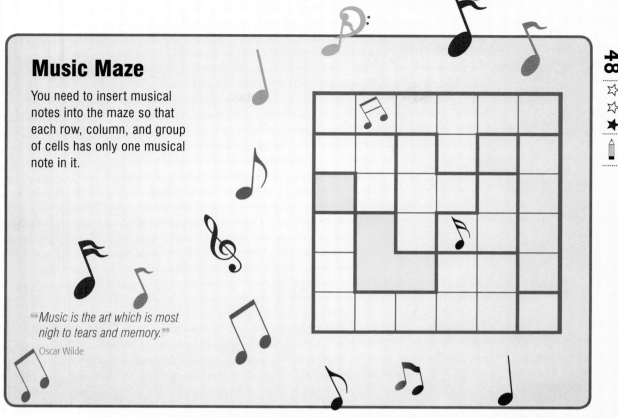

"Music is the art which is most nigh to tears and memory."

Oscar Wilde

49

Find the Numbers

You need to join each pair of numbers with a line without crossing lines for any other connections to know your future. Your lines cannot pass through the shaded blocks.

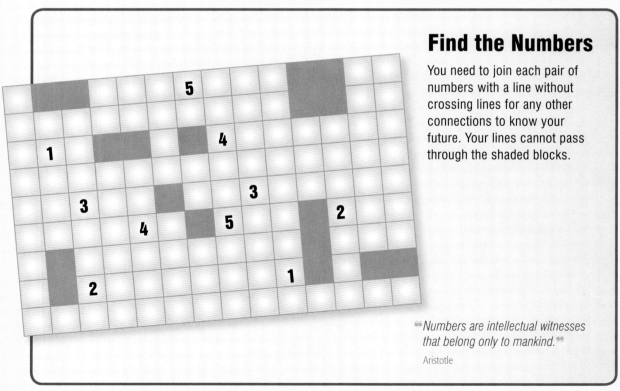

"Numbers are intellectual witnesses that belong only to mankind."

Aristotle

50

Over the Top

Identify which of the pictures below matches the overhead view shown.

"Success is not the key to happiness. Happiness is the key to success. If you love what you are doing, you will be successful."

Herman Cain

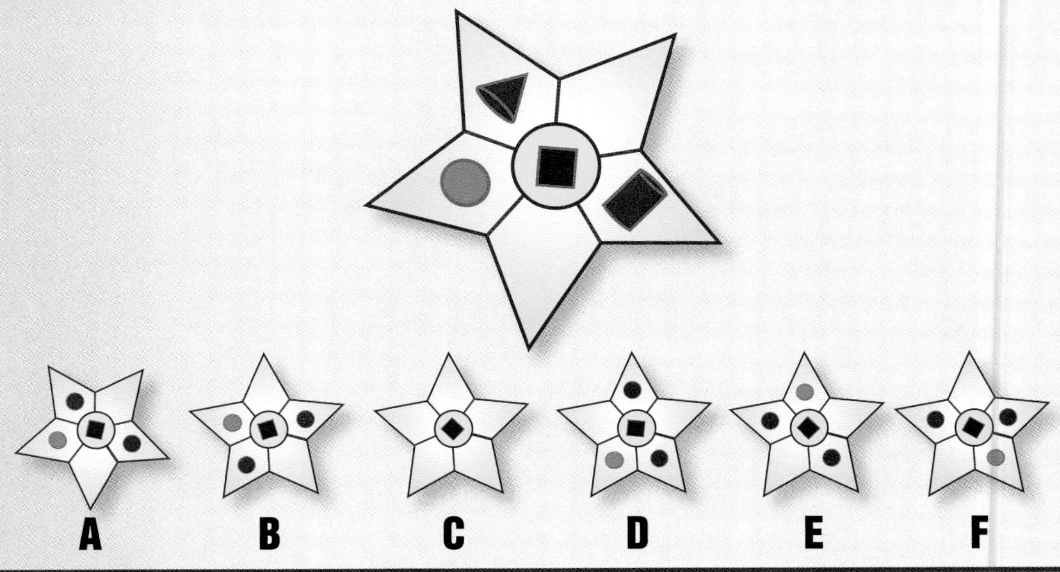

51

Spot the Man

Which image matches the silhouette?

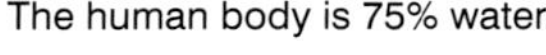

The human body is 75% water.

52

Computer Count

All the computers in the office are numbered to different machines. One of the computers has a missing number. Number the computer based on the logic used to number the other computers in the row.

12 29 46 63 ? 97

"Everybody gets so much information all day long that they lose their common sense."

Gertrude Stein

53

Closed Circuit

The electrician is trying to fix a door bell by joining all the connection points with a single wire. Can you help the electrician join the connections using 3 squares, without lifting your pen or pencil?

"Electricity is really just organized lightning."

George Carlin

54

Alpha Painting

Write the missing letters in the puzzle. Every row, column, and group should have the letters A–I. No letter should be repeated in a row, column, or group.

G			H		F			I
			D				C	
		F		C				
	D	A				I		E
E				I		D	B	
		H					F	
						B	G	H
		I	G		C			

"A picture is a poem without words."

Horace

55

Bucket Pairing

The following buckets have similar color patterns. Each bucket has a pair, except one. Find the bucket that does not have a pair.

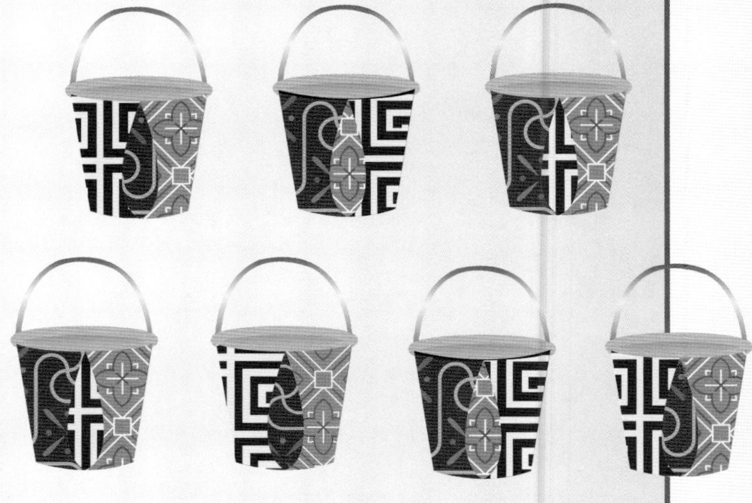

Did you know that an average shower uses two buckets of water per minute?

Find the Only Pair

56

Each shape appears only once apart from one which appears twice. Can you find the pair?

"Hold a picture of yourself long and steadily enough in your mind's eye, and you will be drawn toward it."

Napoleon Hill

Cups and Glasses

57

Place the individual cups and glasses into the circles on the big cup in such a way that no two cups and glasses are together. Also make sure that no two consecutive numbers are placed together. Solve the puzzle to figure out how to arrange them.

6 2 3 8 7 1 9 5 4

"Music is the wine that fills the cup of silence."

Robert Fripp

58

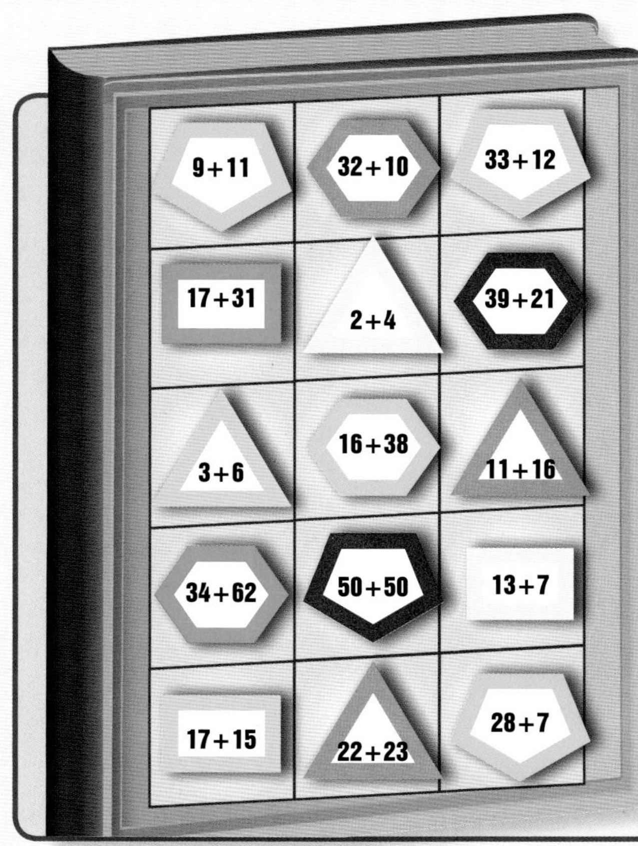

Book Bafflement

The book exhibition has a book with an interesting cover. Each block on the cover has different shapes with calculations inside. Perform the calculation to find the number and add it with the number of edges of the shapes around it. Find 2 adjacent blocks which total 88.

"The worth of a book is to be measured by what you can carry away from it."

James Bryce

59

The Dog and the Bone Mystery

"There is no psychiatrist in the world like a puppy licking your face."

Ben Williams

Can you shade the chipped part of the bone? Use the numbers shown in the squares to shade the adjacent squares that share the same edges. Make sure the squares that you shade are not diagonal.

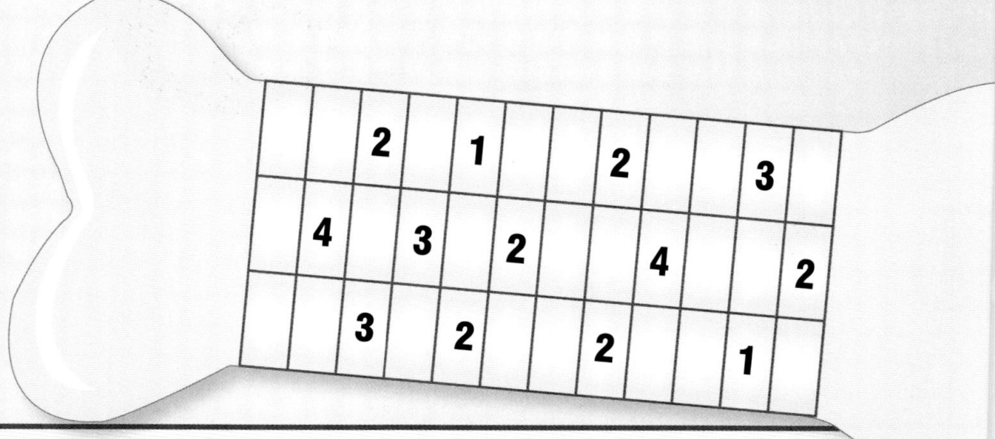

60

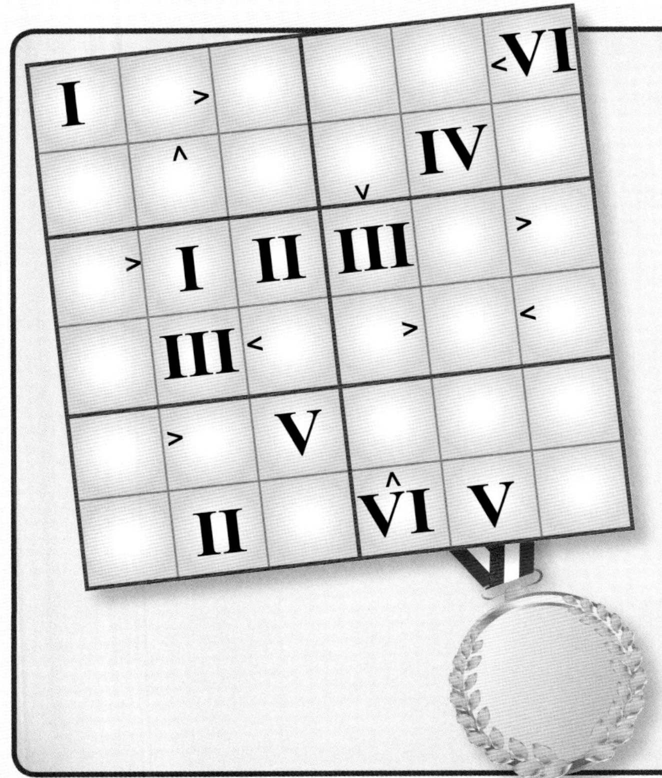

Win a Medal

This gold medal is for the one who can solve this puzzle. Fill up the empty squares with the help of the more or less signs. Every row, column, and highlighted group should have numbers I–VI. No number should be repeated in a row, column, or groups. Complete the empty cells correctly to win the medal.

“The will to win, the desire to succeed, the urge to reach your full potential… these are the keys that will unlock the door to personal excellence.”

Eddie Robinson

61

Math Maze

Create an equation using each number in the puzzle only once to get the result 22. Use only the required mathematical signs in any combination and as many times as required.

62

Candle Confusion

The candles have a unique design of different shapes and letters. Write the number equivalent of the letter, example, N=14. Subtract the number of edges of the shape from the number equivalent of the letter inside each shape. Find 4 adjacent parts whose total is equal to 50.

"A candle loses nothing by lighting another candle."

James Keller

63

Currency Chart

Complete the chart displaying different currencies. The chart has four types of currencies. Every row and column should include each currency. No currency should be repeated in a row or column.

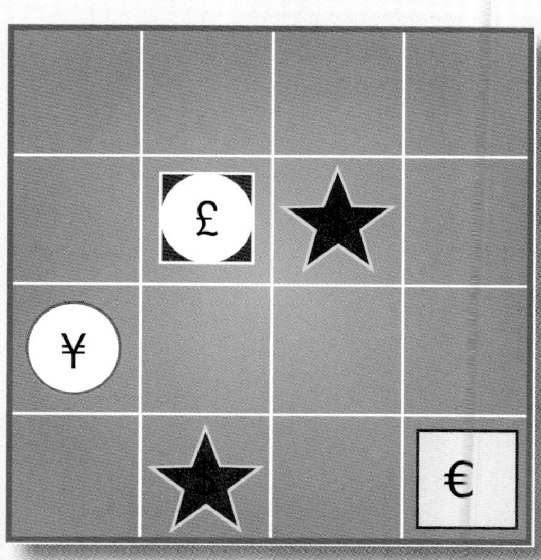

"Money never made a man happy yet, nor will it. The more a man has, the more he wants. Instead of filling a vacuum, it makes one."

Benjamin Franklin

64

★★★

Population Analysis

Perform the calculations in the population chart to find the numbers. Fill up the empty squares with the help of the more or less signs specified. Every row, column, and highlighted group should have numbers 1–9. No number should be repeated in a row, column, or group.

"Population, when unchecked, increases in a geometrical ratio."

Thomas Robert Malthus

		3×2	$9-8$	>		>		$1+1$
$24/4$		>		∧	$14-11$	$15/3$	<	
	>	$16/2$						
<			<	$\sqrt{9}$	$6+3$ ∨	<		
	∨		$13-11$			3×2		2^3
					<		$17-8$	$\sqrt{16}$
	∨				<		4^2	$3+2$
	$12/4$		$\sqrt{81}$	$4+2$	>	$21-14$	>	
∧ $21/3$	$9-7$							

65

Number Board

Join each pair of numbers on the board with a line without crossing lines for any other connections. The lines cannot pass through the shaded blocks.

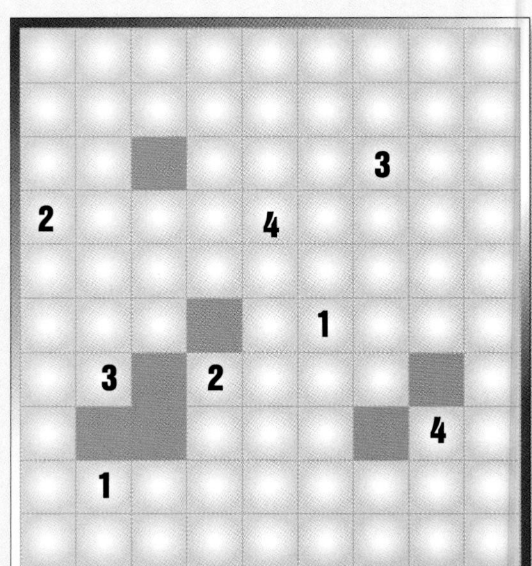

Did you know that 0 is the only complex number which is both real and purely imaginary?

66

Tally the Tile

Two square tiles have been broken into four pieces each. Can you reunite them?

Tiles are made of ceramic, clay, porcelain or stone.

"It takes two to get one in trouble."
Mae West

Triangle Trouble

67

In the sequence below, which of the alternatives, A, B, C, or D, should replace the question mark?

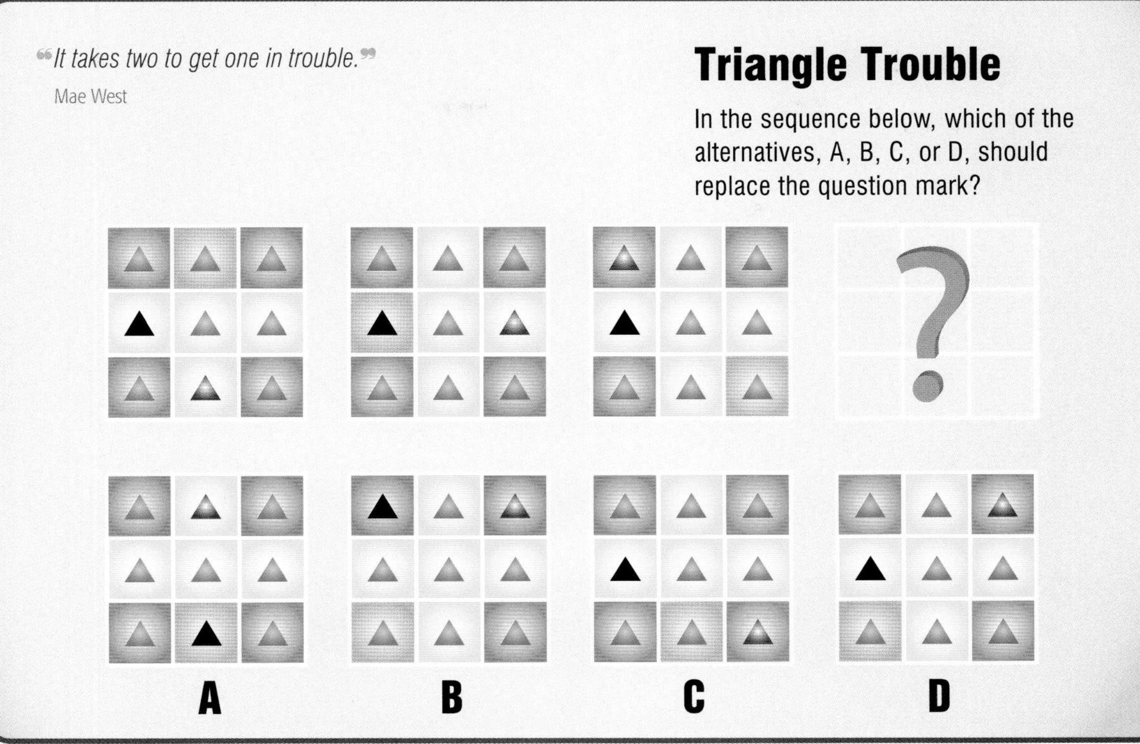

Join the Oranges

68

There are nine oranges arranged in three rows and three columns. Use three lines to join all the oranges without lifting the pen or pencil.

Did you know that all oranges contain "carotene" that makes them orange.

69

Cup Conundrum

Can you work out the number that should appear on the cup in the middle?

"The mere chink of cups and saucers turns the mind to happy repose."

George Gissie

70

Let's do Alpha Doku!

Complete the grid so that every row, column, and group contain all the letters A, B, C, D, E, and F. No letter should be repeated in any row, column, or group.

		B			
D				E	
	F				
		A			C
			C		
	C		D	A	

"The problems of puzzles are very near the problems of life."

Erno Rubik

71

☆★★

Mirror Image?

Compare the pictures. See if you can find five differences.

"God loved the birds and invented trees. Man loved the birds and invented cages."

Jacques Deval

72

Diamond Décor

You are asked to decorate a room for a party. There are different paper diamonds kept for decoration along with an unfolded paper triangle. Find the diamond that matches the unfolded one.

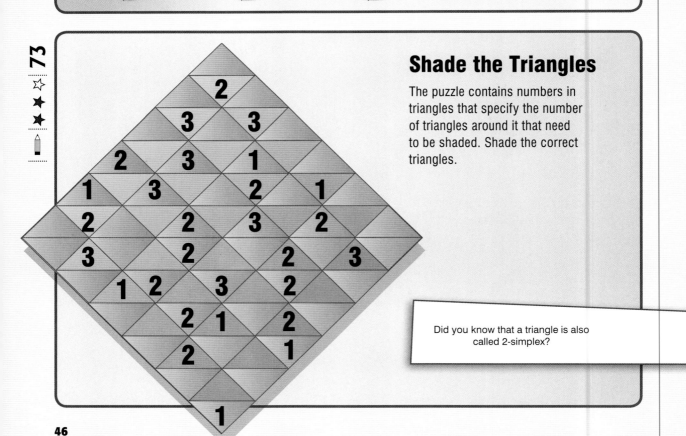

“Colors must fit together as pieces in a puzzle or cogs in a wheel.”

Hans Hofmann

73

Shade the Triangles

The puzzle contains numbers in triangles that specify the number of triangles around it that need to be shaded. Shade the correct triangles.

Did you know that a triangle is also called 2-simplex?

74

Aerial Shapes

Which of the pictures below represents the correct overhead view of this scene?

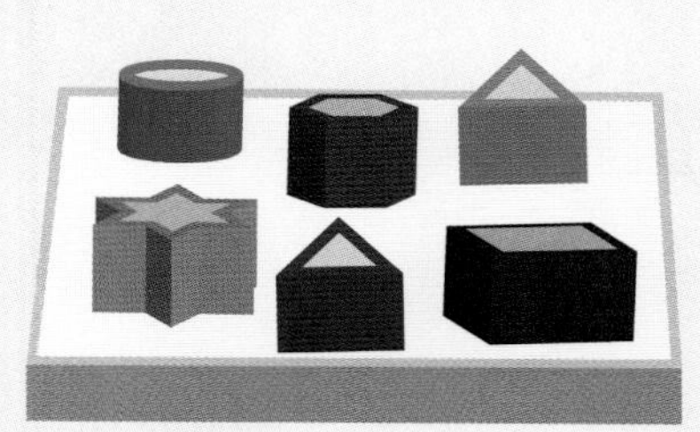

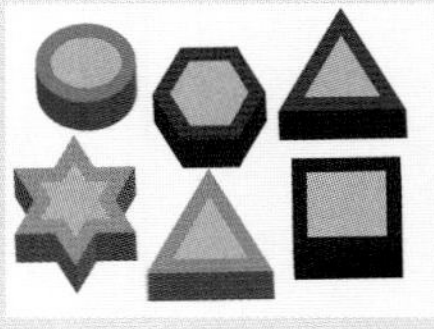

B

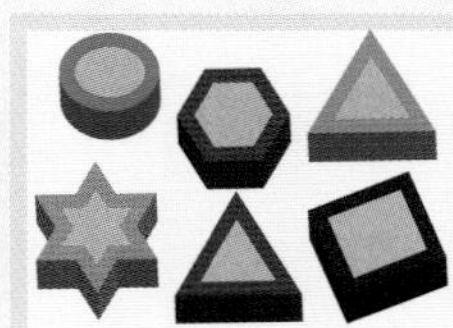

C

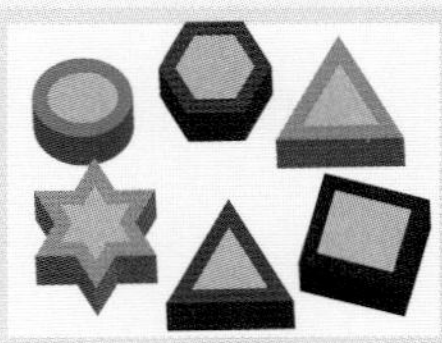

D

75

Tournament Arrangement

Arrange the rackets and shuttlecocks in the squares so that no two rackets or shuttlecocks are placed together. Also, no two consecutive numbers can be placed together. There are multiple ways of arranging these. Solve the puzzle to figure out which method works for you.

"Approach the game with no preset agendas and you'll probably come away surprised at your overall efforts."

Phil Jackson

76

Computer Conundrum

The desktop background has blocks containing different shapes and numbers inside each shape. Add the one or two digits inside the shape and multiply it with the number of edges of the surrounding shape. Find 5 adjacent blocks which make the total 126.

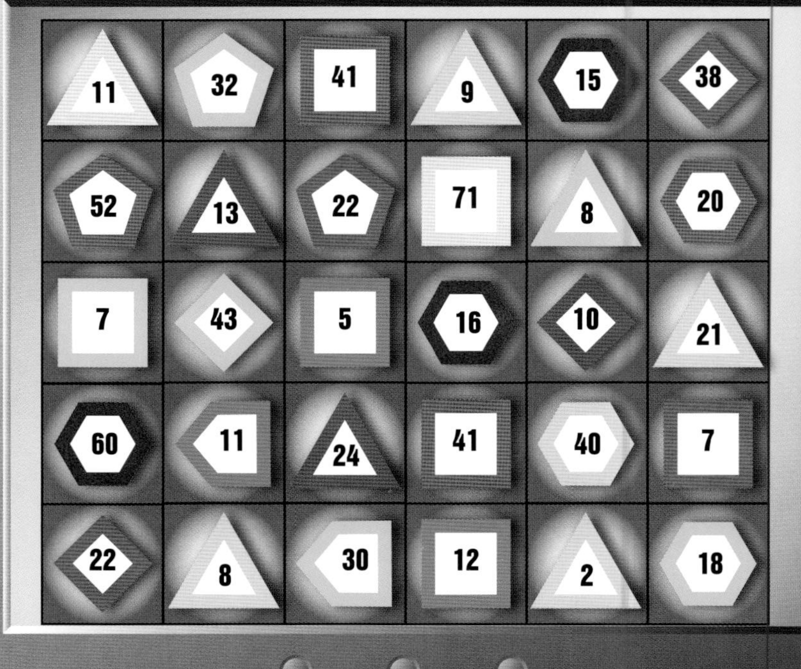

"The question of whether computers can think is like the question of whether submarines can swim."

Edsger W. Dijkstra

77

Shirt Stumper

You walk into a shopping mall and pick up a shirt which is colored blue and green. The numbers in the rectangles specify the number of blue rectangles which surround it. Color the rectangles to find how your shirt looks.

"The quickest way to know a woman is to go shopping with her."

Marcelene Cox

Greater than or Less?

78 ☆☆★

Fill numbers in the empty squares, so that every row and every column should have numbers I–IV. No number should be repeated in a row or column.

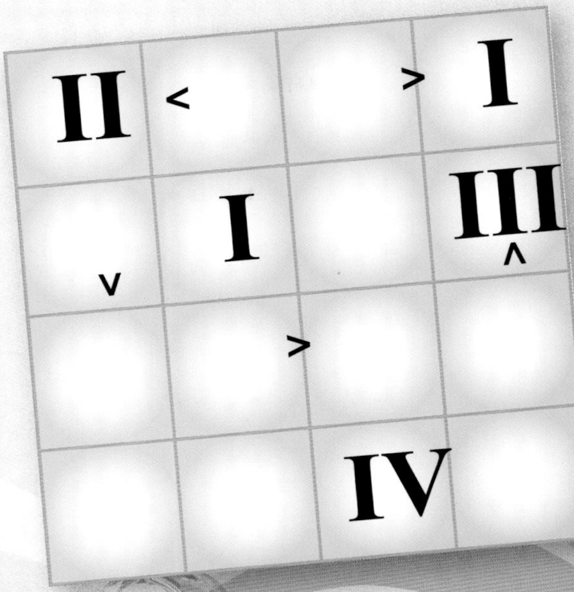

II	<	>	I
∨	I		III ∧
	>		
		IV	

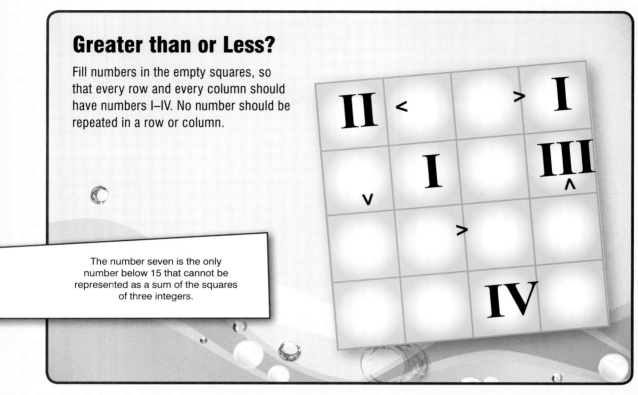

The number seven is the only number below 15 that cannot be represented as a sum of the squares of three integers.

Flower Fun

79 ★★★

Create an equation using each number on the flower only once to get the result 27. Use the mathematical signs in any combination and as many times as required.

27

2

6

8

/

7

( )

−

×

+

=

“Earth laughs in flowers.”

Ralph Waldo Emerson

80

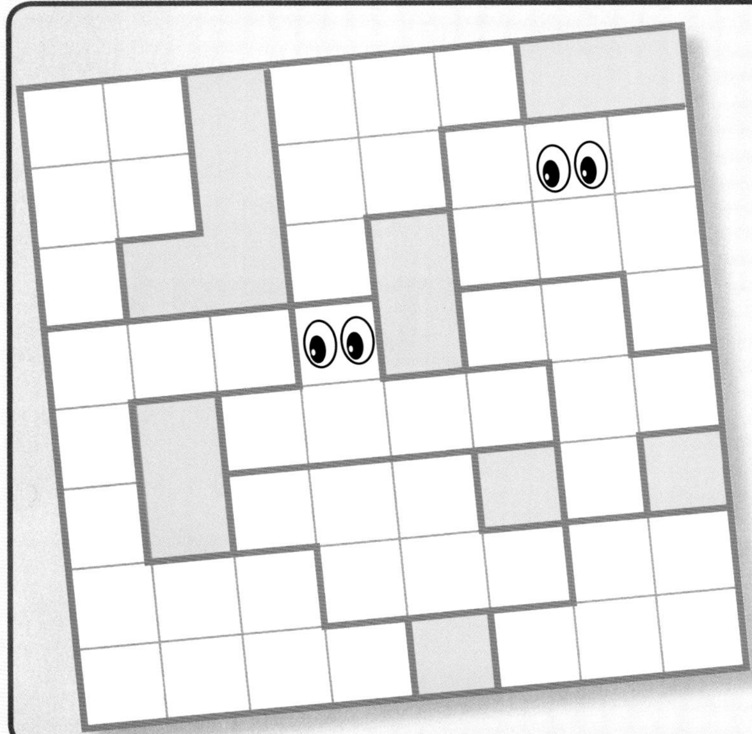

Look for the Answer

Insert the pair of eyes in the grid so that each row, column, and group of cells has only one pair of eyes in it.

"The eye of the master will do more work than both his hands."

Benjamin Franklin

81

Roll the Dice

The game board has pairs of numbers on it. You need to join each pair of numbers with a line without crossing lines for any other connections. Your lines cannot pass through the shaded blocks.

Seven has the highest probability of occurring when rolling two dice.

82

Missing Fruits and Vegetables

There are lots of fruits and vegetables in the boxes below. Look closely to find five that are missing from the box on the left.

83

Coloring Board

Color the coloring board so that no color is repeated in a row or a column. Also, each row and each column should contain all the five colors.

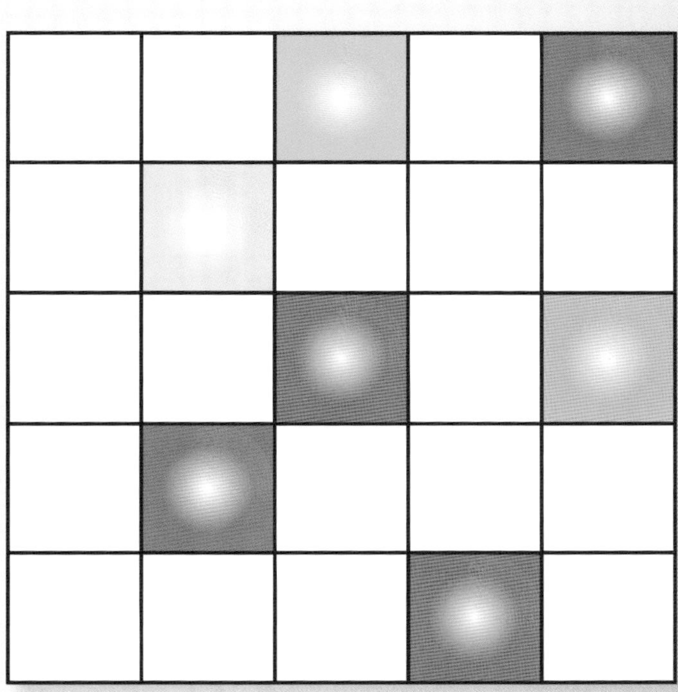

"Colors, like features, follow the changes of the emotions."

Pablo Picasso

84

Complete the Necklace

Find the missing number in the sequence to complete the necklace.

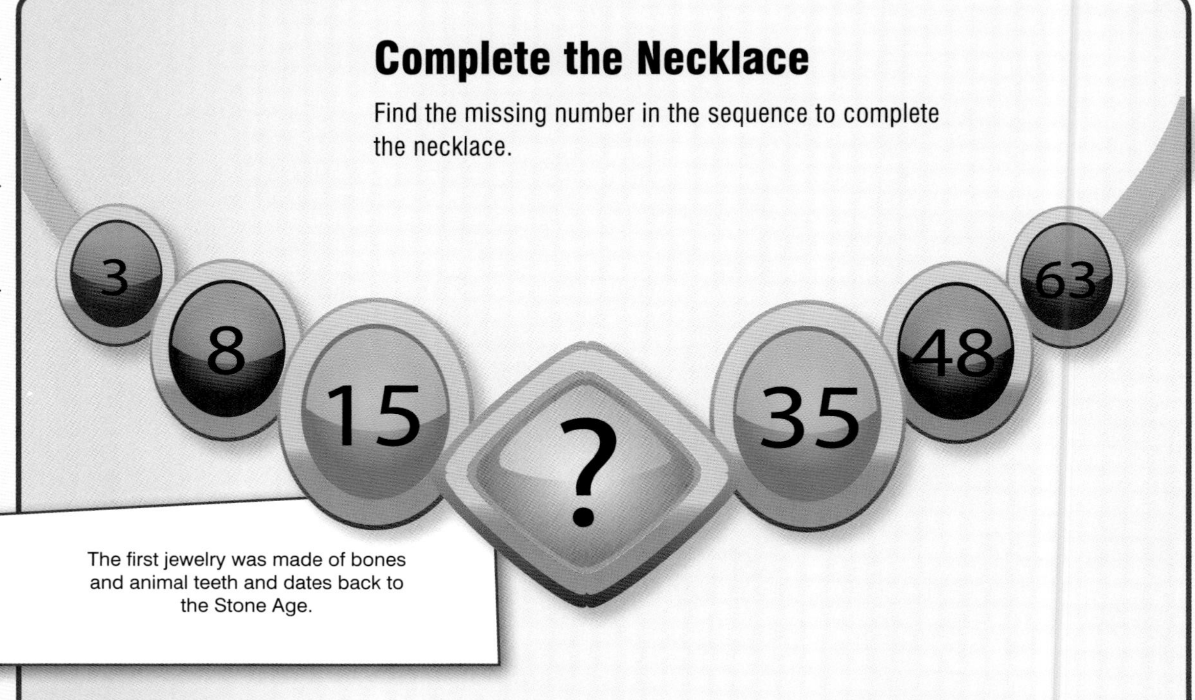

The first jewelry was made of bones and animal teeth and dates back to the Stone Age.

Bird Spotting

A flock of birds is flying in the air. Use three lines to join all the dots on the birds without lifting your pen or pencil.

"It is not only fine feathers that make fine birds."

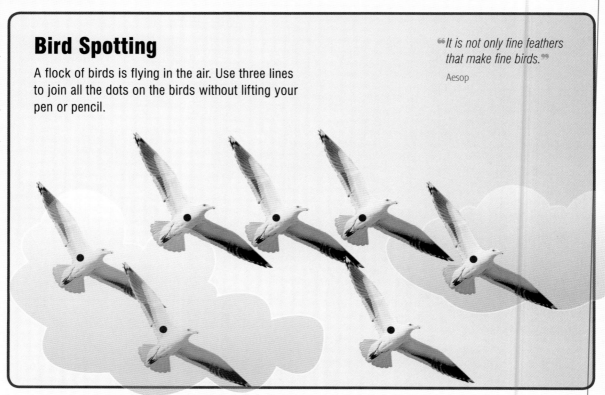

Aesop

86

Alpha Ado

Complete the grid so that every row, column, and group should have the letters A–F. No letter should be repeated in a row, column, or group.

		B			
D				E	
	F				
		A			C
			C		
	C		D	A	

The history of the alphabet letters started in ancient Egypt.

87

Music Mania

You are at a music store. There are 5 boxes on a table out of which one has 10 music CDs inside. This box is the same as the unfolded box. Find the box to win the CDs.

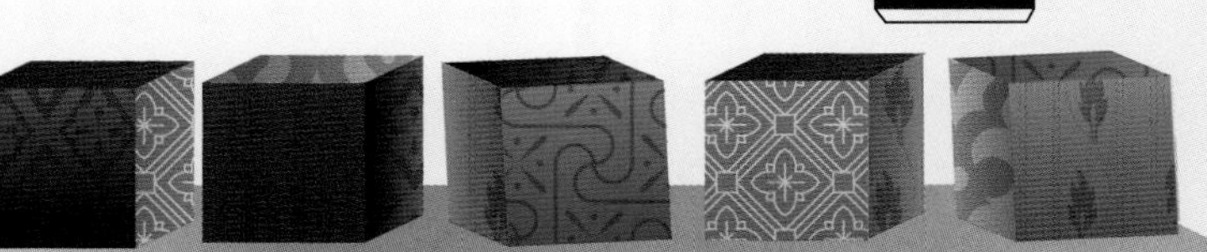

"Music is enough for a lifetime, but a lifetime is not enough for music.."

Sergei Rachmaninov

88 ★★★

The Secret Code

There is a secret code hidden in this grid.You can crack the code only if you fill in the missing numbers correctly. Perform the calculations to find the numbers. Next, fill up the empty squares with the help of the more or less signs specified. Every row, column, and highlighted group should have numbers 1–9. No number should be repeated in a row, column, or group.

"It is as if the ordinary language we use every day has a hidden set of signals; a kind of secret code."

William Stafford

	>			3^2		24/3		∧
			3+1			< $\sqrt{49}$		17-15
1^2		∧	>					
∨	∧			∧	<			3+4 ∨
	2^2	3^2				$\sqrt{25}$		
		3+5 ∨	13-8	3×2	>		1^2	
					$\sqrt{49}$ >			
	$\sqrt{9}$ <				12-11		15-8	
	$\sqrt{64}$			10-5		3^2		

Help the DJ

89

This DJ has been trying to set up his equipment, but there are so many connections that he is all muddled up. Starting from any point, he has to connect all the dots with four continuous lines (without lifting the pen), so that each of the nine dots has at least one line running through it.

Can you get the music going by making the right connections?

"Music is the wine that fills the cup of silence."

Robert Fripp

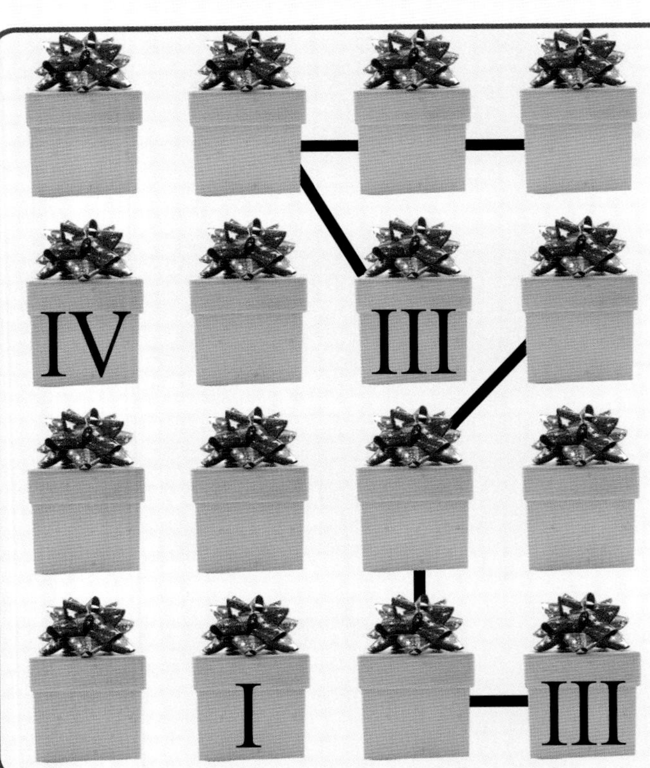

Gift Placement

90

Number the gift boxes so that every row, column, and linked gifts have the numbers I–IV. No numbers should be repeated in a row, column, and the gifts that are linked together.

"The manner of giving is worth more than the gift."

Pierre Corneille

91

Lunch Party

Each fruit has a letter tag in different shapes. Find the corresponding number for each letter. Add each number inside the shape with the number of edges of shape around it. For example, E=5 and 5+4=9. Find 3 adjacent fruits that add up to 30.

Did you know that one orange a day provides enough Vitamin C to fight off flu?

92

Circuit Confusion

Help the confused electrician, repair the fuse by putting the fuse plugs in their proper positions. The plugs are numbered from 1–8 and you must place the fuses in such a way that no two plugs with consecutive numbers touch each other. Solve the puzzle by arranging the rest of the fuses.

If you scuffed your feet long enough without touching anything, you could build up enough electrons to explode your toes!

93 ★★★

No Can Do!

You can open the can by filling up the empty squares with the help of the more or less signs. Every row, column, and highlighted group should have the letters A–F. No letter should be repeated in a row, column, or group. Find the corresponding number for each letter to identify which number is greater than the other. For example, C=3, so the letter in the upper left cell needs to be a letter that corresponds to a number that is greater than 3.

Did you know that the can opener was invented 48 years after cans were introduced?

94 ★

Puzzling Purse

The numbers in the diamond shaped pockets specify the number of surrounding pockets which are filled with diamonds. Color the diamond pockets to find the diamonds in your purse.

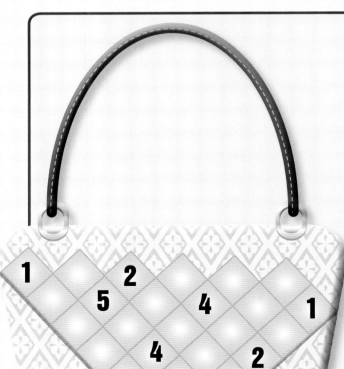

"I have always felt a gift diamond shines so much better than one you buy for yourself."

Mae West

95

Rocket Launch

You need to help the pilot find the secret equation using all the numbers only once and the mathematical signs in any combination and as many times as required to get the result equal to 55.

"A year spent in artificial intelligence is enough to make one believe in God."
Alan Perlis

96

Computer Code

Complete the game on the computer so that every row and column should have each icon in it. No icon should be repeated in a row or column.

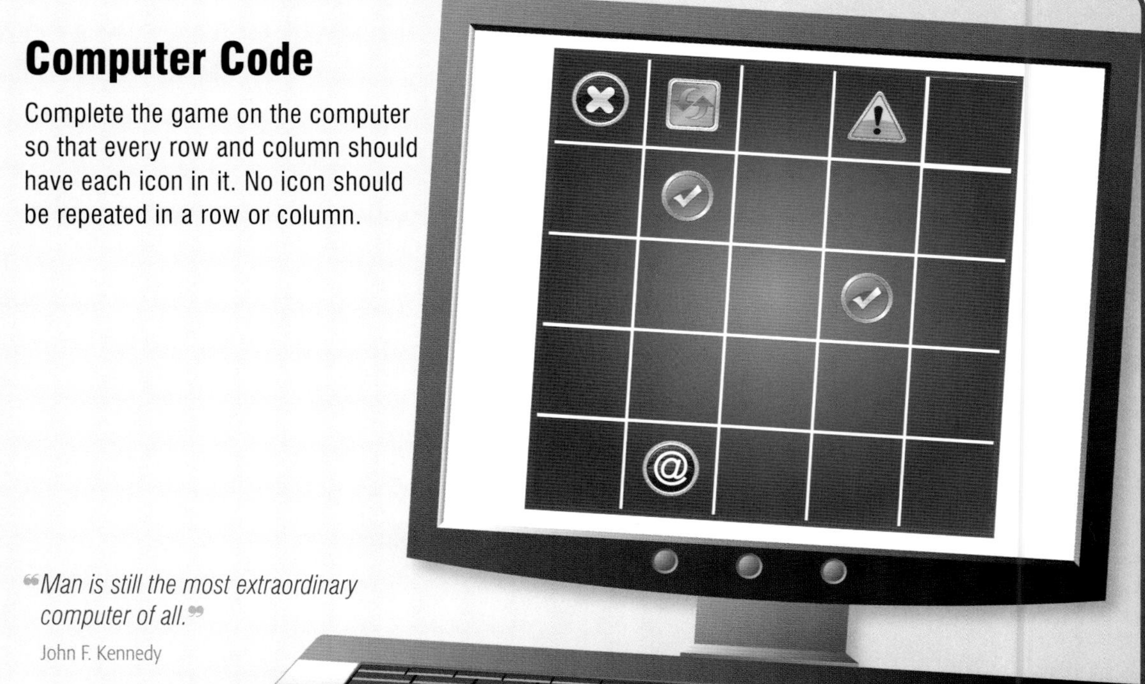

"Man is still the most extraordinary computer of all."
John F. Kennedy

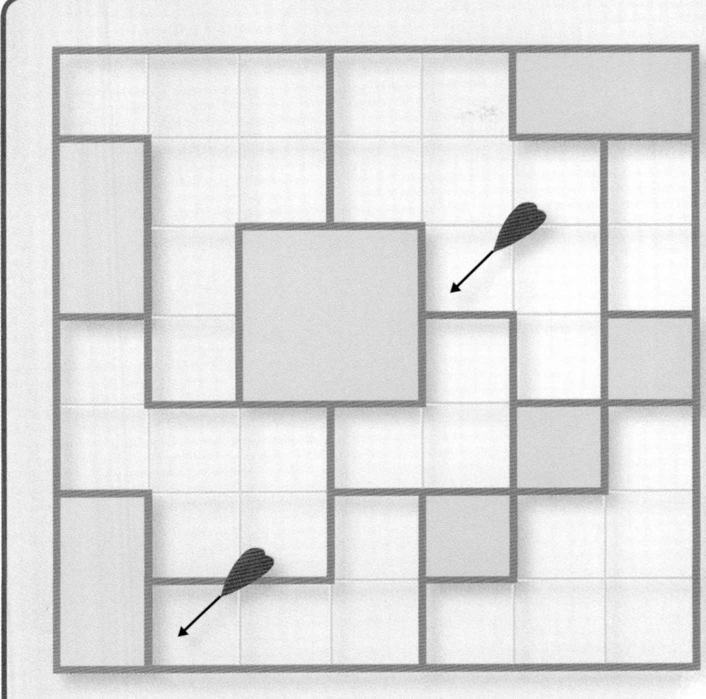

Aim for the Solution

97

Insert arrows in the grid so that each row, column, and group of cells has only one arrow in it.

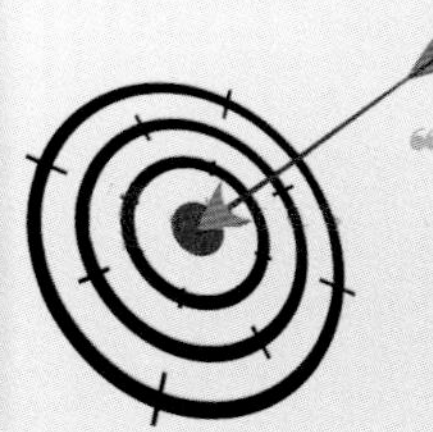

“The odds of hitting your target go up dramatically when you aim at it.”

Mal Pancoast

Table Tops

98

You need to join each pair of numbers on the table with a line without crossing the lines for any other connections. Your lines cannot pass through the shaded blocks.

			1			
					2	
				3		
			2			4
	4					
		3		1		

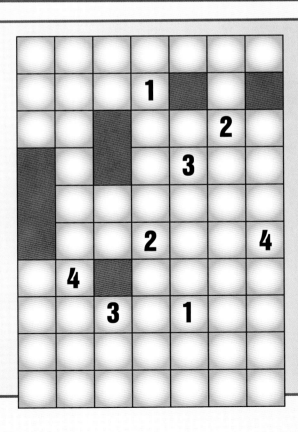

“The only time to eat diet food is while you’re waiting for the steak to cook.”

Julia Child

99

Kitchen Arrangement

The kitchen is arranged, according to the paper plan, with all items in place except one. The items that are placed in the kitchen are displayed in the plus sign below. Find the missing item.

"The problems of puzzles are very near the problems of life."

Erno Rubik

100

Unfold the Colors

The puzzle requires you to complete the colors in the empty squares. Every row and column should have all five colors and no color should repeat in a row or column.

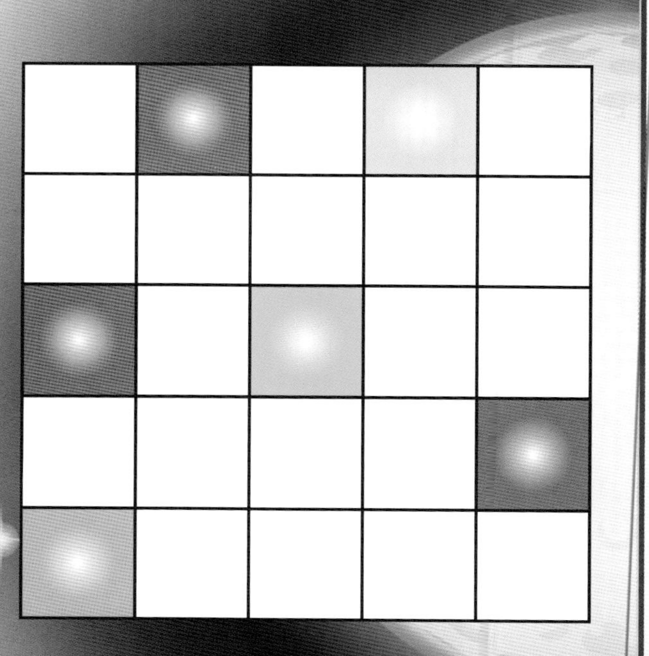

"Green is the prime color of the world, and that from which its loveliness arises."

Pedro Calderon de la Barca

101 ★★★

Box Brain-Teaser

Here is a parcel with a number code on it which reveals the senders name. Can you work out which cube A, B, C or D will fill the empty block to figure out who sent this parcel to you?

2	31	7
13	43	5
11	23	2

29	19	7
3	17	11
2	5	13

37	13	7
7	19	11
23	2	3

The first known use of numbers dates back to around 35,000 BC in the form of Tally Marks.

2	17	11
13	23	7
4	5	19

A

6	13	5
11	47	23
7	11	3

B

13	5	2
3	19	11
2	23	7

C

5	11	7
23	21	31
2	13	3

D

102 ☆☆★

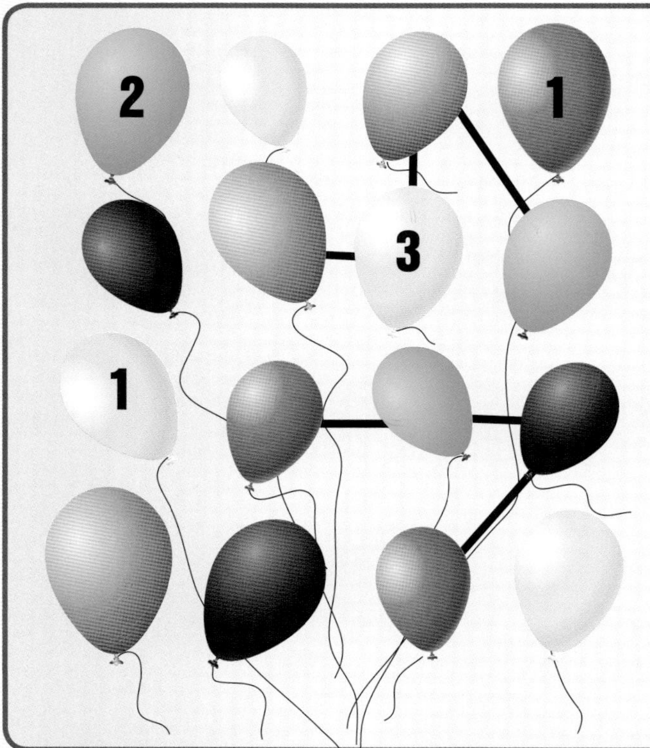

Balloons

You are arranging a birthday party. Each guest in the party gets four balloons to take home. Each balloon has a number written on it. Enter missing numbers in the range of 1–4 in such a way that no numbers are repeated in a row, column and in the balloons that are linked together.

Did you know that a 100-foot-diameter balloon can lift 33,000 pounds?

103 ☆☆★

Slithery Problem

The snake has lost its way home as the path leading to his hole has been covered. Find the missing number using the logic in which the existing number are placed. To help him find an alternate route back.

Did you know that Cobras are the only snakes in the world that can spit their venom, and they are accurate up to about half their own length?

Tea Set 104

Fill the empty cells on the tea cup so that every row and column should have the letters A–D. No letter should be repeated in a row or column.

C			A
A		B	C

Puzzle Gift 105

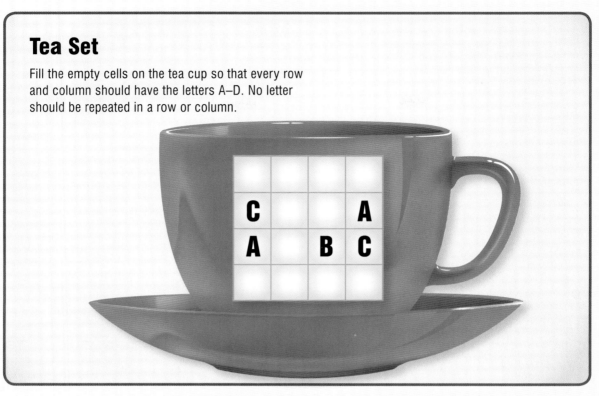

You are at your friend's birthday party. There is a puzzle game in which you have to identify the party cap that matches the unfolded cap.

"Tell the truth, and so puzzle and confound your adversaries."

Henry Wotton, Sr.

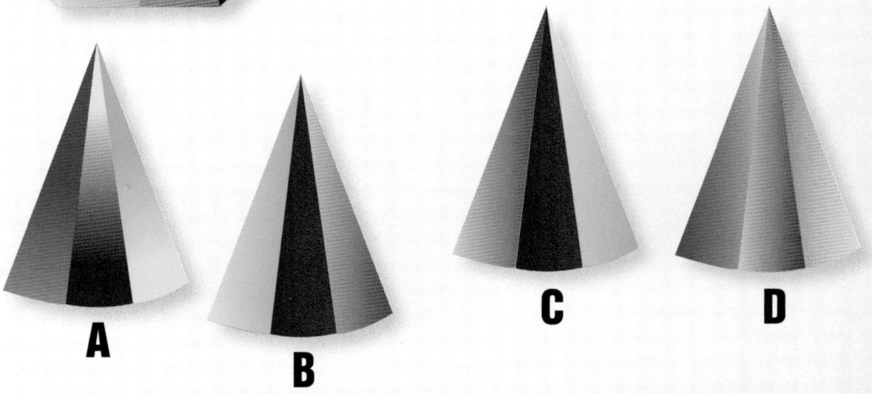

A B C D

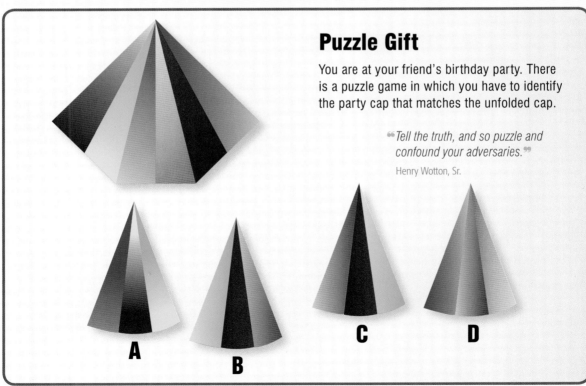

106

Tic Tac Toe Trouble

The pictures show different tic tac toe games. Each game has a pair, except one. Find the tic tac toe game without a pair.

X	O	X
X	O	X
O	X	O

O	X	O
X	X	O
O	O	X

X	X	O
O	O	X
O	X	O

O	X	O
X	X	O
O	O	X

X	X	O
O	O	X
O	X	O

X	O	X
O	X	O
O	X	O

O	X	O
X	X	O
X	O	X

X	O	X
X	O	X
O	X	O

O	X	O
X	X	O
X	O	X

"The art of simplicity is a puzzle of complexity."

Douglas Horton

107

Fireworks Fun

It's New Year's Eve and you need to arrange the labeled crackers in rows and columns. Make sure that no letters are repeated in a row, column, and the crackers that are linked together.

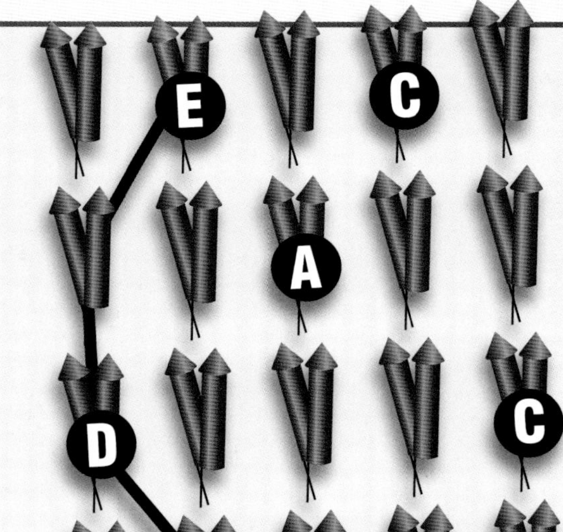

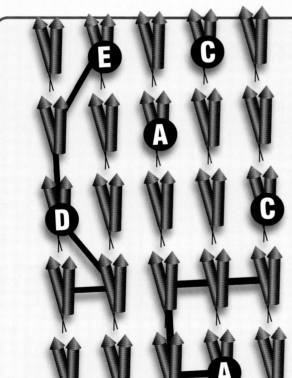

Did you know that blue is the hardest color to create in a firework?

Test your Eyes

Can you spot 10 differences between these two pictures.

"One picture is worth 1,000 denials."

Ronald Reagan

109

Find the Clock

You have arranged clocks at the store. A customer messed up the arrangement of all the clocks while shopping. You find that a clock is missing. Arrange all clocks as before and find the missing ones.

Electric clocks were made in the second half of the 19th century.

110

Flower Color

You are organizing a flower exhibition. You have to arrange flowers of six different colors in a square box. Every row, column, and highlighted group should have all six colors of flowers, without repeating any color.

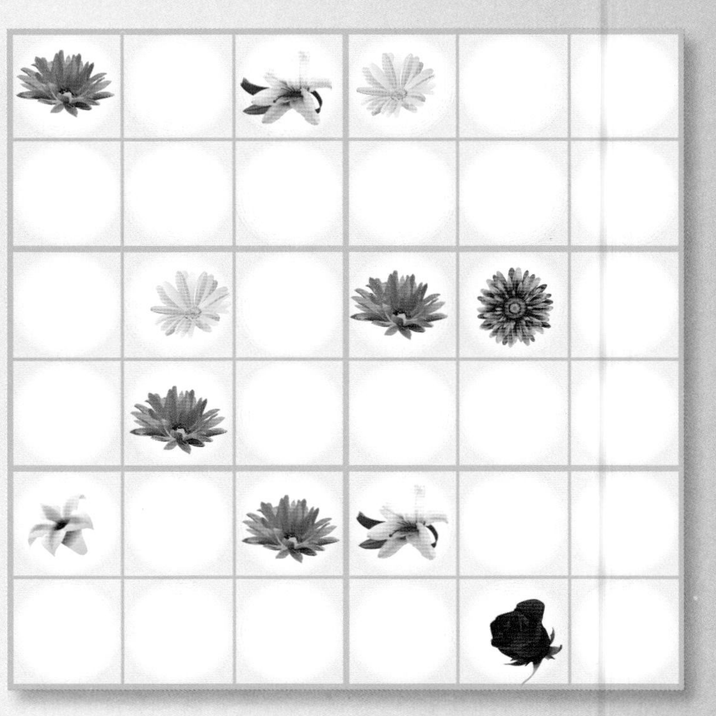

"As you walk down the fairway of life you must smell the roses, for you only get to play one round."

Ben Hogan

111

Repair the Guitar

The guitarist has some broken strings on the guitar and he can't continue to play the songs. He's been trying to join the strings by joining the dots on the guitar with no more than six lines, but doesn't seem to get it right. Can you help him join the dots?

Traditionally, guitars were constructed with combinations of various woods. The strings were made of animal gut.

112

Baffled Baker

The baker is preparing some cakes with numbers as instructed by the customer for a game. He forgot to place the number on one of the cakes. Can you help the baker find the missing number?

"A great empire, like a great cake, is most easily diminished at the edges."

Benjamin Franklin

113

Gigantic Grid

Complete the missing letters in the grid so that every row, column, and group should have the letters A–F. No letter should be repeated in a row, column, or group.

E		A	D		
			B	C	
C		F	E		
	D				A
					E

Did you know the alphabet letters and twinkle-twinkle little star have the same tune?

114

Match the Bucket

There are buckets with different designs in a store. You need to identify the bucket that matches the unfolded one.

115

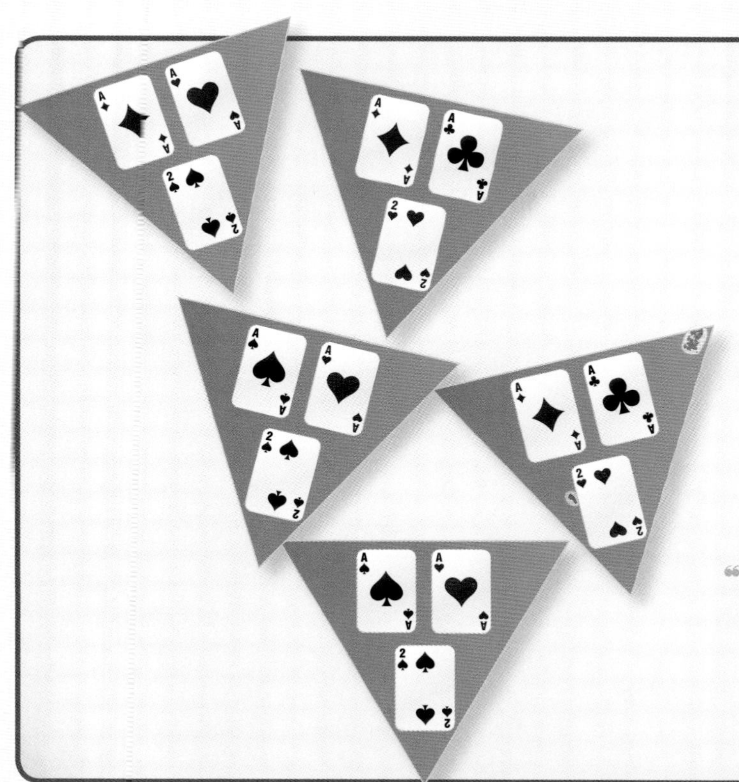

Identify the Pack of Cards

Each triangle has three playing cards placed in it. You can find pairs for triangles with similar placement of cards. However, one triangle does not have a pair. Find the odd triangle.

"Life is not a matter of holding good cards, but of playing a poor hand well."

Robert Louis Stevenson

116

Struggling with Certificates

Lucy has got a job offer and is struggling to assemble all the certificates to be taken. Arrange the certificates so that no certificate number is repeated in a row, column, or linked certificates. Also, each row, column, and linked certificates must contain each number 1–5.

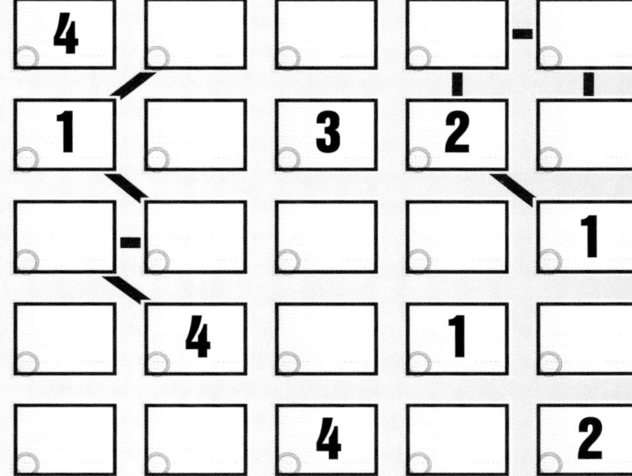

"If there is no struggle, there is no progress."

Frederick Douglass

117

Food Fest

At a food stall, you need to arrange pizzas and burgers in a tray so that no pizza and burger are placed next to each other and no consecutive numbers should be together. There are multiple ways to achieve this. Find which one works best for you.

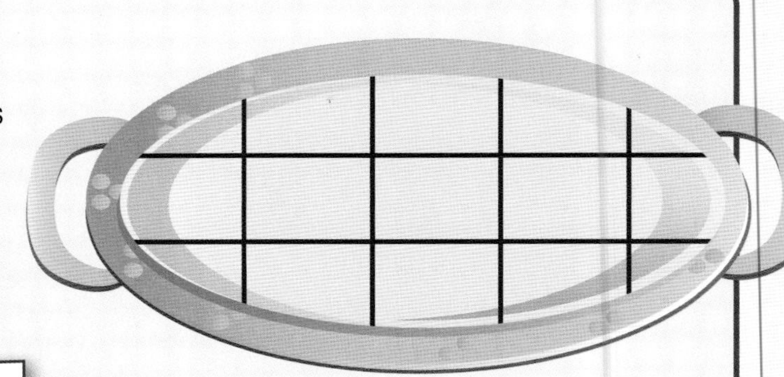

The Hamburger hall of fame is located in Seymour, Wisconsin.

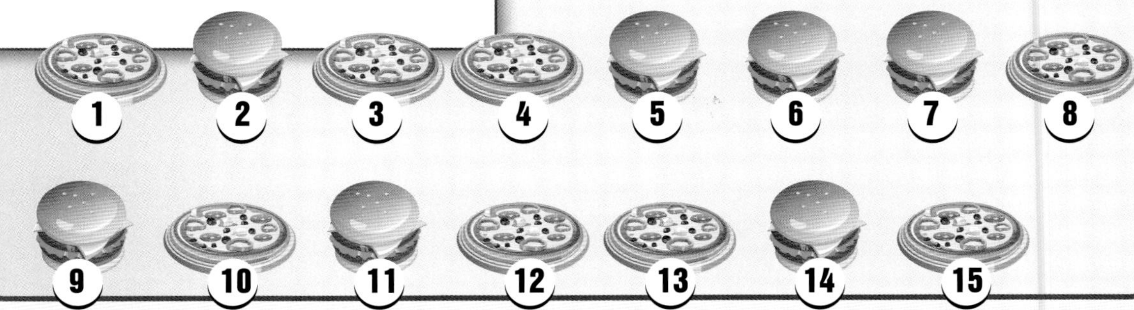

118

Rug Puzzle

You come across a fancy rug that has multiple cubes. Each cube has different shapes and calculations inside each shape. Perform the calculation and multiply the result with the number of edges of the shape around it. Find 4 adjacent cubes that add up to 90.

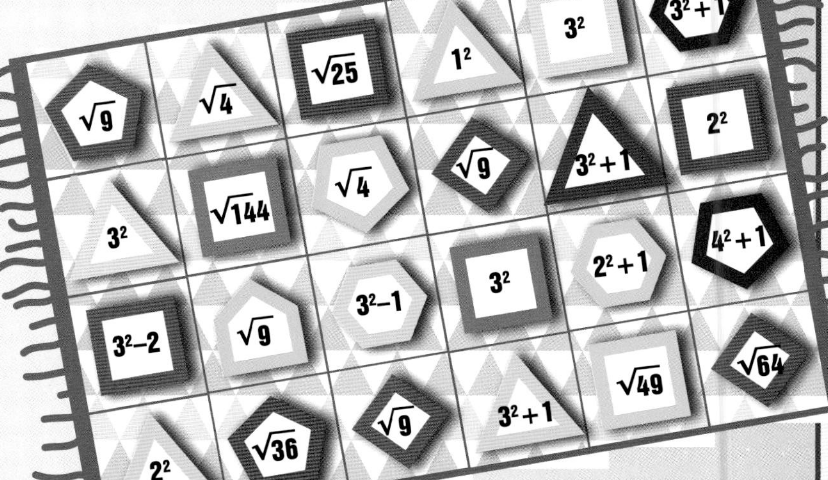

"Problems emerge and some people try to sweep them under the rug."

Bill Condon

119

Count the Eggs

A fish has laid eggs in the ocean and is wondering how many they are. The numbers in the circles specify the number of eggs touching it that need to be shaded. Help the fish to color the eggs to find the count.

Did you know that amphibious fish can live on land?

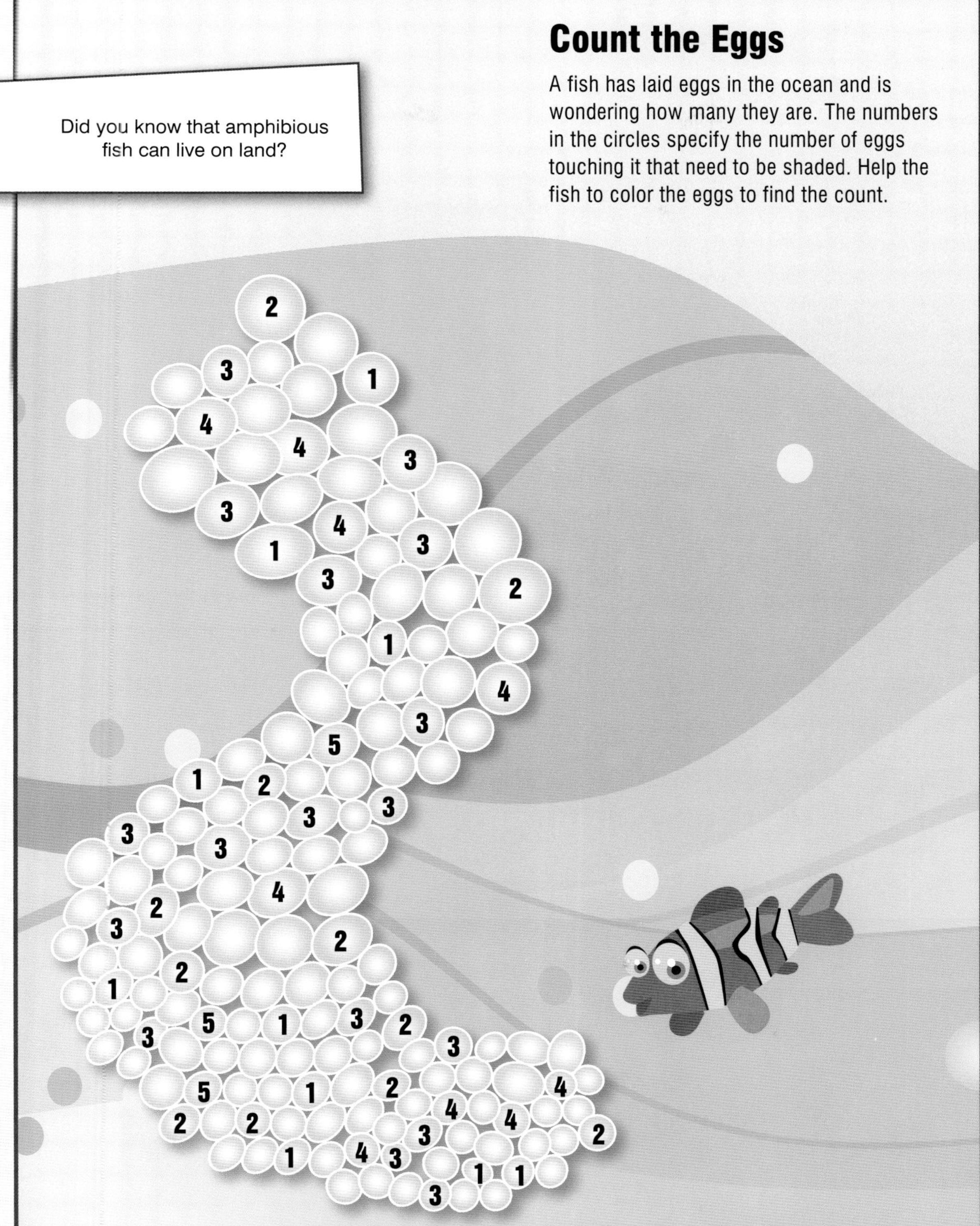

120

Letter Equation

Every row and column should have the letters A–E. No letter should be repeated in a row or column. Find the corresponding number for each letter to identify which number is greater than the other. For example, C=3, so the letter in the second cell of the first row needs to be a letter that corresponds to a number that is less than 3 (A or B).

C >		< B	>	
v			A	B
	D >	>		
E v		A	v	

An onion, apple and potato all have the same taste. The differences in flavor are caused by their smell.

121

Paint the Equation

Create an equation using each number on the color palette only once to get the result of the color you require. Use the mathematical signs in any combination and as many times as required.

"Poetry is the impish attempt to paint the color of the wind."
Maxwell Bodenheim

122

Laws of Nature

The chart contains different elements of nature. Complete it in such a way that every row and column has an element in it. No element should be repeated in either a row or a column.

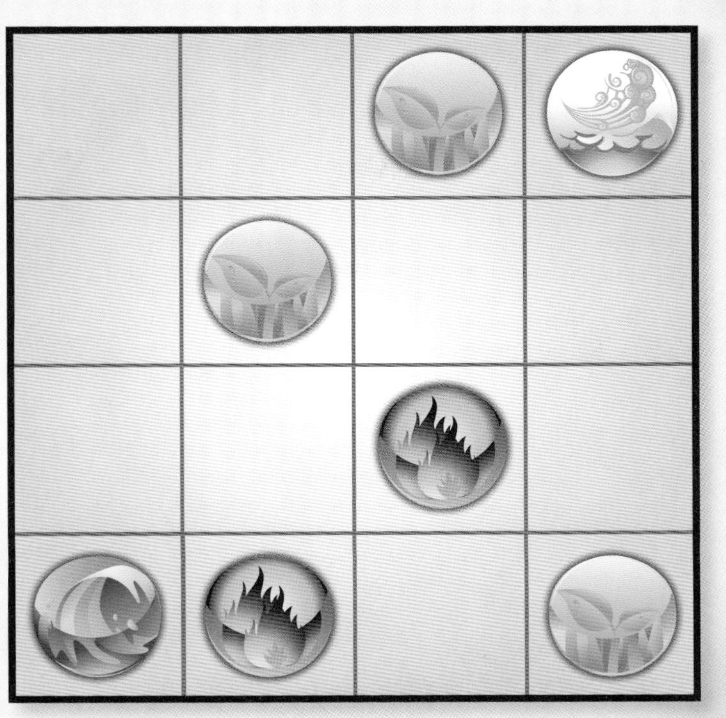

"We cannot command nature except by obeying her."

Francis Bacon

123

Find the Hidden Smileys

Insert smileys in the grid so that each row, column, and group of cells has only one smiley in it.

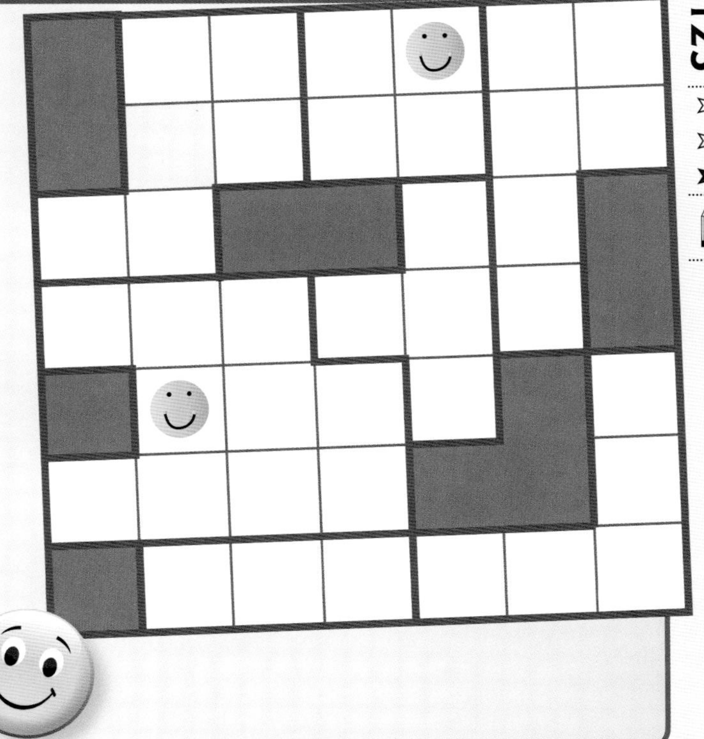

"The robber that smiles, steals something from the thief."

William Shakespeare

124 ☆☆★

Join the Pairs

The blackboard has pairs of numbers on it. You need to join each pair with a line without crossing lines for any other connections? Your lines cannot pass through the shaded blocks.

								4	
				1					
						3	5		
	1		2						
			5		4				
			2	3					

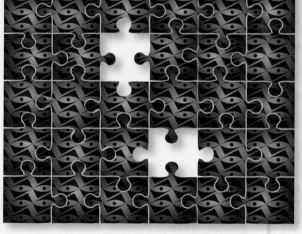

"The whole purpose of education is to turn mirrors into windows."

Sydney J. Harris

125 ☆★★

Jigsaw Puzzle

While arranging all the pieces, you realise that two pieces are missing. Can you find it?

"People who work crossword puzzles know that if they stop making progress, they should put the puzzle down for a while."

Marilyn vos Savant

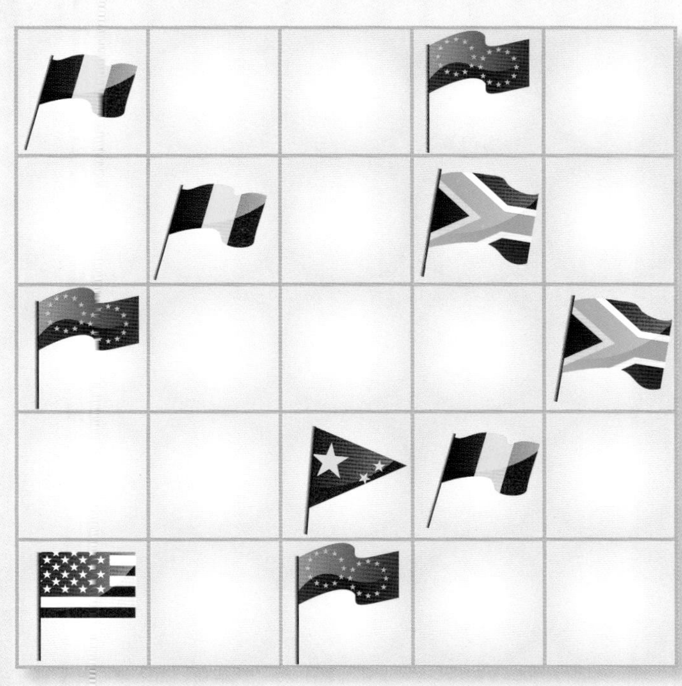

126

Place the Flags

The puzzle has flags of different countries. You need to fill flags in the empty cells so that every row and column has all five flags, without repeating any flag.

"Nationalism is an infantile disease. It is the measles of mankind."

Albert Einstein

127

Achieve the Impossible

Join all the dots with 12 lines without lifting your pen or pencil.

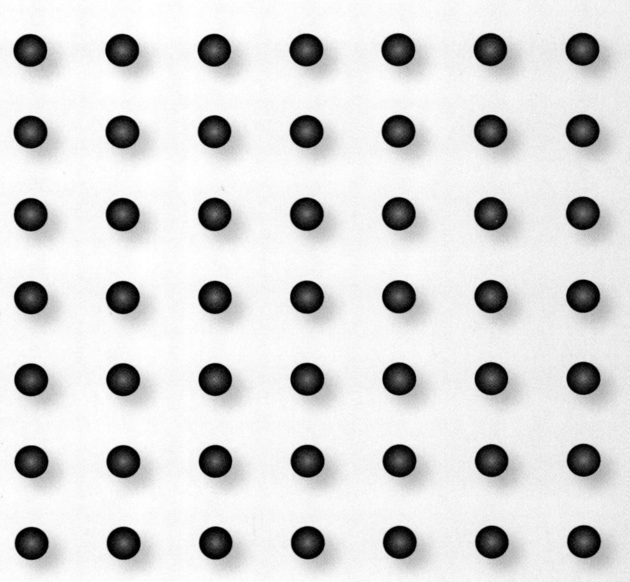

"It always seems impossible until it's done."

Nelson Mandela

128 

Let's Play Baseball

The sports store has numbered all its items. Each bat and ball is related by a number logic. Find the missing number on the last ball.

The first professional baseball league was initiated in 1871.

129 

Complete the Name Game

Mike challenges his wife Macy on her birthday to write her name on this board game. Write the letters M, A, C, and Y in such a way that each row and column has them.

"A diplomat is a man who always remembers a woman's birthday but never remembers her age."

Robert Frost

Match the Box 130

Anna has arranged a game for her children where they need to select the matching box. Help them identify the correct box that matches the unfolded pattern.

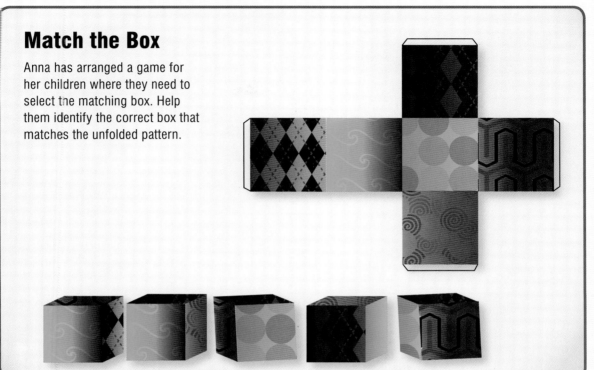

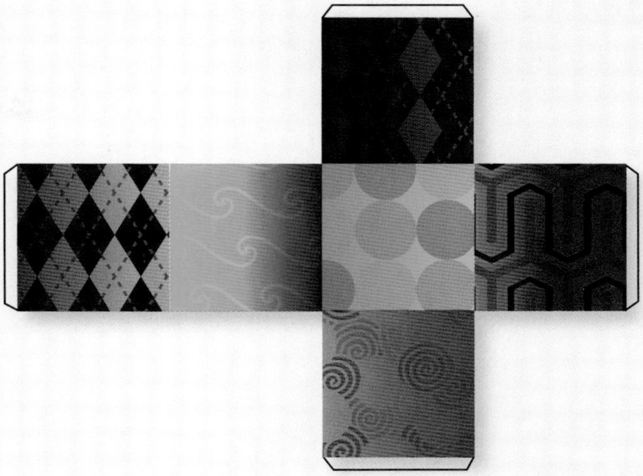

Animal Search 131

Each animal appears twice apart from one which appears once. Can you find the odd one out?

"Animals can communicate quite well. And they do. And generally speaking, they are ignored."

Alice Walker

132 ★★★

Flower Numbering

Number the flowers in such a way that each row, column, group and linked flowers have the numbers I–VI. You cannot repeat a number.

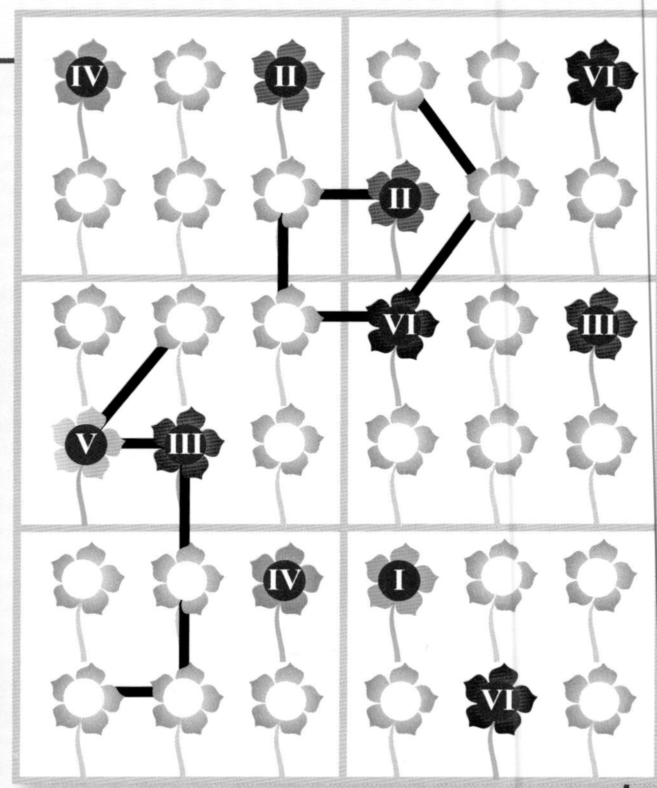

Did you know that the largest flower in the world is the Rafflesia arnoldi, which weighs 7 kg (15 pounds)?

133 ★★☆

Jewel Jumble

You are at a jewelry store and the jeweler is making a pendant out of Amber and Sapphire gems. There are multiple ways of making the pendant. Can you help him find one way? No gem of the same type and consecutive number should be placed together.

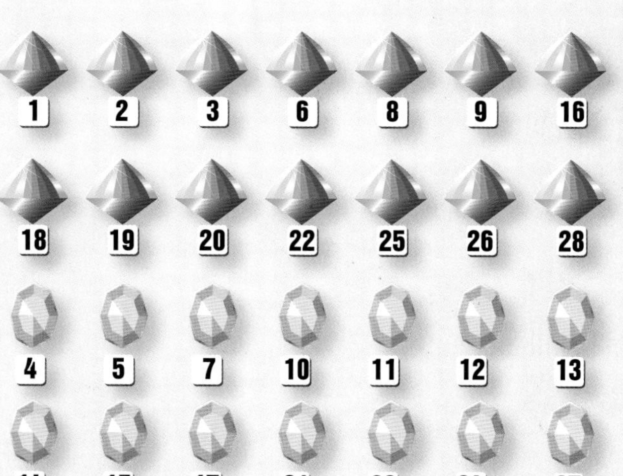

Amber is resin of pine that has fossilized and was formed 50 million years ago.

134 ☆☆★

Unfold the Laptop

Here is a laptop that has a really interesting cover. It has multiple blocks with different shapes and numbers. Add each number inside the shape with the number of edges of the shape around it. Find 3 adjacent blocks that add up to 31.

"The great thing about a computer notebook is that no matter how much you stuff into it, it doesn't get bigger or heavier."

Bill Gates

135 ☆★★

Open the Safe

Solve the puzzle on the electronic safe locker to open it. Fill the empty squares using the more or less signs. Every row, column and highlighted group should have the numbers 1–6, without repeating any number.

"He that's secure is not safe."

Benjamin Franklin

	2×2 ∨		<		∨
18/3				∧	
		<7−4	>	3+2	12/6
∨	4+1 ∨	>		∨	
1×1		<			15/3
	>		<	12/6	2×2

136 ★★★

Flower Maze

Each flower has a number or a sign. Create an equation using each number only once to get the result as written on the large flower. Use only the required mathematical signs in any combination and as many times as required.

During the 1600s, Tulips were so valuable that their bulbs were worth more than gold!

137 ★★☆

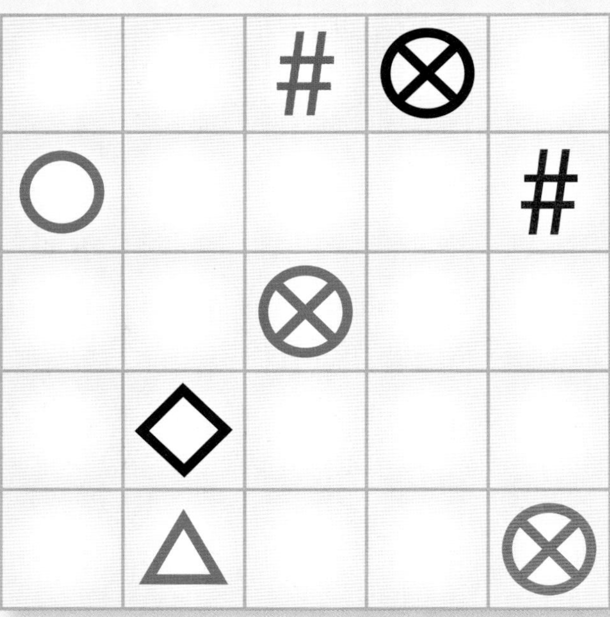

Place the Shapes

The puzzle has five different shapes with five colors. Every row and column should have each shape and color in it, without repeating any shape or color.

"Eagles come in all shapes and sizes, but you will recognize them chiefly by their attitudes."

E. F. Schumacher

Spot the Difference

Can you spot 10 differences between these two pictures of a day at the amusement park?

"Photograph: a picture painted by the sun without instruction in art."

Ambrose Bierce

139

Egg Connection

The eggs have to be placed in the egg tray but some of them are cracked. Arrange them in such a way that no two consecutive numbers are together. You also need to ensure that no cracked eggs are placed together. There are multiple ways of arranging them. Solve the puzzle to figure out which method works for you.

Did you know – If you spin a fresh egg, it wobbles, while a hardboiled egg spins easily.

140

Cookie Puzzle

The cookie wrapper has pairs of numbers on it. You need to join each pair with a line without crossing the lines for any other connections. Your lines cannot pass through the shaded blocks.

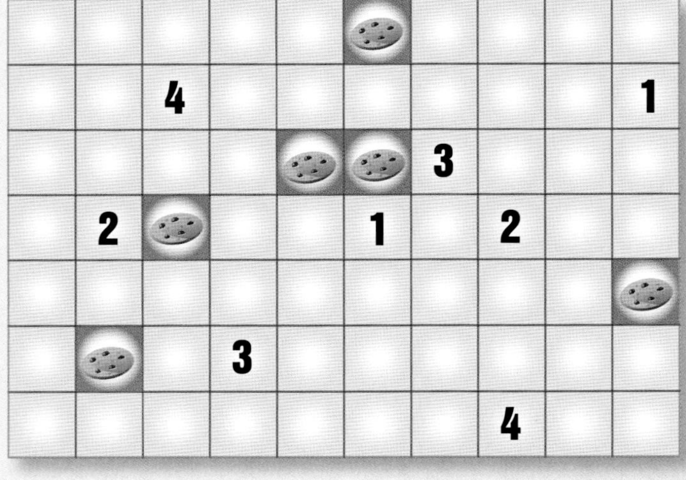

141

Seeing Stars

Which of the pictures below represents the correct overhead view of this scene?

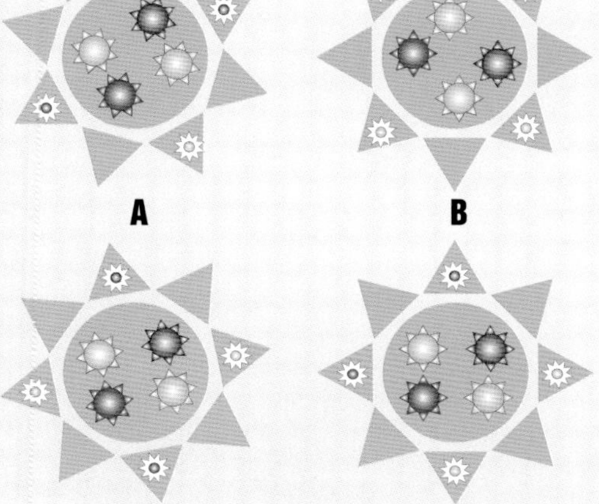

Did you know that stars are not visible from space?

142

Arrange the Bottles

There are bottles in six colors. Arrange them in such a way that every row, column and highlighted group has all six without repeating any color.

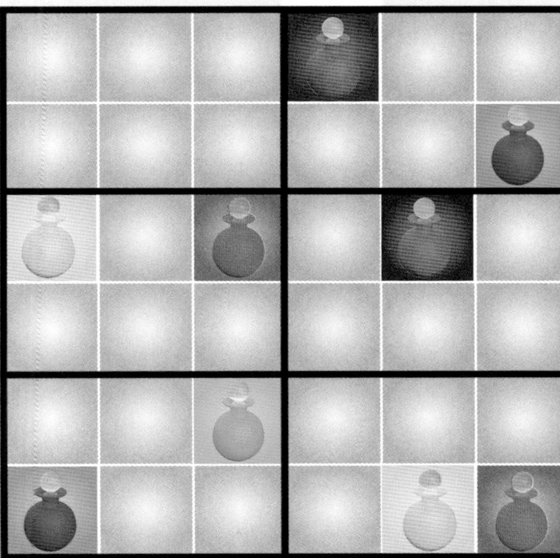

Recycling a single plastic bottle can conserve enough energy to light a 60-watt light bulb for up to six hours.

143

Join the Dots

There is an image hidden in these 16 dots. Join the dots without lifting your pen or pencil to see what it is.

"From now on, I'll connect the dots my own way."

Bill Watterson

144

Lock and Key

Each lock and key is paired based on a number pattern. Can you find the missing number on the key?

"Continuous effort - not strength or intelligence - is the key to unlocking our potential."

Winston Churchill

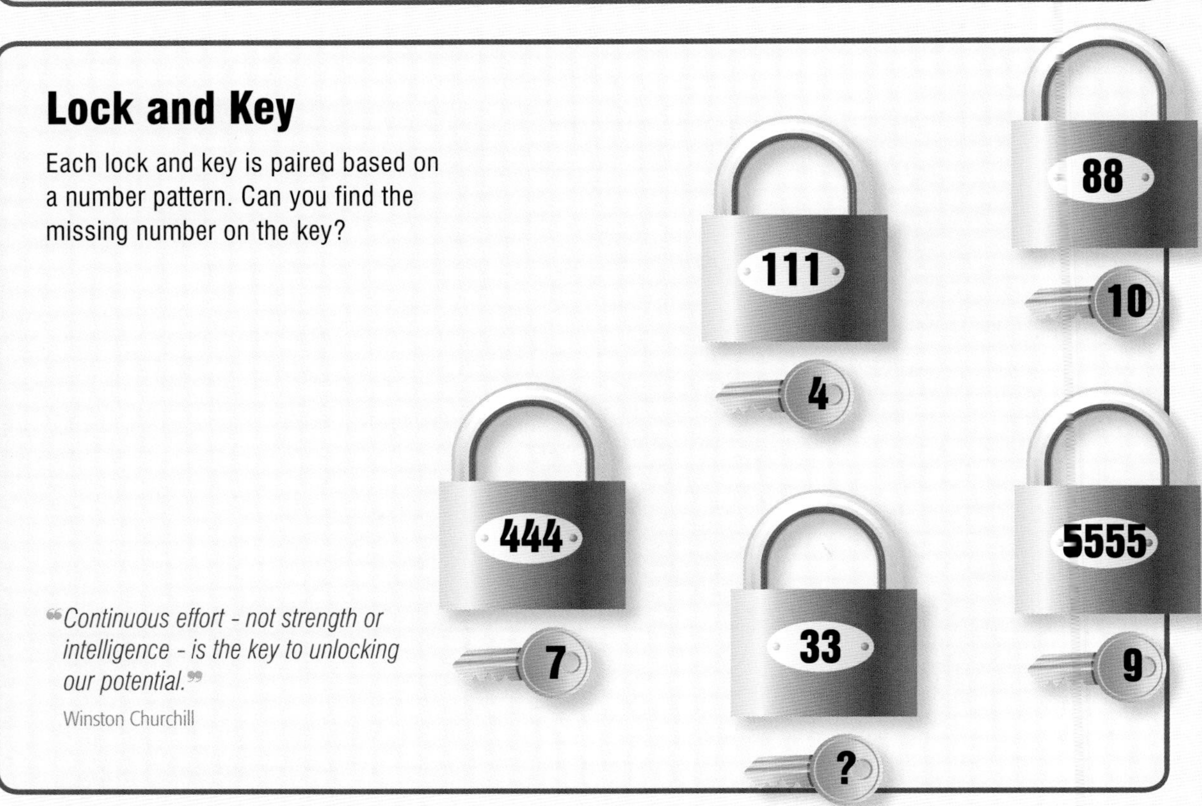

Matching Mirrors

You are at a mirror store and every mirror except for one has an identical one. Find the mirror that is not an identical twin.

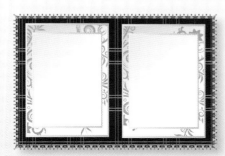

"A game is like a mirror that allows you to look at yourself."

Robert Kiyosaki

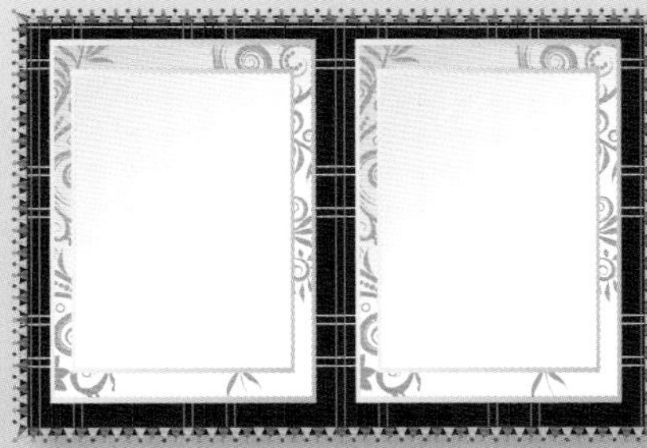
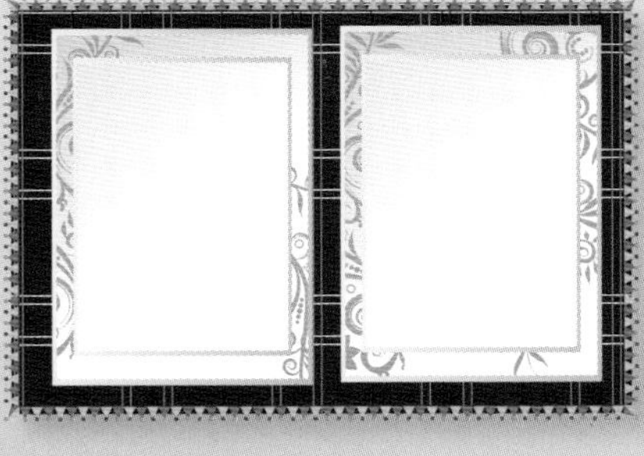
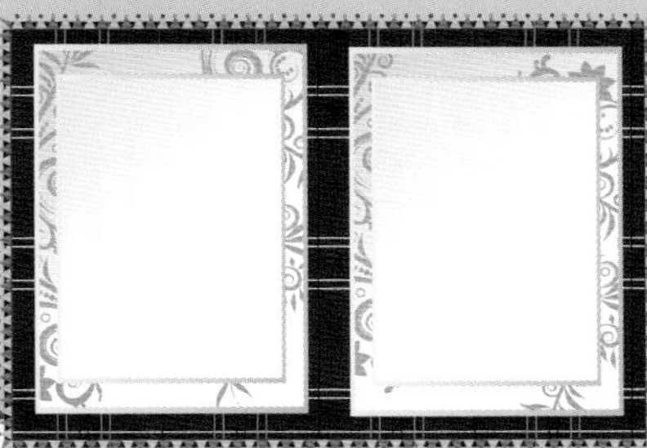

146

Calculate the Profit

Help Mike open the password protected file to calculate the business profits. The letters in the third column of the puzzle form the password. Every row and column should have the letters A–E. No letter should be repeated in a row or group.

	D	A		
			E	D
E			A	
	B			
		C		A

"A business that makes nothing but money is a poor business."

Henry Ford

147

Match the Skirt

There are six wraparound skirts on display and one is left unfolded. Find the skirt that matches the unfolded one.

Did you know that the skirt is the second oldest women's garment in history?

148 ☆★★

Number the Homes

Number the homes in such a way that each row, column, group and linked homes has the numbers 1–6 without repeating any number.

"Home is the place where, when you have to go there, they have to take you in."

Robert Frost

149 ☆☆★

Arrange the Cans

You need to place 36 cans in a refrigerator in such a way that no consecutive or even numbers are together. Identify any one of the multiple ways of doing so.

1 2 3 4 5 6 7 8 9
10 11 12 13 14 15 16 17 18
19 20 21 22 23 24 25 26 27
28 29 30 31 32 33 34 35 36

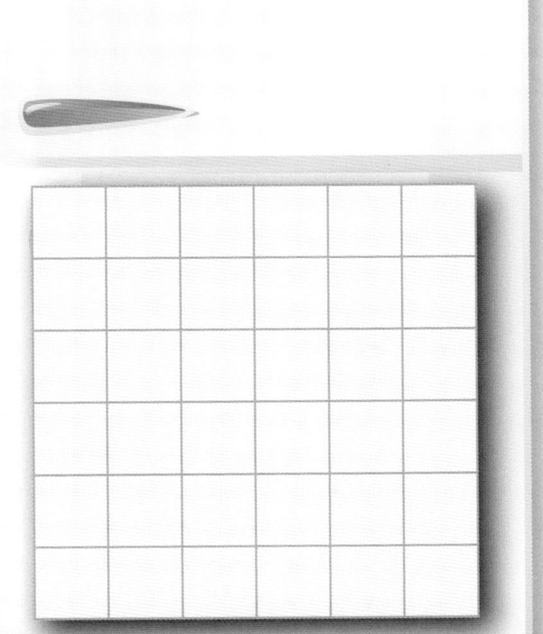

Drinking cola can affect the ability of white blood cells to kill bacteria in the body for up to seven hours.

150

Bag Confusion

Here is a school bag that has multiple cubes. Each cube has different shapes and calculations in it. Calculate and add the result with the number of edges of the shape around it. Find 2 adjacent blocks that add up to 21.

"Poverty often deprives a man of all spirit and virtue; it is hard for an empty bag to stand upright."

Benjamin Franklin

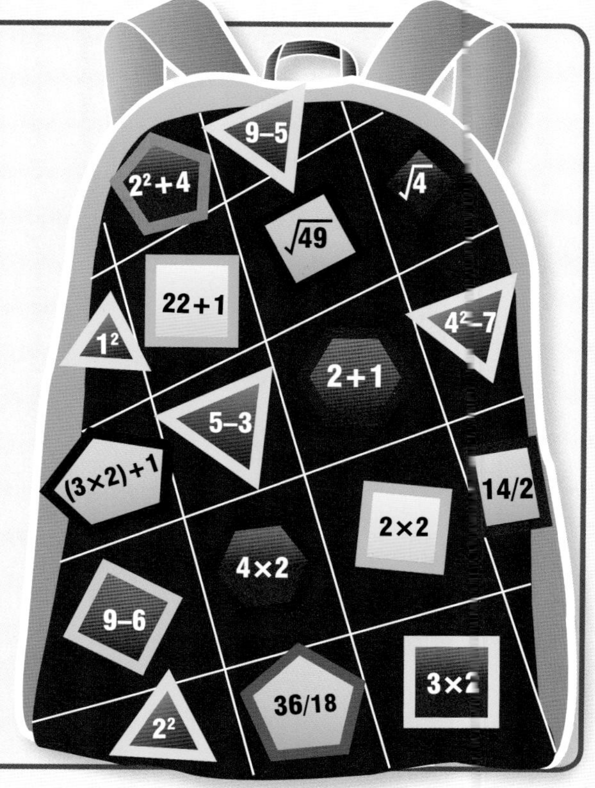

151

Paint the Flower Pyramid

Here is a pyramid that needs to be painted. It has numbers written on the flowers that specify the number of flowers touching it that are pink colored. Start coloring your pyramid pink.

Count the Cattle 152

Here's a chart that maintains a count of the number of cattle in the Savanna region. Fill the empty squares using the more or less signs so that every row and column has the numbers I–IV, without repeating any number.

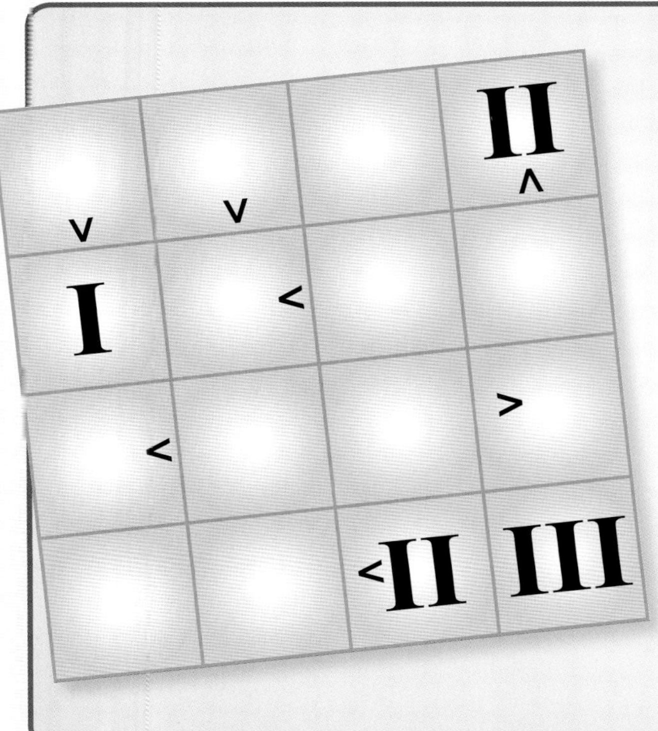

"To make a goal of comfort or happiness has never appealed to me; a system of ethics built on this basis would be sufficient only for a herd of cattle."

Albert Einstein

Egg Equation 153

Create an equation using each number on the egg only once to get the result written on the large egg. Use only the required mathematical signs in any combination and as many times as required.

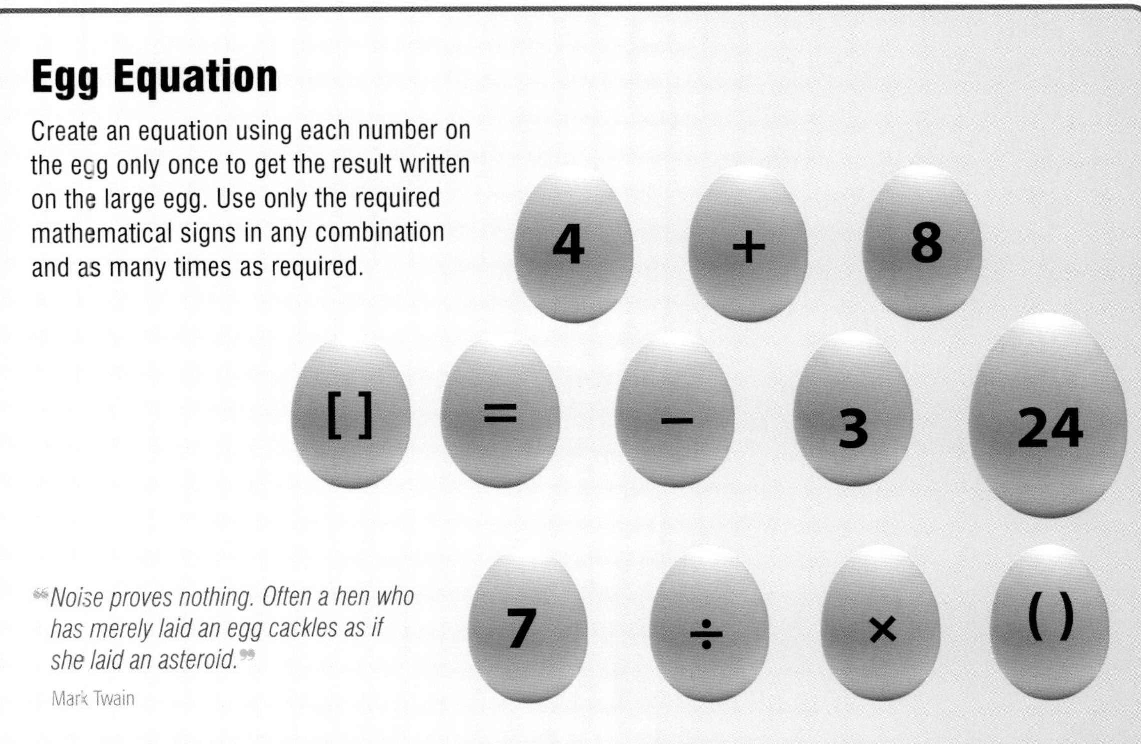

"Noise proves nothing. Often a hen who has merely laid an egg cackles as if she laid an asteroid."

Mark Twain

154

Spot the Tree

Which image matches the silhouette?

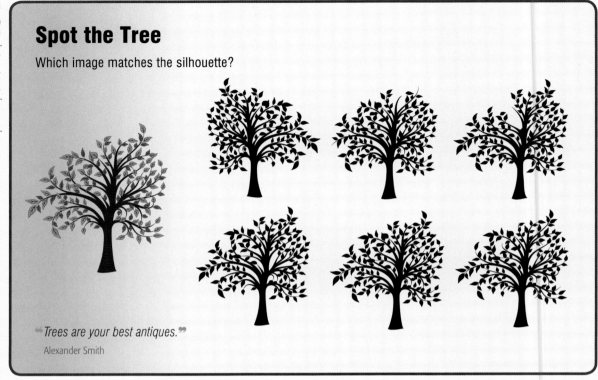

"Trees are your best antiques."

Alexander Smith

155

Spring Confusion

Insert flowers in the grid in such a way that each row, column and group has only one flower in it.

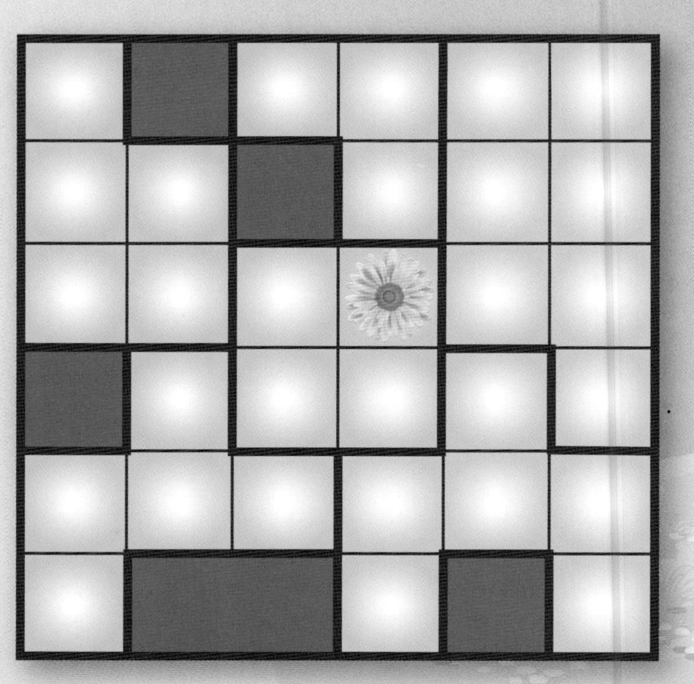

"Spring is nature's way of saying, "Let's party"!"

Robin Williams

156

Doughnut Store

Arrange the cream and chocolate doughnuts in such a way that no doughnuts of the same type and with adjacent numbers are placed together. Also, group the first eight doughnuts into the first two rows, the next eight in the next two rows and so on.

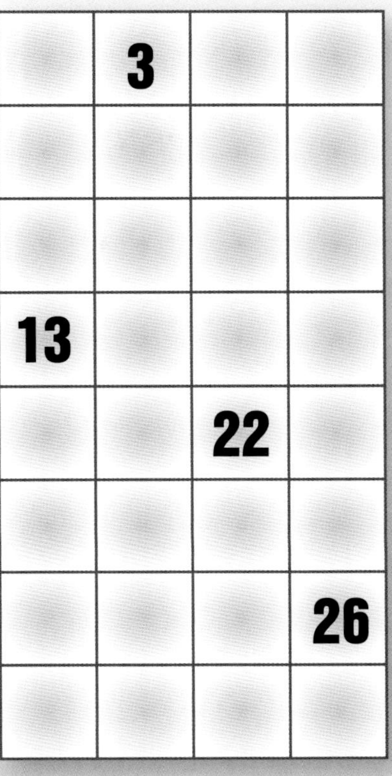

Did you know that the first doughnut machine was invented in 1920, in New York, by Adolph Levitt.

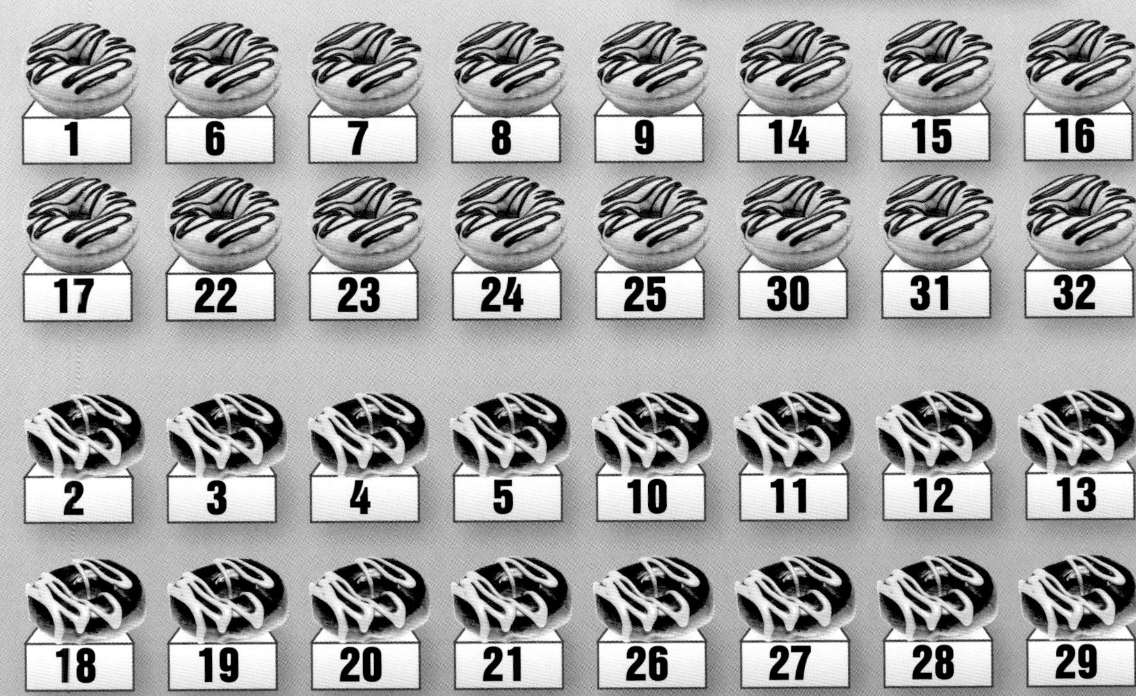

157

Mysterious Ship

Join each pair of numbers with a line without crossing lines for any other connections. Your lines cannot pass through the shaded blocks.

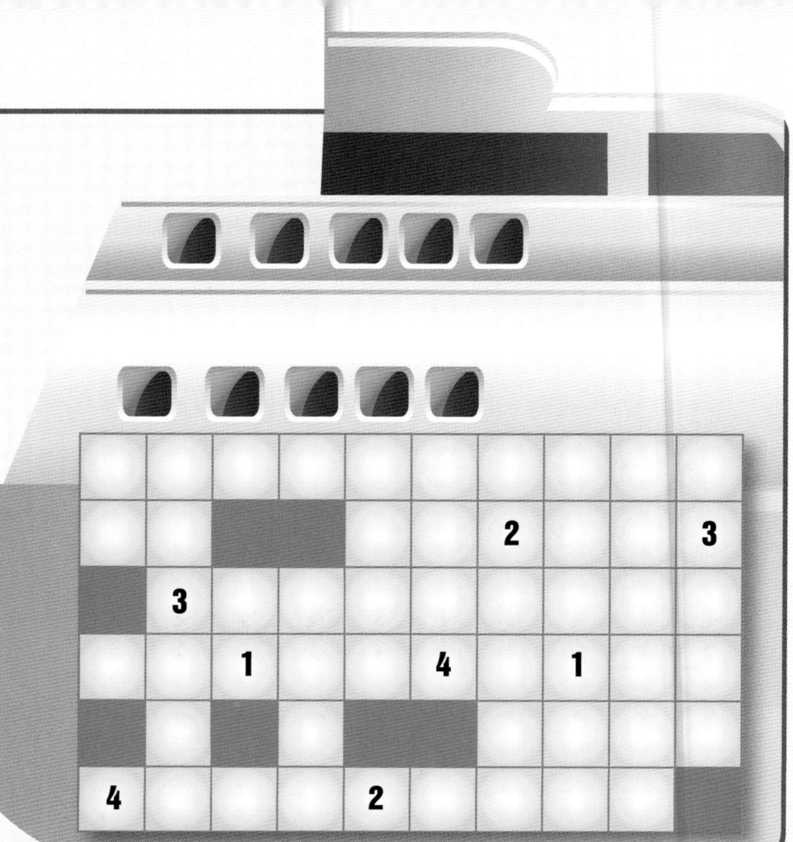

						2			3
	3								
		1			4		1		
4				2					

"Beware of the little expenses; a small leak will sink a great ship."

Benjamin Franklin

158

Balloon Maze

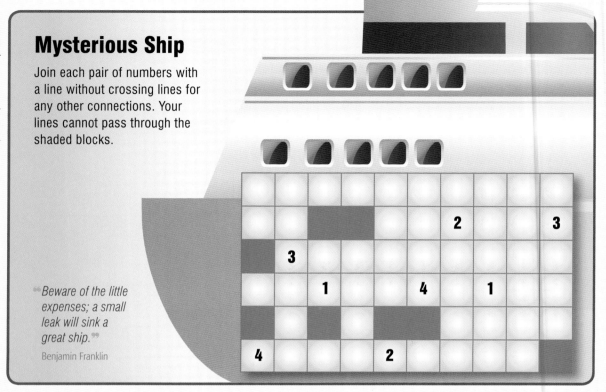

Find the number on the last balloon. Use the numbers provided on the other balloons to find the number that should replace the question mark for the third balloon.

Balloons were invented in 1824, the same year as the electromagnet.

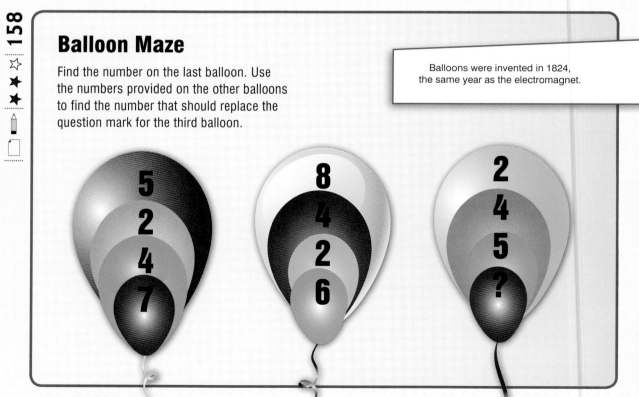

159

Complete the Vegetable Chart

Complete the vegetable chart in such a way that four vegetables are there in each row and column without any repetition.

Did you know that mushrooms have no leaves, roots, or seeds, and does not need any light to grow?

160

Draw the Boat

Join the drops to form the shape of the boat by using six lines without lifting your pen or pencil. Find one of the multiple ways of doing so.

"He who loves practice without theory is like the sailor who boards ship without a rudder and compass and never knows where he may cast."

Leonardo da Vinci

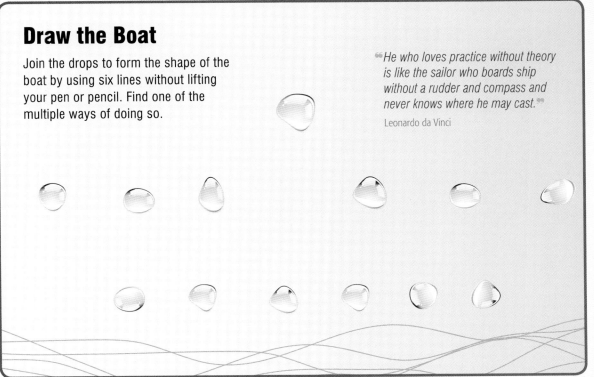

161

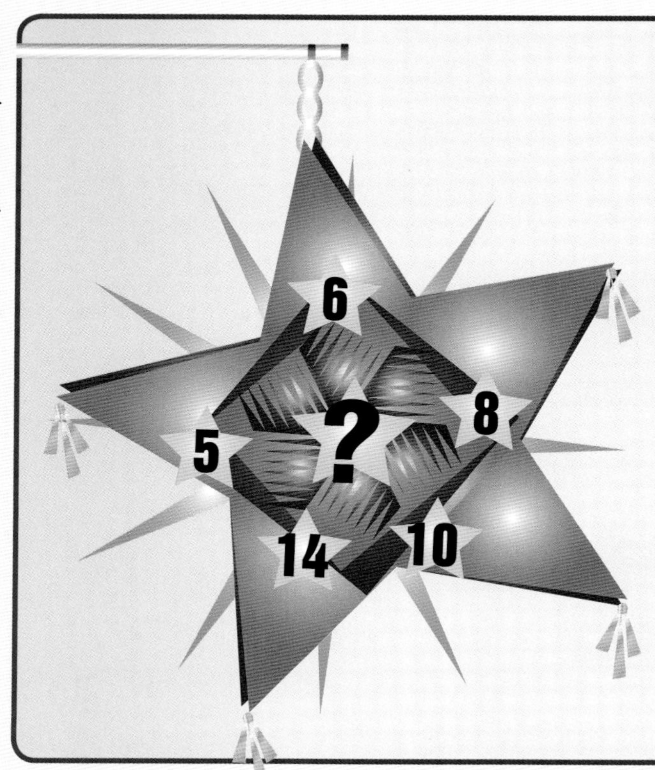

Make the Star Glow

The numbers placed on the star follow a sequence. Complete the sequence to replace the question mark.

"He turns not back who is bound to a star."

Leonardo da Vinci

162

Dazzling Diamonds

In the sequence below, which of the numbered alternatives, A, B, C, or D, should replace the question mark?

Cullinan is the world's largest diamond that was found in South Africa in 1905.

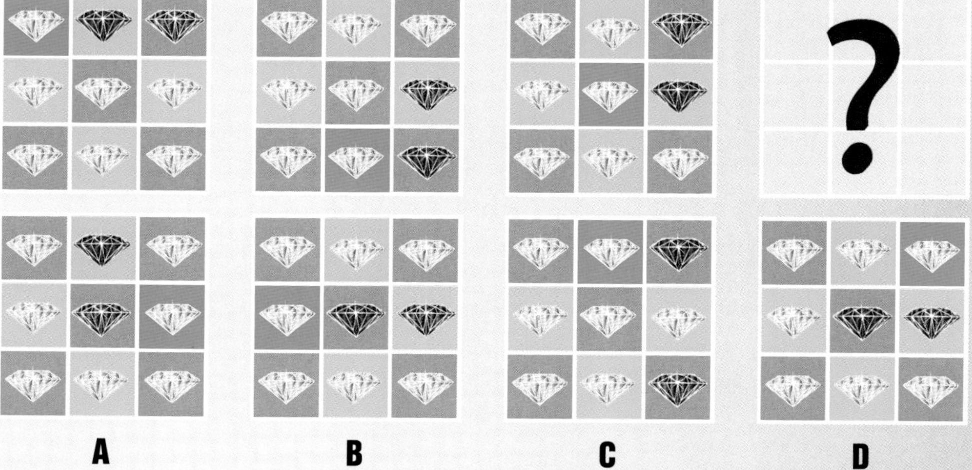

Find the Watch

163 ☆★★

You are giving your friend a watch. There are six boxes that are gift wrapped but only one box has the watch. The box with the watch matches the unfolded box. Find it.

Did you know that Peter Henlein from Germany created the first pocket watch in 1500s.

Find the Odd One Out

164 ☆★★

All the earrings are in pairs except for one. Can you find the odd one out?

165

Arrange the Display

Arrange these three gift items in the placeholder in such a way that no item is repeated and no consecutive numbers are together. Some of the items have already been placed, complete the rest.

"Joy in looking and comprehending is nature's most beautiful gift."
Albert Einstein

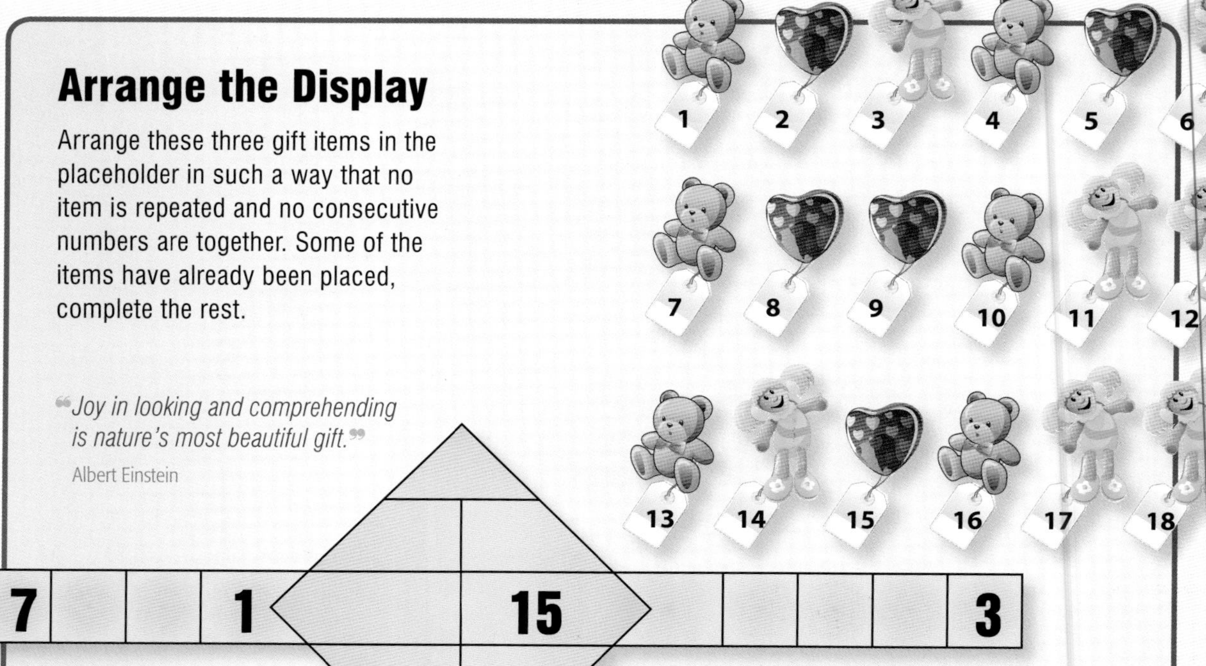

166

Number the Balls

Number the balls in such a way that each row, column and linked balls has the numbers 1–4 without repeating any.

$\sqrt{9}$ $\sqrt{4}$

2^2 1^2

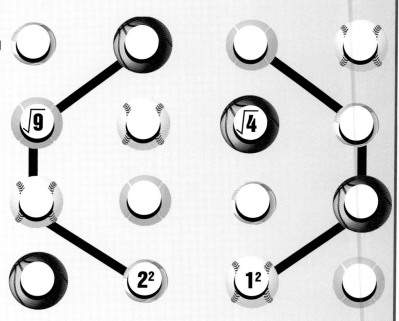

167

Bottle Game

The bottle has multiple shapes with a letter inside. Find the corresponding number for each letter. Multiply the number you found with the total number of edges of the shape around it. For example, B=2 and 2X6=12. So the number for the first block is 12. Find 4 adjacent blocks that total 84.

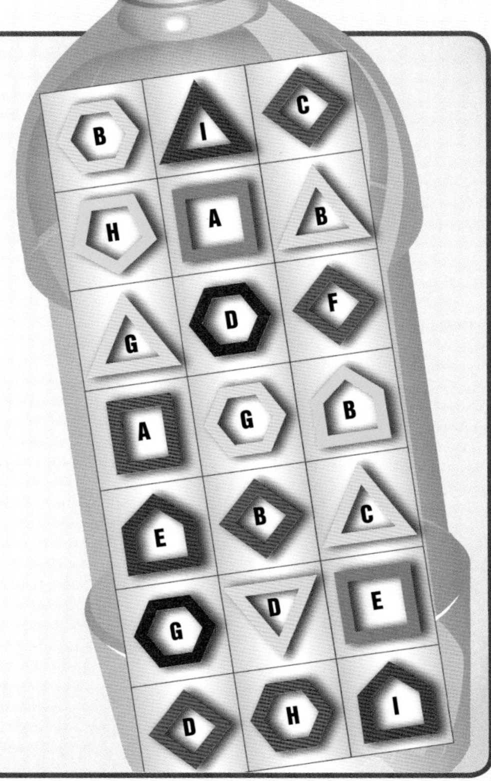

The safest types of plastic water bottles are polyethylene (marked with a 2), polyethylene (marked with a 4) or polypropylene (marked with a 5).

168

Color the Fish

The fish bowl contains colorful fish. You need to color the yellow ones. The numbers on the fish specify the number of yellow fish. Find them.

Did you know that fish were well established long before the dinosaurs roamed the earth?

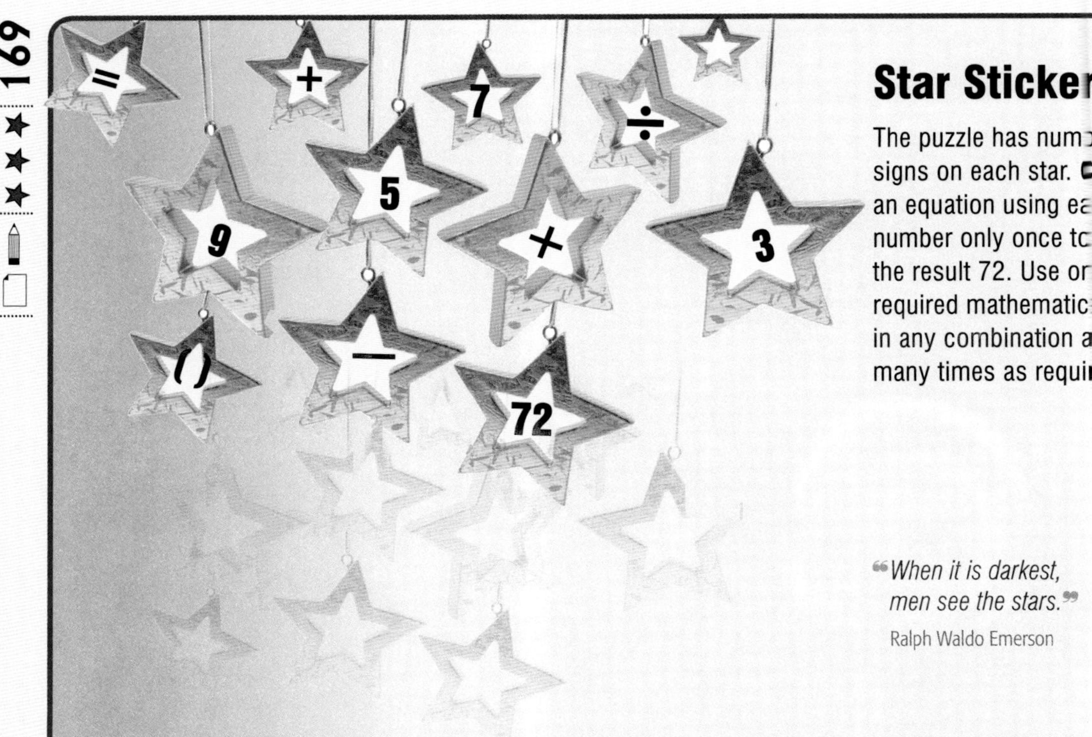

Star Sticker

The puzzle has numbers or signs on each star. Create an equation using each number only once to get the result 72. Use only the required mathematical signs in any combination and as many times as required.

"When it is darkest, men see the stars."

Ralph Waldo Emerson

170 ★★★

Number Logic

Fill the empty squares using the more or less signs. Every row, column and highlighted group should have the numbers 1–9 without any repetition.

			>					
>	7	<		4 <		1		
			9	>			6 >	
2	^	>	7		9	^ 5		
			8	3 >			^	
	^		1			2		8
3 >		^		v	<		9	
9	8	6 >		<	3		2	
	1	7			>		3	v

Did you know that September 11 is the 254th day of a year and 2+5+4 = 11?

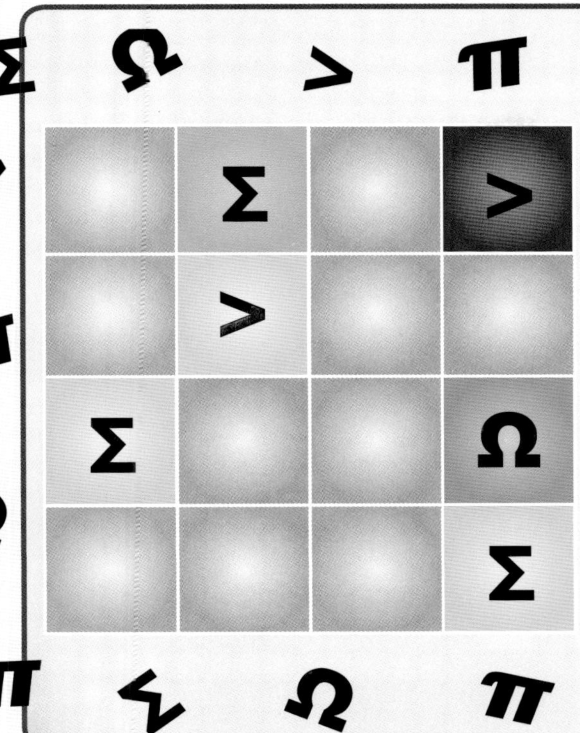

Find the Missing Signs

171

You have to create a chart of mathematical signs for your project. Arrange all four signs with four different colors in such a way that every row and column has each sign and color without any repetition.

Did you know that Omega is the 24th and last letter of the Greek alphabet?

Decorate the Stage

172

Decorate the grid with bouquets in such a way that each row, column and group of cells has only one bouquet in it.

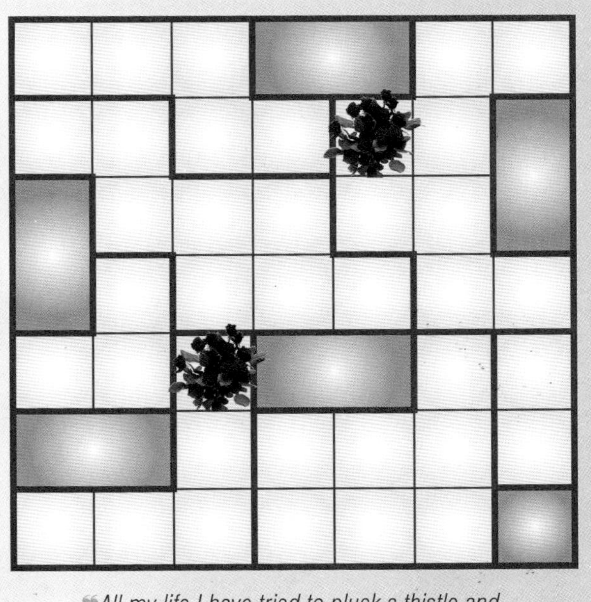

"All my life I have tried to pluck a thistle and plant a flower wherever the flower would grow in thought and mind."

Abraham Lincoln

173 ☆☆★

Join the Pairs

Join the pairs of numbers on the board without crossing lines for any other connections. Your lines cannot pass through the shaded blocks.

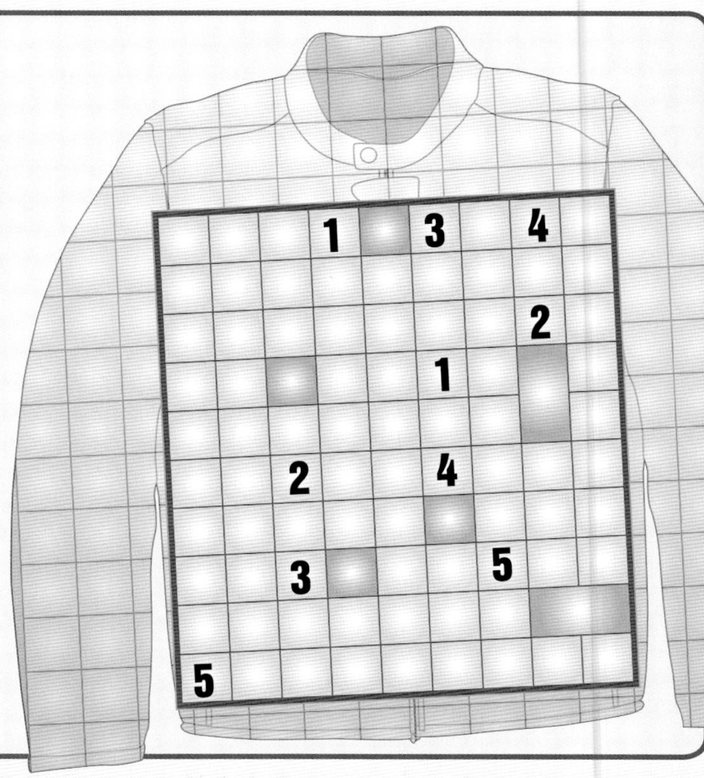

Did you know that the number five is classified as a Fermat prime because it can be written as 2^2+1.

174 ☆★★

Reuniting the Bricks

Three rectangular bricks have been broken into three pieces each. Can you reunite them?

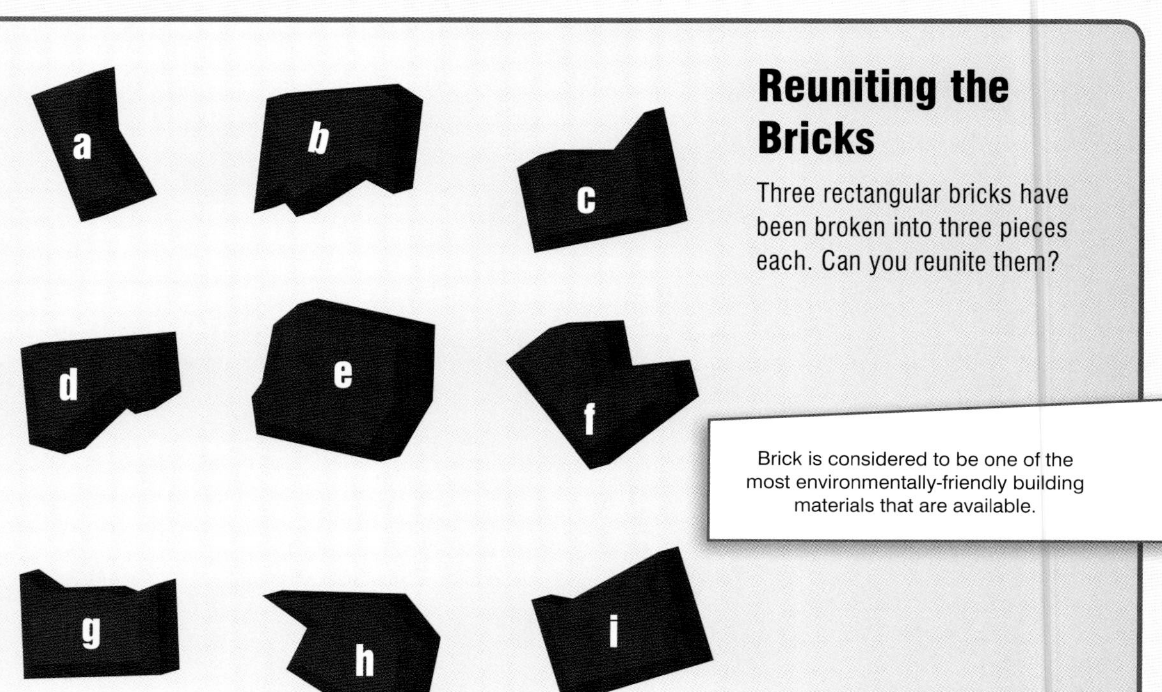

Brick is considered to be one of the most environmentally-friendly building materials that are available.

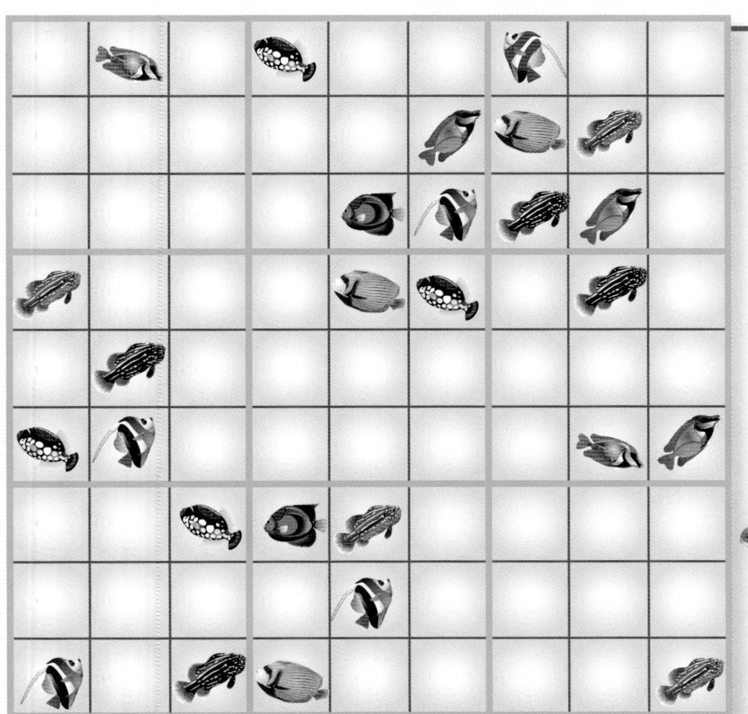

175 ★★★

Fill the Tank

The fish tank has fish in different colors. Draw the missing ones so that each row, column and highlighted group has all nine colors.

Did you know that there are over 25,000 identified species of fishes on the earth?

176 ☆★★

Join the Musical Notes

You are attending a concert and the musician has forgotten some tunes. Help him remember by joining the 16 notes with 6 lines. You cannot lift your pen or pencil.

"A painter paints pictures on canvas. But musicians paint their pictures on silence."

Leopold Stokowski

177

Logic and Calculations

The numbers are placed in a sequence. Replace the question mark to complete the sequence.

"The idea of a being who interferes with the sequence of events in the world is absolutely impossible."

Albert Einstein

178

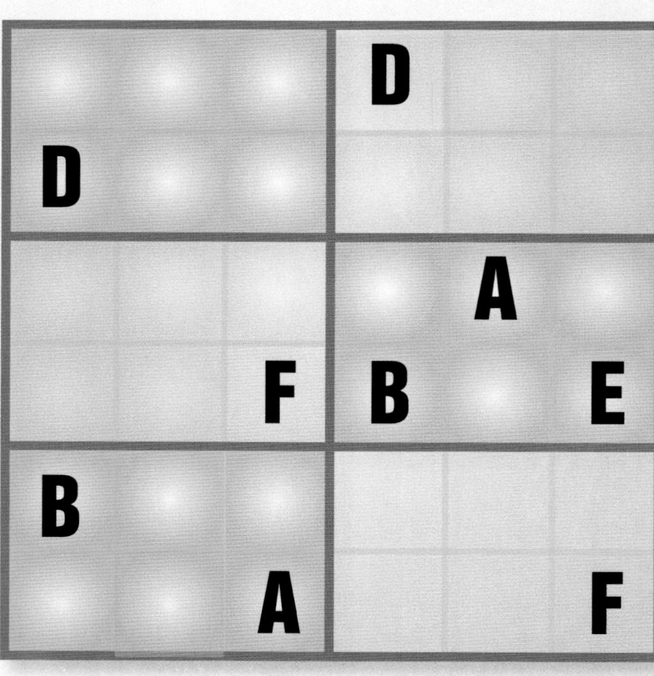

Fun with Letters

Complete the letters in the grid in such a way that every row, column and group has the letters A–F. No letter should be repeated in a row, column or group.

"Whatever games are played with us, we must play no games with ourselves."

Ralph Waldo Emerson

179

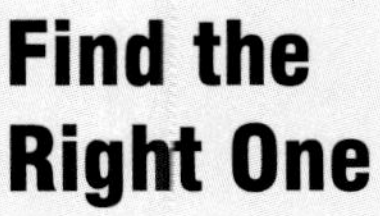

Find the Right One

Only one out of the four flower pots matches the unfolded flower pot. Find the right flower pot.

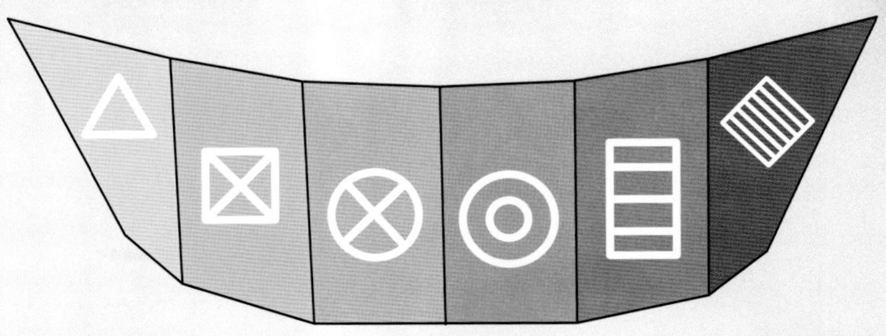

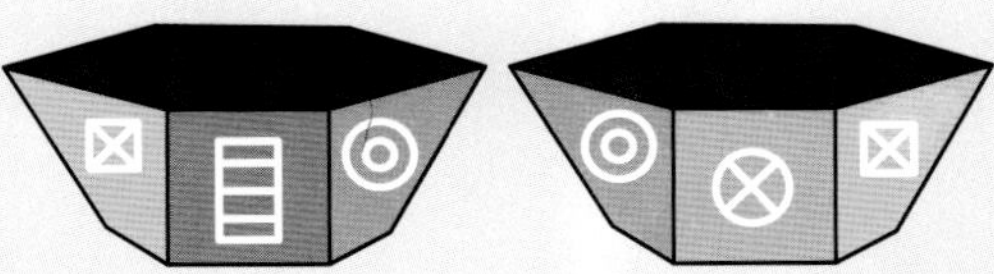

"A person born to be a flower pot will not go beyond the porch."

A Mexican Proverb

180

Number the Umbrellas

The puzzle has umbrellas that are numbered 1–5. Put the numbers on the empty umbrellas in such a way that each row, column and linked umbrellas has all 5 numbers, without repeating any number.

181

Music Store

Arrange the CDs and DVDs in such a way that no two consecutive numbers, CDs or DVDs are together horizontally or vertically.

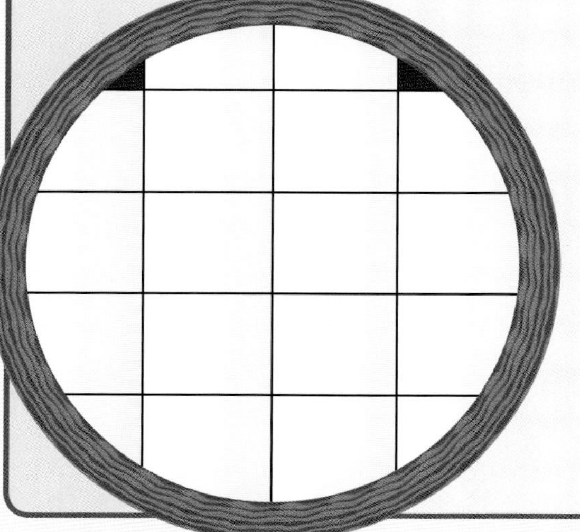

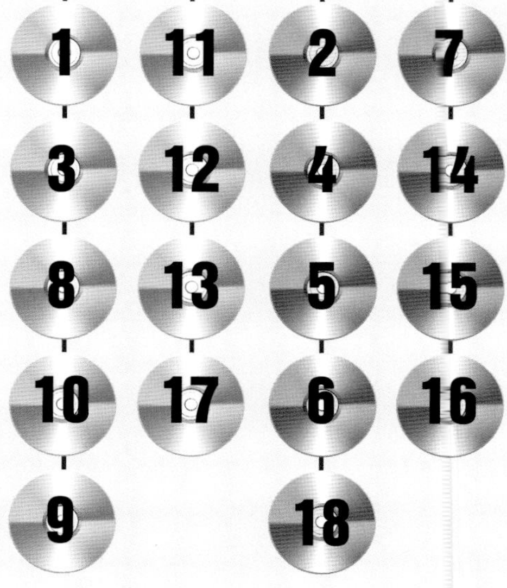

"Music washes away from the sou the dust of everyday life."

Berthold Auerbach

182

Tray Mystery

The tray has blocks containing different shapes that have numbers inside them. Multiply each number with the number of edges around each shape. Find 4 adjacent blocks that add up to 65.

"Governing a great nation is like cooking a small fish - too much handling will spoil it."

Lao Tzu

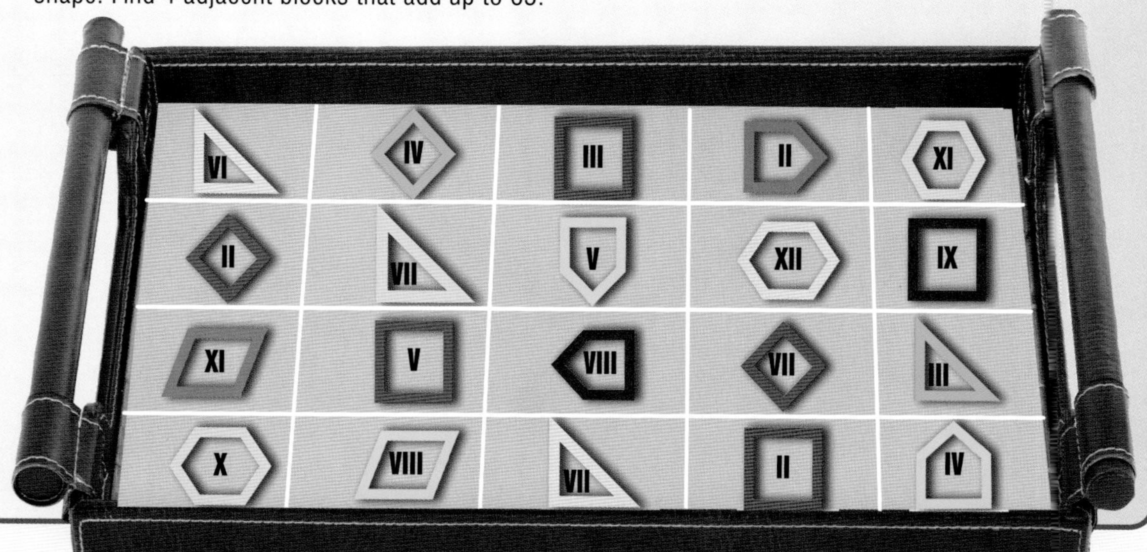

183

Aqua Plants

The mall that you are visiting has multiple tanks with aqua plants. Each tank except for one has a pair. Find the odd tank.

Did you know that aquatic plants have specialized roots that are able to take in oxygen?

184 ★☆☆

Pyramid Trick

Color the Egyptian pyramid using the numbers written on it. The numbers in the triangles specify the number of triangles sharing common sides that need to be shaded.

The ancient Egyptians took almost 20 years to build one pyramid!

185 ★★★

Fill it up

In this book exhibition you need to solve the given puzzle to win a free book. Fill the empty squares using the more or less signs. Every row, column and highlighted group should have the numbers 1–6, without any number being repeated.

>	3	5	^	>	
	<				
		6	4	<	3
4 >			5 v	6	
5	>				
<			1	>	4

"A good decision is based on knowledge and not on numbers."
Plato

186 ★★★

Circles and Squares

Create an equation using the number in the circles only once to get 22 as the result. Use only the required mathematical signs in the squares in any combination and as many times as required.

"Pure mathematics is, in its way, the poetry of logical ideas."

Albert Einstein

187 ☆☆★

Elements of the Universe

You are creating a chart to teach children about the different elements of the universe. Arrange the four objects in such a way that every row and column has each object, without any repetition.

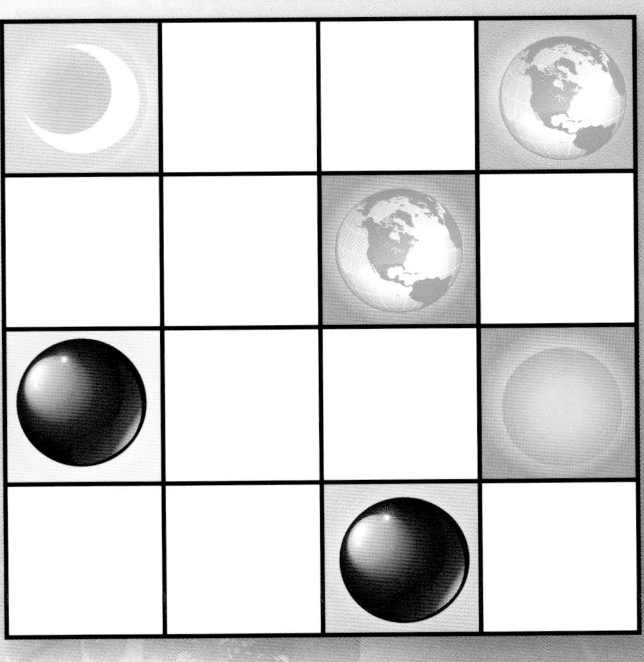

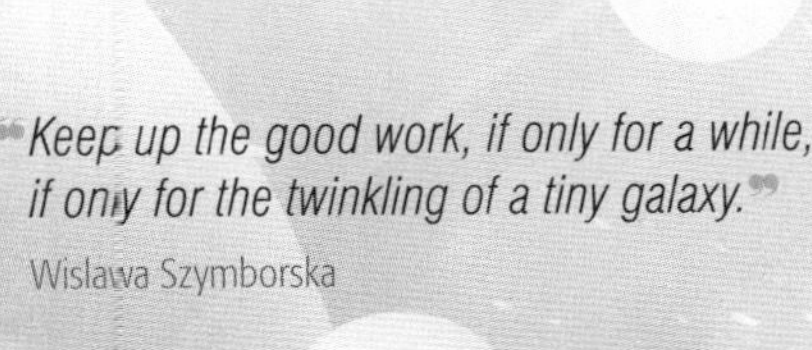

"Keep up the good work, if only for a while, if only for the twinkling of a tiny galaxy."

Wislawa Szymborska

188

Design the T-Shirt

Your friend has designed a T-shirt with a puzzle on it. You need to fill the empty cells without repeating the letters A–H in a row, column or group.

E			A			B	
		G	C			F	D
A				B	C		
		B					A
	F		H			E	
				C	H		
D						C	H
	C		B	G			

"Don't play what's there, play what's not there."

Miles Davis

189

Complex Counts

Can you work out which cube from A, B, C and D will fill the empty box?

"Do not worry about your problems with mathematics; I assure you mine are far greater."

Albert Einstein

2	9	6
4	3	1
5	7	3

8	5	3
3	7	2
4	4	4

11	2	10
5	1	2
3	3	3

A

1	5	2
3	6	9
11	4	2

B

5	13	2
1	7	2
4	4	2

C

6	5	4
9	8	7
1	1	1

D

4	7	2
6	5	5
3	2	5

"The next best thing to being wise oneself is to live in a circle of those who are."

C.S. Lewis

Puzzling Puzzle

190

In the sequence below, which of the numbered alternatives, A, B, C, or D, should replace the question mark?

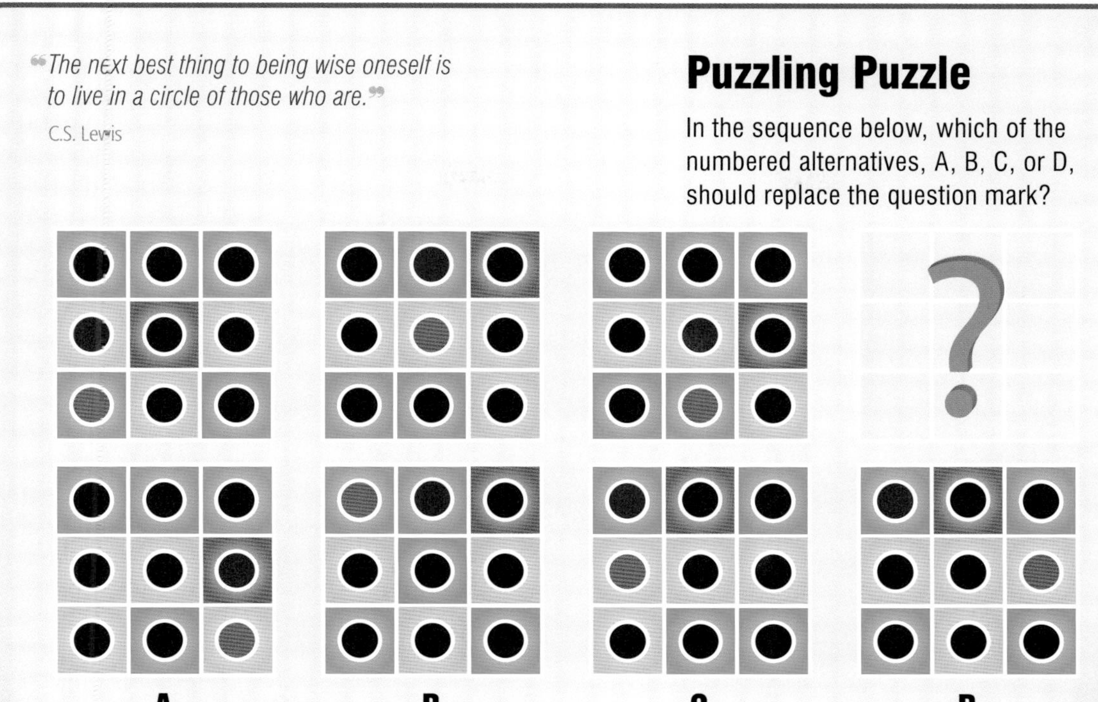

Crack a Smile

191

This grid has equal number of rows and columns with some cells blocked. Also, there are groups of cells highlighted. Can you insert smileys in such a way that each row, each column and each group of cells has only one smiley in it?

When a person studies laughter they are known as a "gelotologist".

192

Complete the Puzzle

You have a box full of puzzles but it is locked. Find the missing number to open the box and enjoy the games.

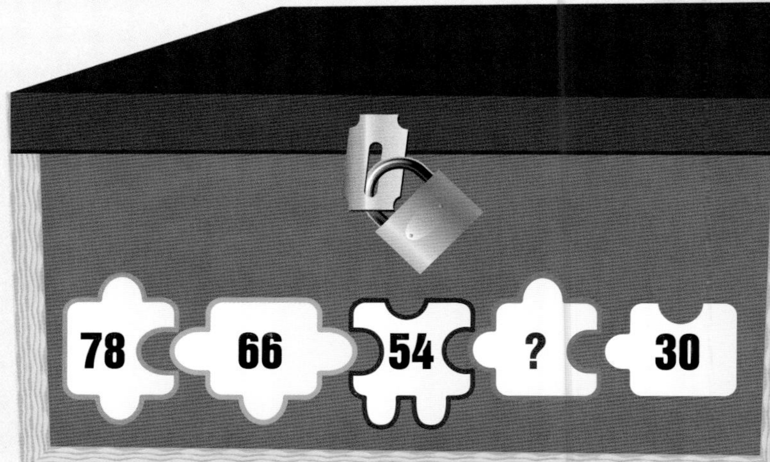

"The art of simplicity is a puzzle of complexity."

Doug Horton

193

C		B	
	D	A	

Logical Letters

Add the missing letters to the puzzle in such a way that every row, column and group has the letters. No letter can be repeated.

194

Road Maze

Join each pair of numbers on the pathway with a line without crossing lines for any other connections. Your lines cannot pass through the shaded blocks.

"The best road to progress is freedom's road."

John F. Kennedy

195

Find the Correct Bangle

Here are five bangles. One of these bangles matches the unfolded bangle below. Can you find it?

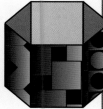

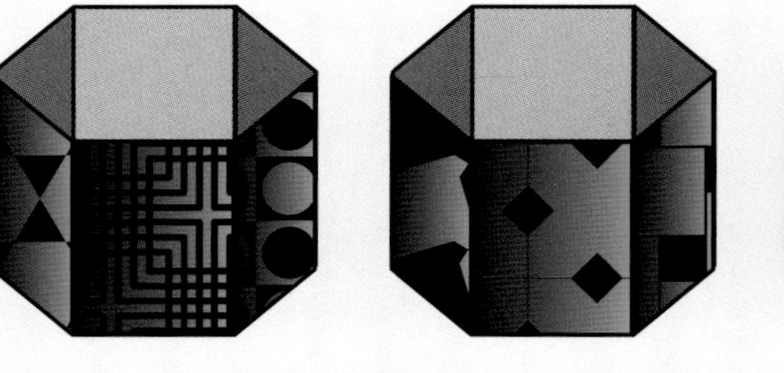

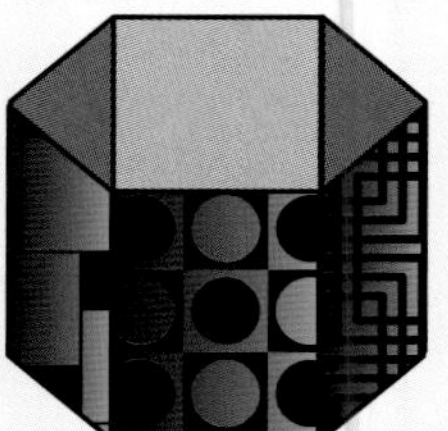

"A woman wears her tears like jewelry."

Anonymous

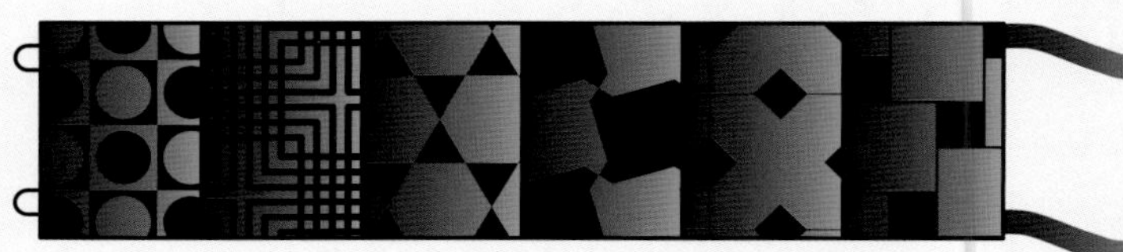

196

Find the Odd Dish

At a restaurant, there are seven fruit dishes kept on a table, three are pairs. Find the odd one out?

"All good things which exist are the fruits of originality."

John Stuart Mill

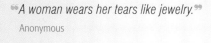

Number the Fruit Bowls 197

Number the fruit bowls from 1–5 in such a way that no number is repeated in a row or column, and the bowls that are linked together.

Did you know that it takes two years for a pineapple plant to produce a fruit. Each plant typically produces at the most two

Coin Puzzle 198

Fill the empty coins using the letters A–E in such a way that each row and column has all the letters without any repetition.

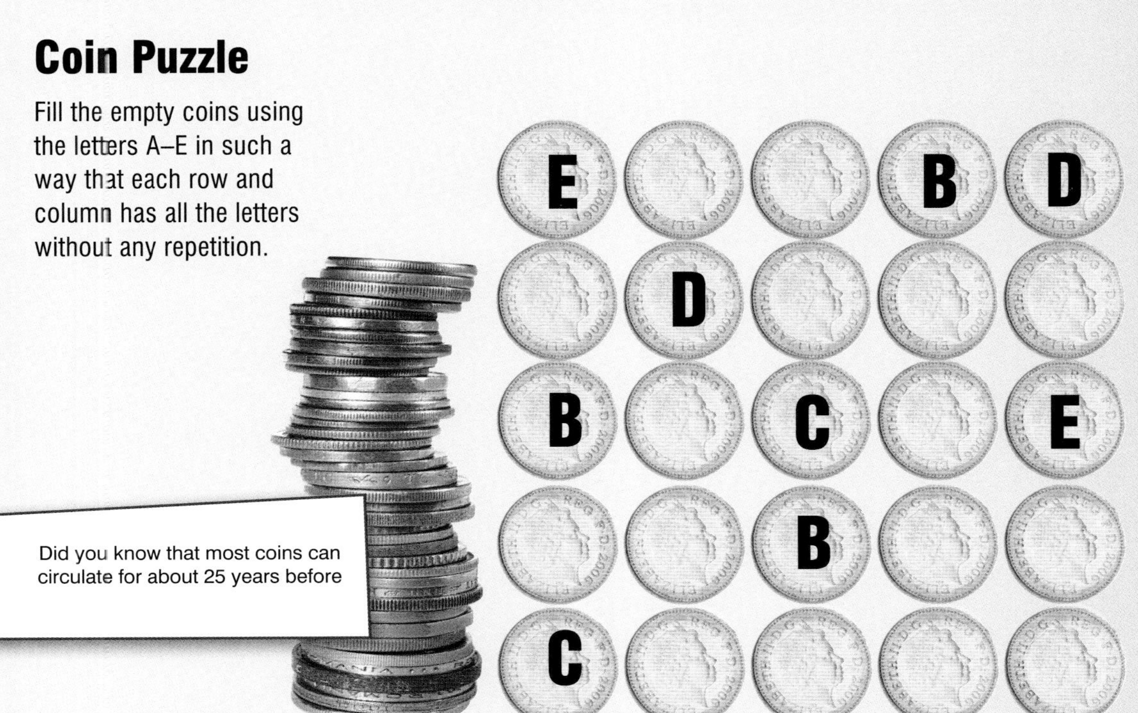

Did you know that most coins can circulate for about 25 years before

199

Follow the Arrow

You need to shade the octagons in the arrow. Each number specifies the adjacent octagons that need to be shaded.

"As the eagle was killed by the arrow winged with his own feather, so the hand of the world is wounded by its own skill."

Helen Keller

200

Look for the Star

The star has blocks which have different shapes and numbers. Add each number inside the shape with the number of edges around it. Search the star to find 5 adjacent blocks that add up to 52.

Did you know that you can see stars from the bottom of a well even in daylight?

Challenge your Intelligence

201

Fill the empty squares using the more or less signs. Every row and column should have numbers I-V, without repeating any number.

I		<III		<
		>	II	^
^	I		<	IV
	v	v		II ^
II				

"I know that I am intelligent, because I know that I know nothing."

Socrates

Equation Time

202

Create an equation using each number only once to get the result 35. Use only the required mathematical signs in any combination and as many times as required.

203

Crack the Answer

Complete the chart of basic shapes so that every row and column has each shape and color in it. No shape and color should be repeated in a row or column.

"Colors answer feeling in man; shapes answer thought; and motion answers will."

John Sterling

204

Fashion Show

You go to a fashion show and find one of your friends walking on the runway. You view the magazine for pictures of all the models, however your friend's photo is missing. Which one is your friend?

"Acting and modeling have nothing to do with each other."

Elle Macpherson

Colorful Bricks

205

In the sequence below, which of the numbered alternatives, A, B, C, or D, should replace the question mark?

"Mere color, unspoiled by meaning, and unallied with definite form, can speak to the soul in a thousand different ways."

Oscar Wilde

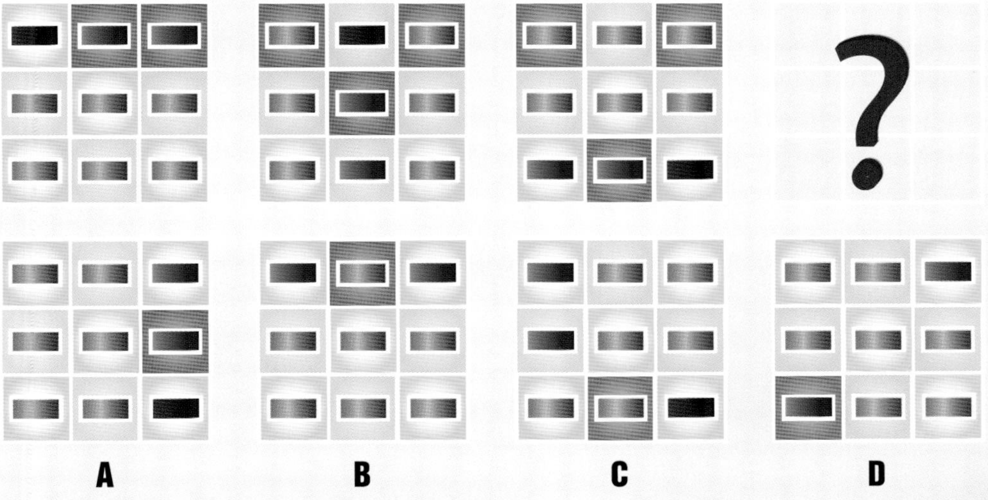

A B C D

A Helping Hand

206

You are helping your friend with their studies. There is a question that requires you to join all 25 dots using 8 lines without lifting your pen or pencil. Help your friend answer the question.

"The antidote for fifty enemies is one friend."

Aristotle

207

Switch on the Lamp

In the given puzzle, each bulb and switch is related with a number logic. Find the missing number to switch the bulb on.

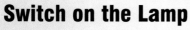

"Live in rooms full of light."

Cornelius Celsus

208

Word Twister

Here is an interesting puzzle. You need to fill the empty cells without repeating the letters A–F in a row, column, or group.

B		E	C		
	C		B	D	
	B				
A		B	E		
				F	

209

"An animal's eyes have the power to speak a great language."

Martin Euber

Find the Pairs

There are five frames with pictures of cats, in them. Two frames have pairs and one frame does not. You need to find the frame without a pair.

210

Find the Mat

The store has many folded mats for sale. One of them is unfolded for display. Find the folded mat that matches the unfolded one.

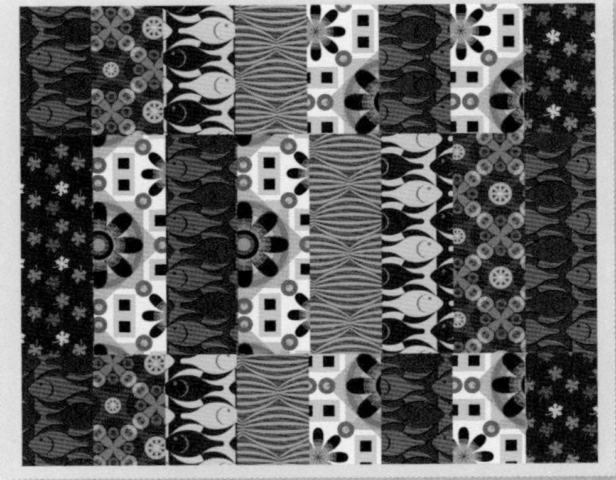

A door mat made of polypropylene is one of the most durable door mats.

211 ☆☆

Fix the Flower

Which of the three petal shapes below can be fixed together to create the top flower?

> *"Flowers seem intended for the solace of ordinary humanity."*
>
> John Ruskin

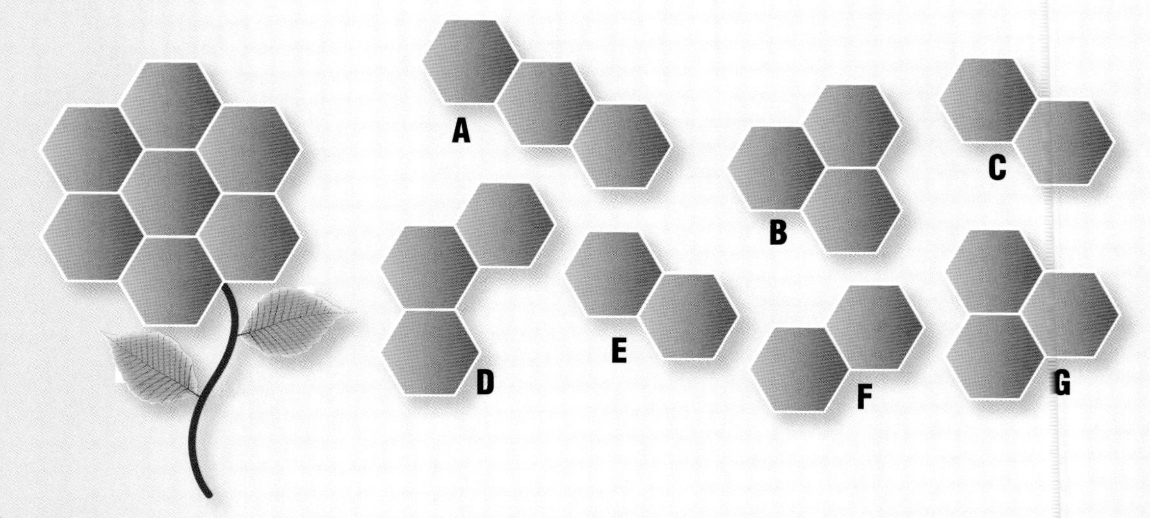

212 ★★

Letter Time

Fill the empty blocks using the letters A–I. You need to enter all the letters in each row, column, and group, without repeating any letter.

E	D		A		H			
					D	I		
I						F		
B	E				G			
				F	B		G	
				D				
	C			B			A	
	G	B	H				I	D
			D				F	

213 ★★★

What's your Score?

Your examination results are hidden in the question mark. Each number in the square specifies the adjacent squares (horizontally, vertically and diagonally) to be shaded. Count the squares that are not shaded to find your score out of 50.

> *"There is no such thing as failure. There are only results."*
>
> Tony Robbins

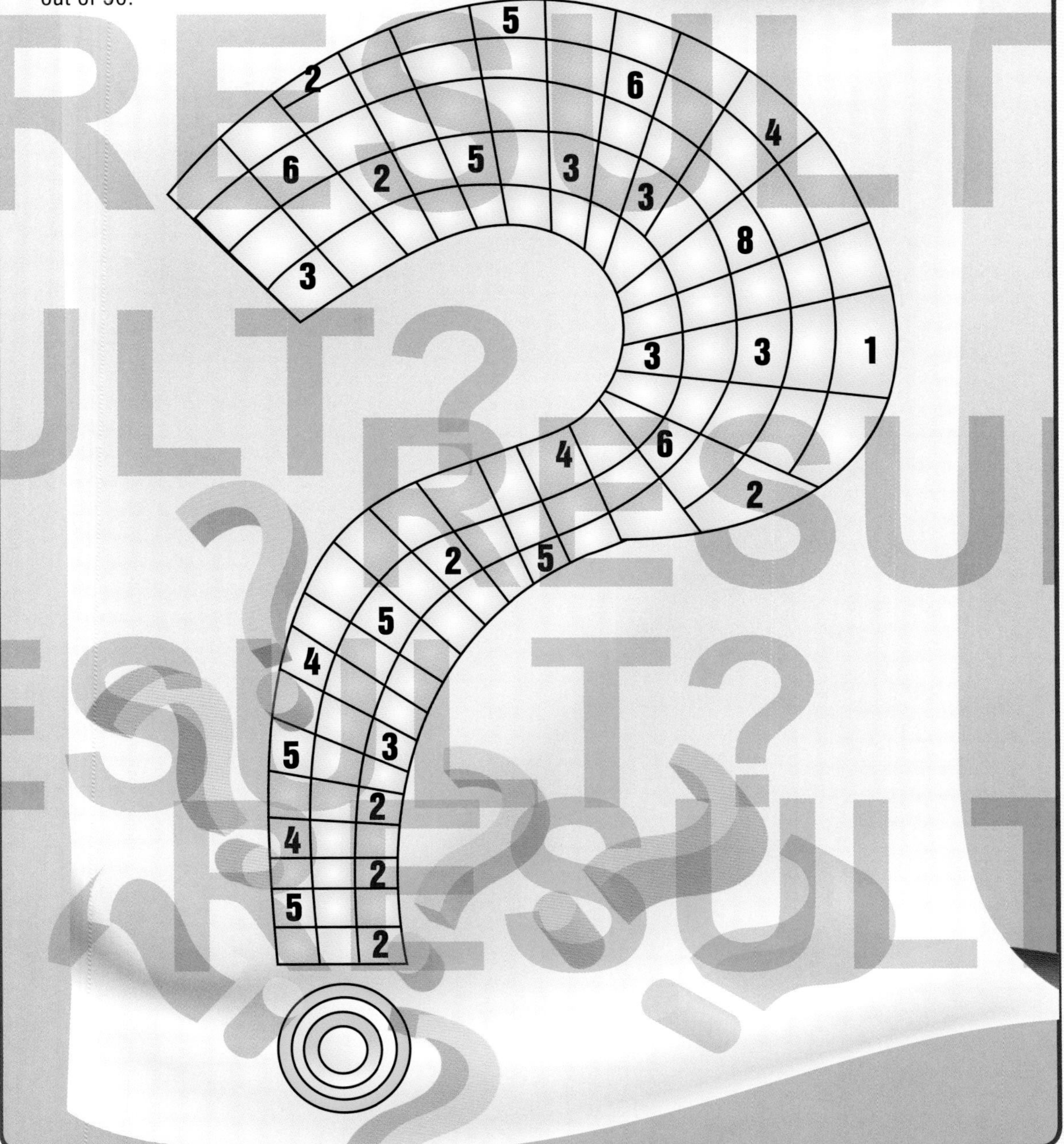

214 ★★★

Chocolate Grid

Fill the empty squares using the more or less signs. Every row and column should have the letters A–H. No letter should be repeated in a row or column. Find the corresponding number for each letter to identify which number is greater than the other. For example, D=4, so the letter in the first cell of the first row needs to be a letter that corresponds to a number that is greater than 4 (E, F, G, or H).

>	D	<				<	B
		A		G >			H
B	>				v	v	
	^	H		> B		G	F
		F	<		B <		
A	>		D	H	>		
<		E	A	v		B	C
F		>			A	<	

"It is not once nor twice, but times without number that the same ideas make their appearance in the world."

Aristotle

215 ★★☆

Pool Decoration

The swimming pool is surrounded by the sitting area with multiple blocks. Each block has different shapes with calculations. Perform the calculations to find the number inside each shape. Multiply the digits found and add the result with the number of edges. For example, for the first block, 13+9=22, and (2X2)+4=8. Find 4 adjacent blocks whose total is 46.

"All good writing is swimming under water and holding your breath."

F. Scott Fitzgerald

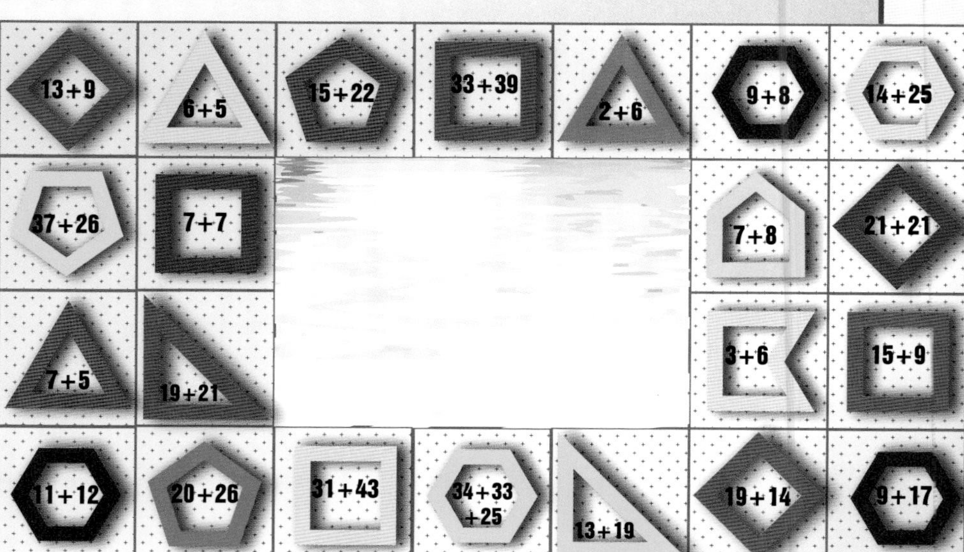

216 ☆☆★

Sandwich Hunger

You are hungry for a sandwich and at a store you see various numbers written on each sandwich, except one. Find the missing number to get a discount on your sandwich.

217 ★★★

Home Sweet Home

There is a cross sign on the back door of a home with different numbers and mathematical signs. Create an equation using each number only once to get the result nine. Use only the required mathematical signs in any combination and as many times as required.

"Home is a place you grow up wanting to leave, and grow old wanting to get back to."

John Ed Pearce

218 ★★☆

Arrange the Signs

You need to create a chart of arithmetic signs. Arrange four signs with four different colors. Every row and column should have each sign and color, without repeating any sign and color.

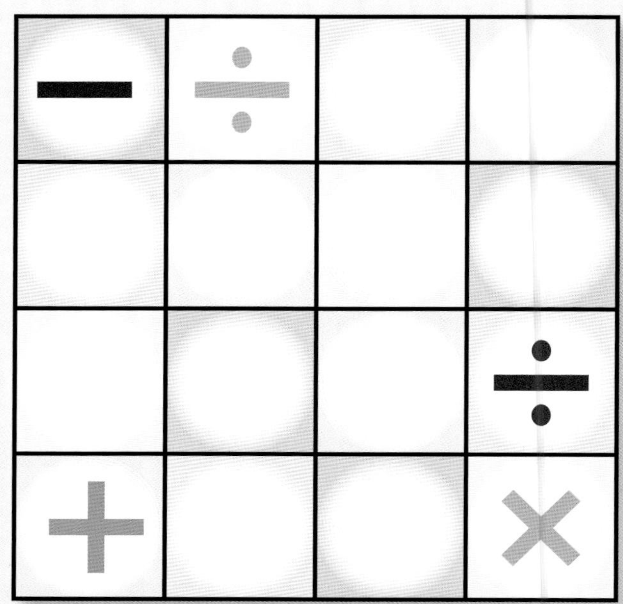

"What would life be without arithmetic, but a scene of horrors?"

Sydney Smith

219 ★☆☆

Air Show

Compare the aircraft within and outside the square to find the missing aircraft.

"Nothing can stop the attack of aircraft except other aircraft."

Billy Mitchell

220

Open the Door

To open the door you need to join each pair of numbers with a line without crossing lines for any other connections. Your lines cannot pass through the shaded blocks.

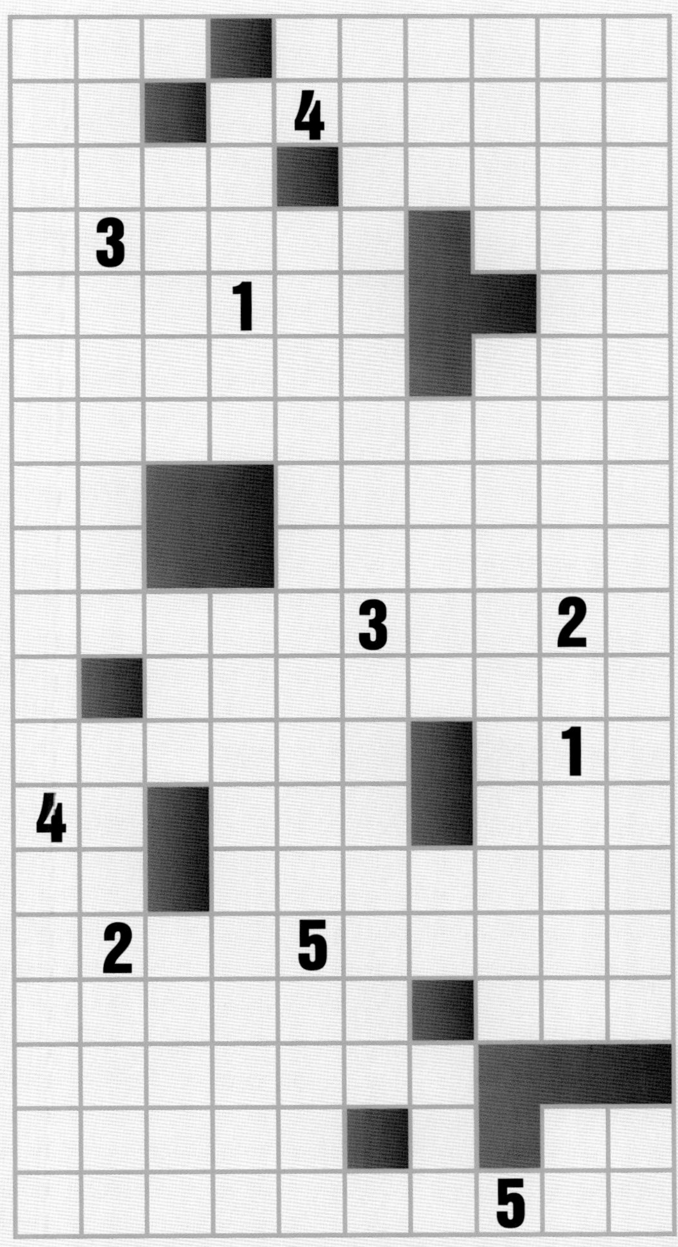

"Knowledge of what is does not open the door directly to what should be."

Albert Einstein

221 ★★★

Find the Marker Pens

There are different colors of marker pens lying on the table. Arrange these pens so that every row, column, and group will have all eight colors of marker pens, without repeating any color.

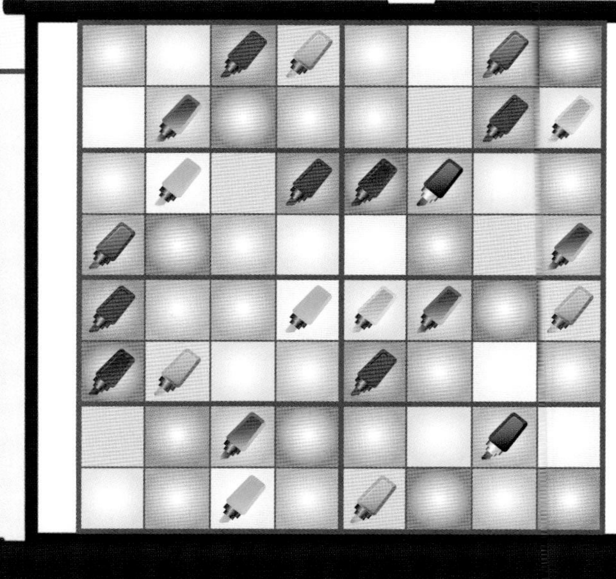

"Be regular and orderly in your life, so that you may be violent and original in your work."

Gustave Flaubert

222 ★★★

Join the Bricks

Can you join all the 36 bricks with maximum 10 lines without lifting your pen or pencil?

"A brick layer, lays bricks... I'm an Actor, that's what I do."

Michael Chiklis

Number the Tin 223

There are six large tins placed in front of you. Each tin has a number on it, except one. You need to find the missing number to open the tin and get the baked beans.

"A life coach does for the rest of your life what a personal trainer does for your health and fitness."

Elaine MacDonald

Classroom Puzzle 224

Complete the puzzle on the blackboard so that every row, column, and group should have all letters A–I. No letter should repeat in a row, column, or group.

"The classroom should be an entrance into the world, not an escape from it."

John Ciardi

225

Find the Correct Cube

Below are five cubes, but only one matches the unfolded one. Find the correct cube.

"The cube is an imitation of life itself or even our improvement of life."

Erno Rubik

226

Coloring Time

You decide to paint a picture over the weekend and go to buy a box of colors. Each box has a pair except one. Find the odd one out.

227 ★★★

Diamond Numbering

Fill the numbers I-VIII on blank diamonds. Each row, column, group and diamonds that are linked together should have all eight numbers, without repeating any number.

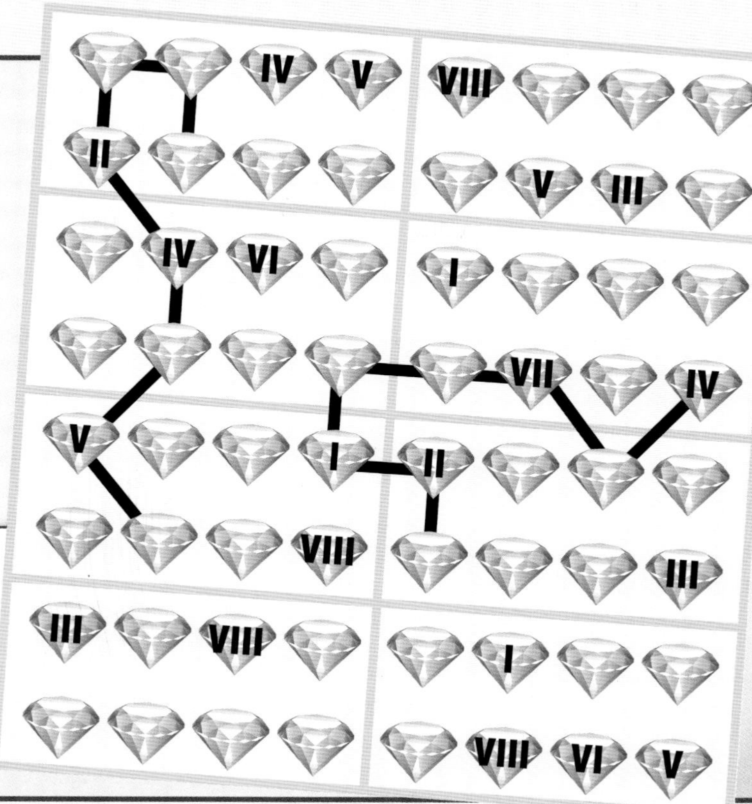

The diamond is the hardest natural substance on earth. But if it is exposed to a temperature of 1405 degrees Fahrenheit, it will simply vanish, without even a trace of ash!

228 ★★★

Help the Postman

The letters have a number of pages included written on the front of the envelope. On the back of the envelope is the home number where it needs to be delivered. The home number on one of the envelopes is missing. Help the postman find the correct address.

41 25 12 33

25 49 ? 36

"To send a letter is a good way to go somewhere without moving anything but your heart."

Phyllis Theroux

229

Tennis Game

The tennis racket cover has blocks containing shapes and calculations. Perform the calculations and add the result with the number of edges around it. Find 3 adjacent blocks that add up to 780.

200/20
114/19
93/31
98/14
51/17
120/15
54/18
98/7
78/13
182/91
108/27
144/16
165/33
112/16

230

Fit the Kite

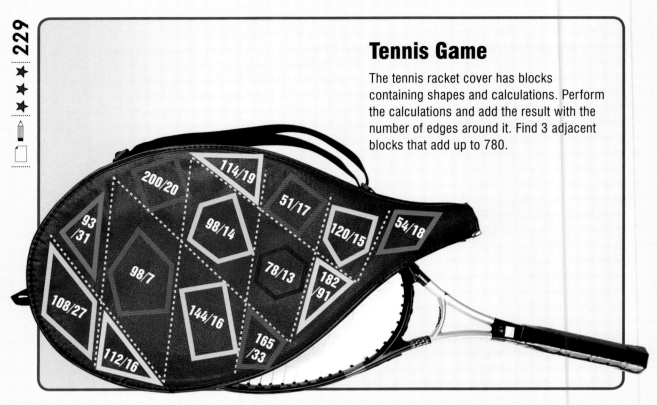

Which one of the two shapes below can be paired to create the kite shape above?

The world record for the longest kite-fly is 180 hours.

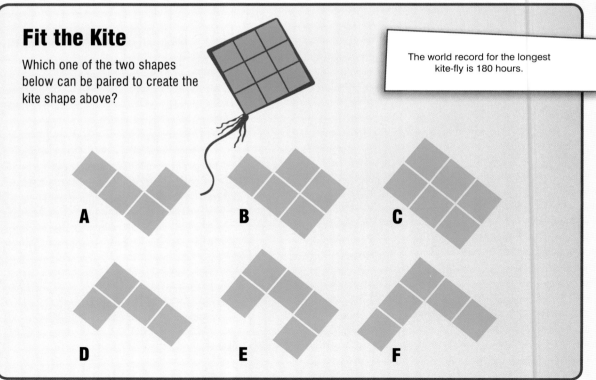

A

B

C

D

E

F

Puzzling Letters

231 ★★★

Every row, column, and highlighted group should have letters A–I, without repeating any letter. Find the corresponding number for each letter to identify which number is greater than the other. For example, H=8, so the letter in the third cell of the first row needs to be a letter that corresponds to a number that is less than 8.

	H >			>		<		
			<	<	D	F	G <	
^		A		v		B <		
	>	B			I			G
A	v		>		E <			
v		I	A			^		F
		>	C			E	<	H
I	^		<				^	
H	G	D	B		>	C		A

Did you know that the letters a, b, c and d, do not appear anywhere in the spellings of the numbers 1 to 99.

Rings of Fire

232 ★★

You visit a circus where they have displayed the “Rings of Fire” on the stage. The ring has different numbers and mathematical signs. Create an equation using each number only once to get the result 36. Use the required mathematical signs in any combination and as many times as required.

“Temptation is the fire that brings up the scum of the heart.”

William Shakespeare

233

Baby Toys

You came to a toy shop, to help your friend who works there, you need to arrange different types of rattles in the showcase such that every row, column, and group will have each type of rattle. No rattle should be repeated in a row, column, or group.

Did you know that Barbie's full name is actually Barbara Millicent Roberts?

234

Picture Maze

Find the missing part to complete the picture as shown in the image.

"Nature has given women so much power that the law has very wisely given them little."

Samuel Johnson

Hand fans are made up of straw, bamboo, wood, paper, or horn.

Fumbled Fan

235 ☆ ☆ ★

You have bought a hand fan with numbers on it. Each number has a relation to the next number. Find the missing number.

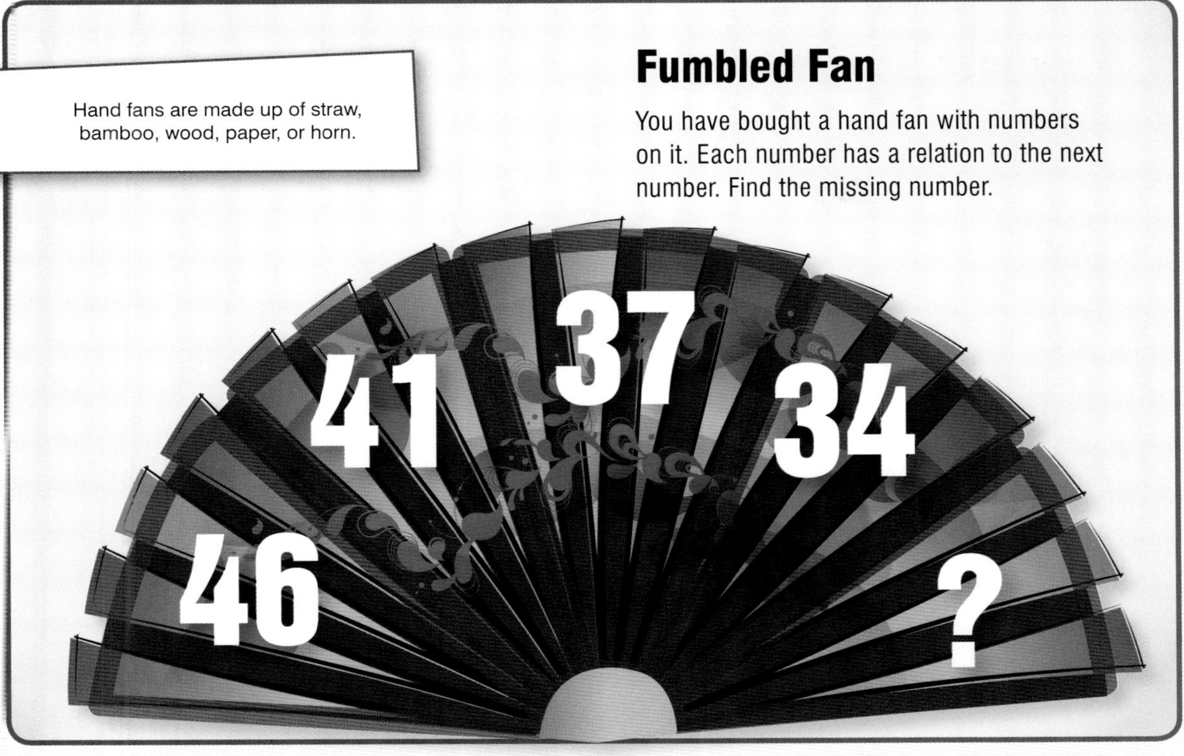

Missing Letters

236 ☆ ☆ ★

Complete the missing letters on the box so that every row and column has all five letters A–E, without repeating any letter.

	B	D		
B			A	
			E	C
C				
		A		

"I've always thought of the T-shirt as the Alpha and Omega of the fashion alphabet."

Giorgio Armani

237 ★★★

Match the Designs

There are different designs shown in the puzzle. Each design has a pair, except one. Find the design that does not have a pair.

"A common mistake that people make when trying to design something completely foolproof is to underestimate the ingenuity of complete fools."

Douglas Adams

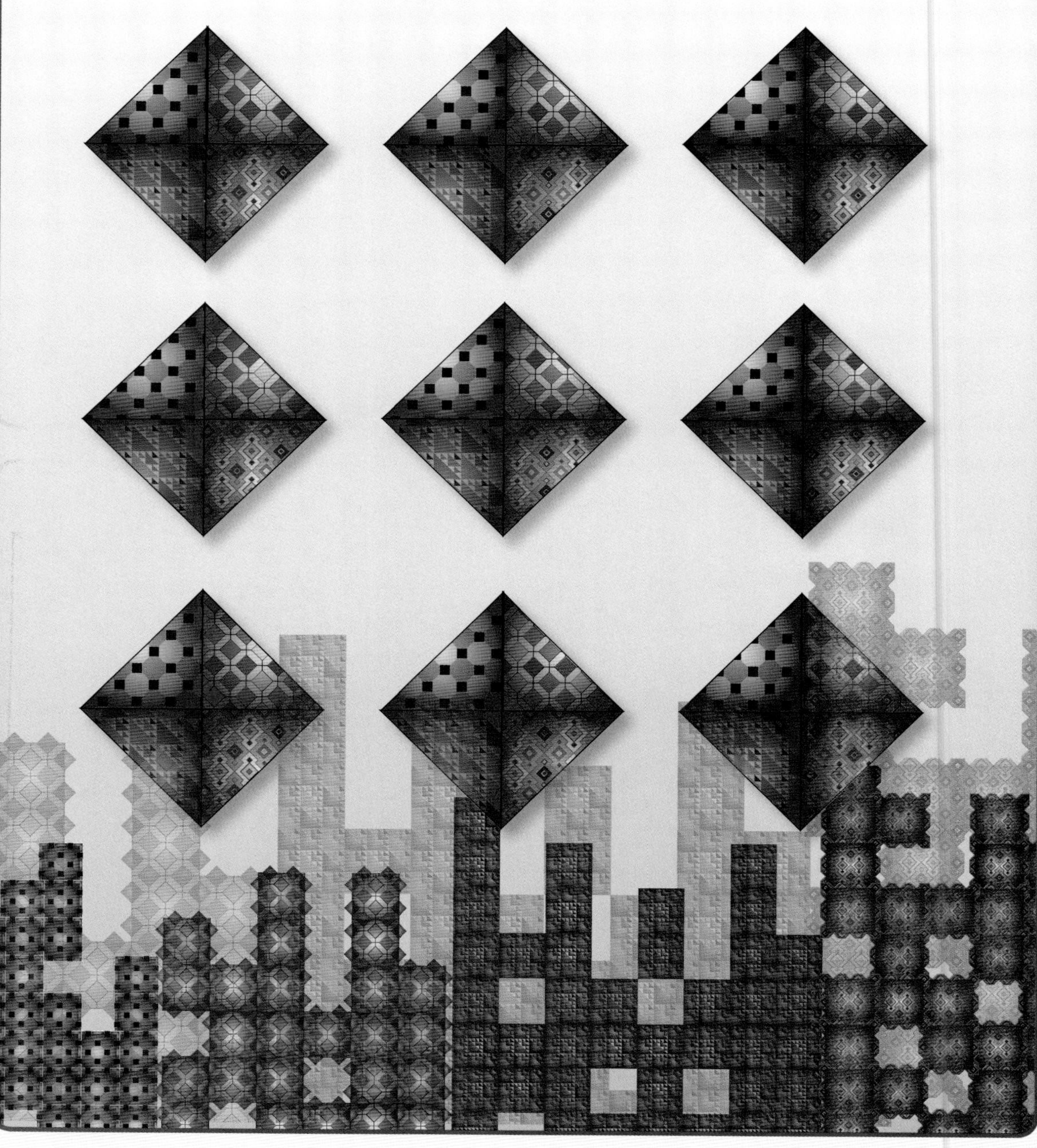

238 ★★★

Number Jumble

Fill the empty squares using the more or less signs. Every row, column, and highlighted group should have numbers 1–9, without repeating any number.

$(26/13)+3$ v	$(1+1)^2$	<	1/1	>	$(4^2-10)+2$		<	
		>			$(2^2+2^2)-28/7$ ^	√81		
$13^2-(8x2x10)$		v	<			$(7x3)-(5x3)$ v	<	
$(14x3)-(10x2^2)$ ^	$(42/14)+2$ ^			>	49/7	>		
			<	$[(48/16)-1]+(51/17)$	2^2-2		59-52<	
		<	<	$(2^2/2)+(2^2/2)$	<			
>	5^2-22	v		$(32.5x2)-(15.75x4)$	>		$(23x2)-45$	
	$(36/12)+4$	$(2^2/2)$	$8^2-(14x4)$	<			36/4	8/2
<		>	3^2-5				√36<	

239 ★★★

Envelope Numbering

Fill the numbers on the blank envelopes so that each row, column, and linked envelopes have all nine numbers, without any repetition.

"The man who works for the gold in the job rather than for the money in the pay envelope, is the fellow who gets on."

Joseph French Johnson

240 ★★★

Tent House

The tent has multiple blocks with different shapes and numbers. Divide each number inside the shape by the number of edges around it. Find 4 adjacent blocks whose average is 14.

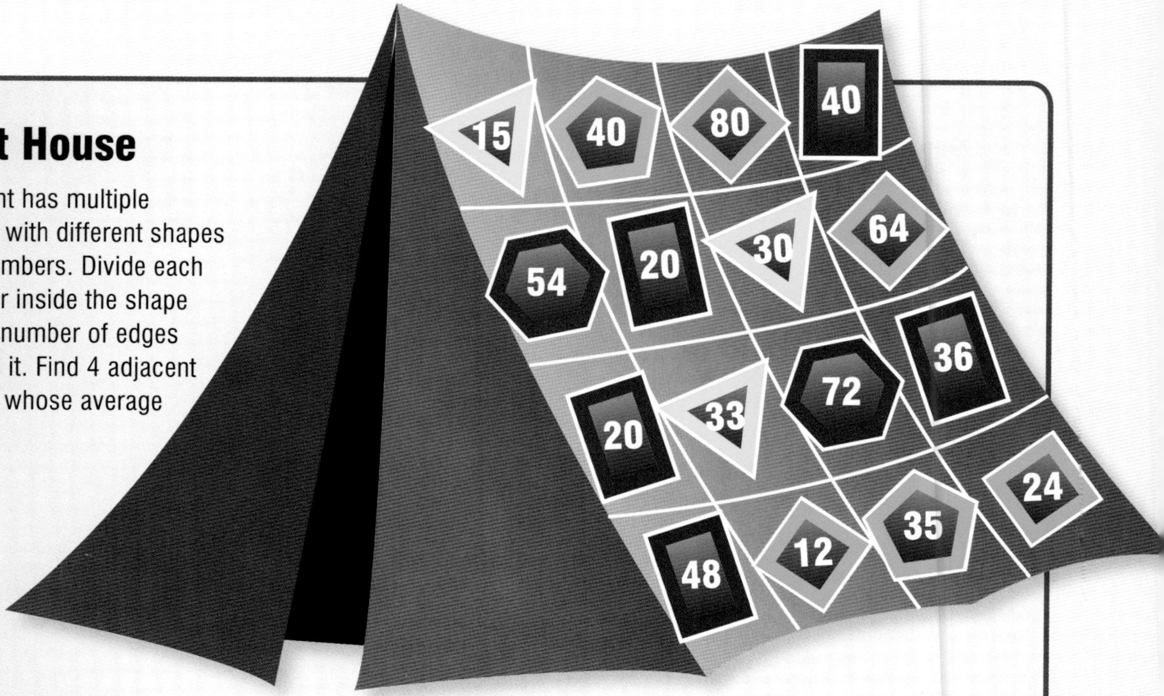

"I never saw a man who looked with such a wistful eye upon that little tent of blue which prisoners call the sky."

Oscar Wilde

241 ★☆☆

Rainy Day

It's a rainy day today and the clouds are getting heavier. You need to color the clouds grey. Each number specifies the number of clouds around it that need to be shaded.

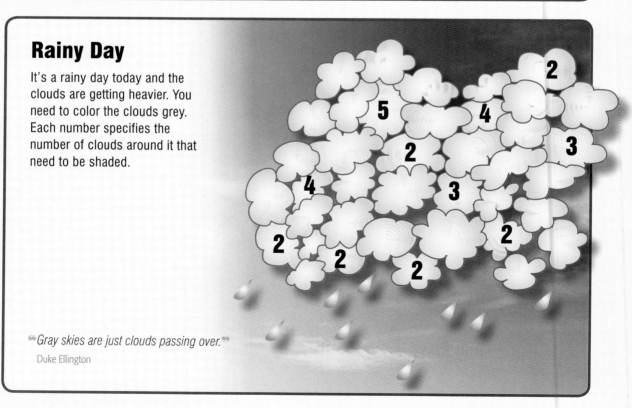

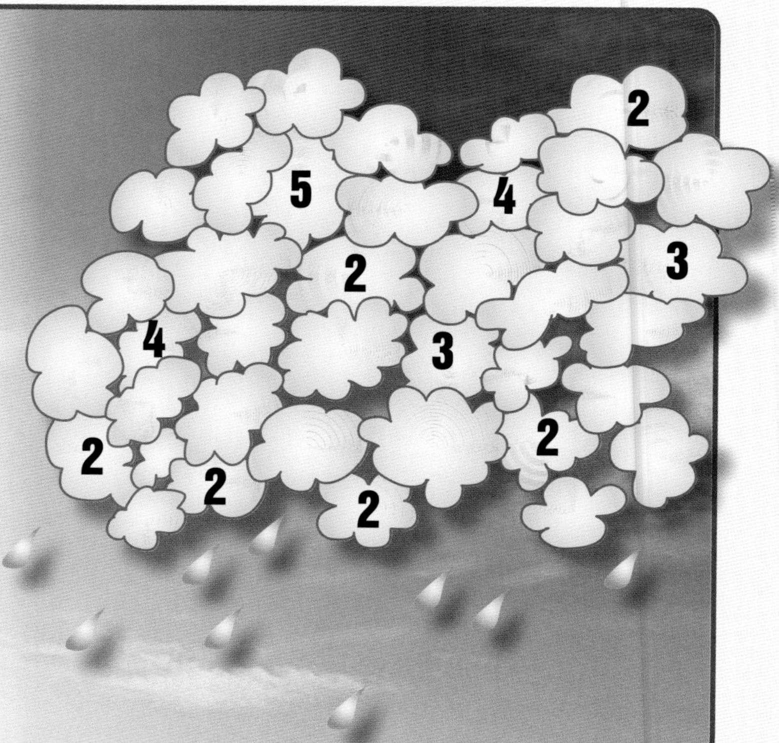

"Gray skies are just clouds passing over."

Duke Ellington

Gaming Time 242

Tedd has ordered 12 video games, but also received some extra ones. He knows 10 of the video games that were definitely ordered. Can you assist him in working out which two of the six boxed figures completes the set?

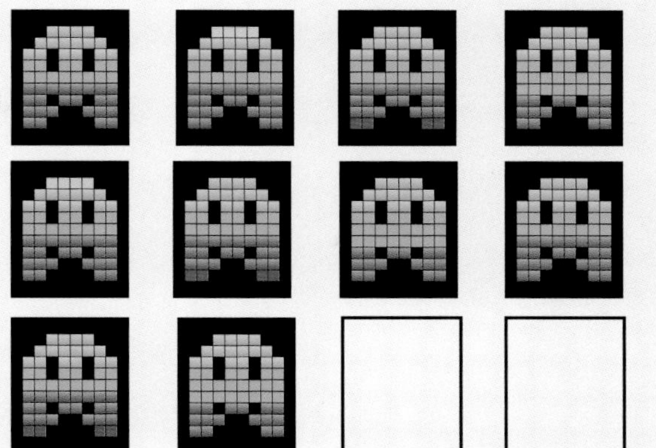

"Talent wins games, but teamwork and intelligence wins championships."

Michael Jordan

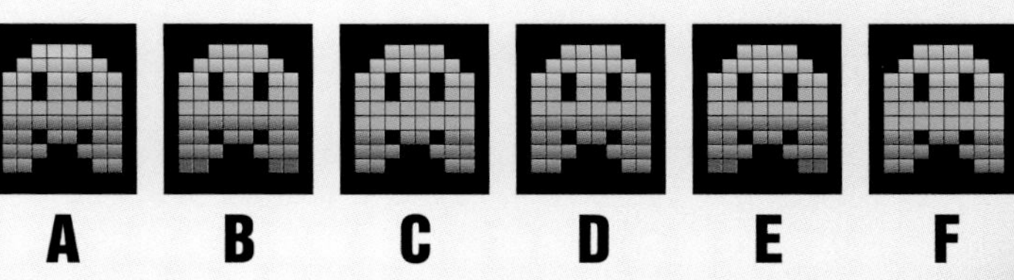

Number the Mitten 243

Complete the empty squares on the pair of mittens using the more or less signs. Every row and column should have the numbers 1–4, without repeating any number. Replace the existing letters with their corresponding number for example, C=3.

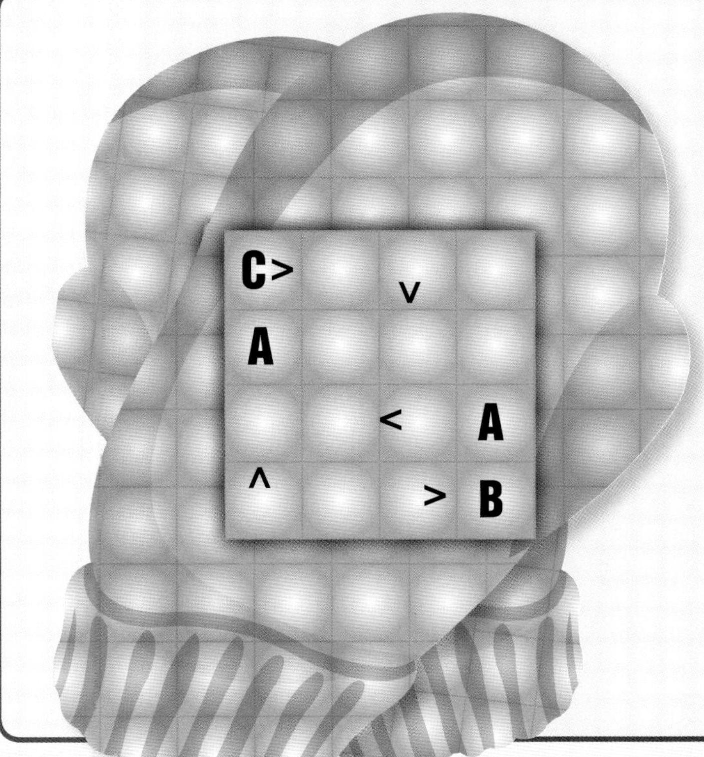

"Statistics are no substitute for judgment."

Henry Clay

244 ☆☆★

Arrange the Glasses

The glasses that have juice and cold water in them are numbered from 1–9. You need to place these glasses in the empty squares that are on the big glass so that no juice glass or cold water glass are together. No consecutive numbered glasses should be placed together. Find one of the multiple ways in which you can arrange the glasses.

"We never know the worth of water till the well is dry."

Thomas Fuller

245 ☆★★

Hide and Seek

The numbers on each row and column identify black squares and groups of black squares that are adjoining in that row or column. Color in all the black squares to find a four number combination.

									1	
				1	5				1	
				1	1	1			1	1
				2	1	2		5	1	3
				2	1	2		3	1	5
		1	3							
		2	1							
		1	3							
1	1	1	1							
		3	3							
		3	3							
1	1	1	1							
		1	3							
	1	1	1							
		3	1							

"The secret to creativity is knowing how to hide your sources."

Albert Einstein

246

Diamond View

Which of the pictures below represents the correct overhead view of this scene?

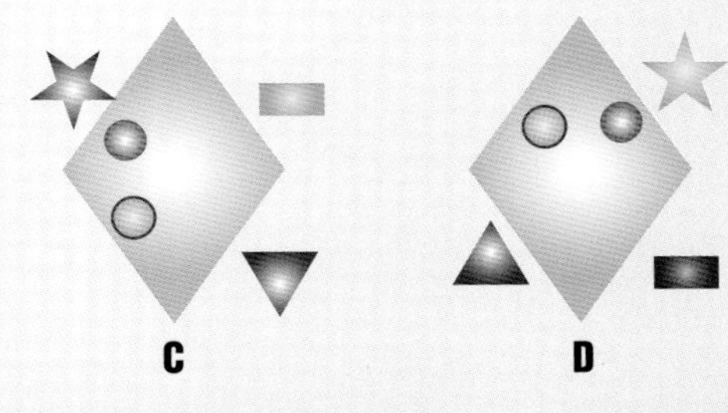

Did you know that a diamond is
58 times harder than the next hardest mineral on earth,
but if hit hard with a hammer, it will shatter.

A B C D

247

Double your Money

Complete this puzzle at the Royal Casino to double your earnings. Fill the empty squares with the help of the more or less signs specified in the puzzle. Every row and column should have the numbers I–IV, without repeating any number.

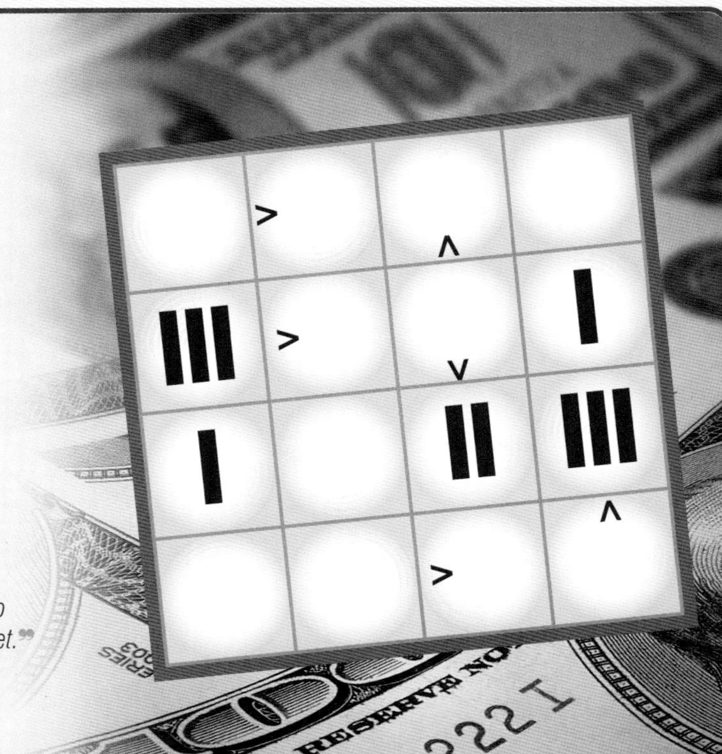

"The safe way to double your money is to fold it over once and put it in your pocket."

Frank Hubbard

248

Something Fishy!

Find the missing numbers so that each pair of triangles multiply to form the triangle directly above them.

Did you know that a Parrotfish makes its own sleeping bag to sleep in?

249

Santa Caps

These Santa caps have calculations on them. You need to number the caps 1–6 in such a way that no number is repeated in a row, column, or group. The caps that are joined by the lines can't have the same numbers on them.

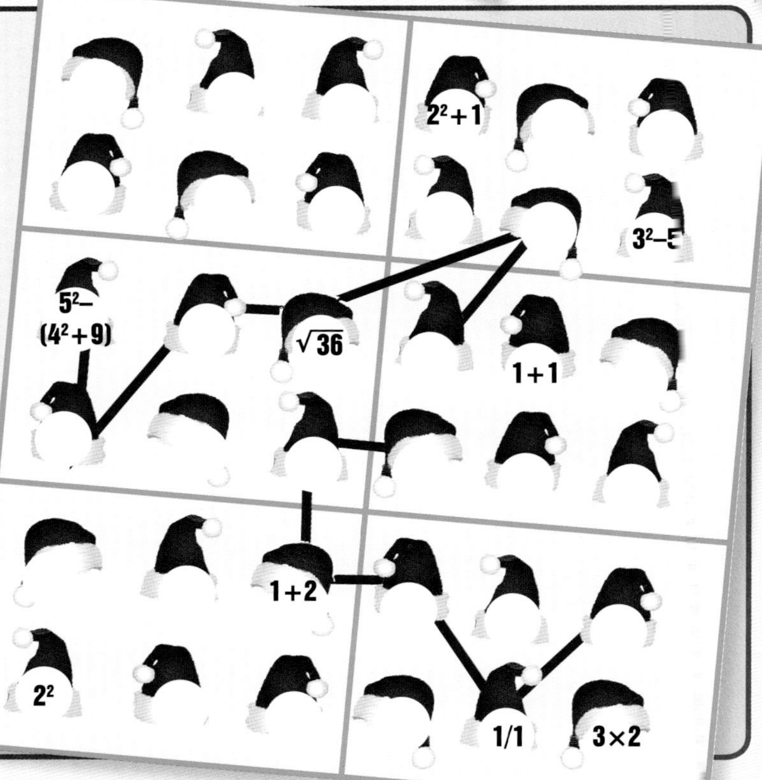

"Gifts of time and love are surely the basic ingredients of a truly merry Christmas."

Peg Bracken

Arrange Sally's Wardrobe

Arrange the dresses and pants in Sally's wardrobe in such a way that two dresses are always together horizontally, vertically or both. No consecutive numbers should be together horizontally, vertically, or diagonally. Some of the clothes have already been placed, you need to arrange the rest.

"Clothes and manners do not make the man; but, when he is made, they greatly improve his appearance."

Henry Ward Beecher

	4			
16				39
			46	
32				
		9		

Dresses:

		33
1	17	34
2	18	36
4	20	37
5	21	38
7	23	40
8	24	43
11	25	44
12	26	45
14	28	47
16	31	50

Pants:

	29
3	30
6	32
9	35
10	39
13	41
15	42
19	46
22	48
27	49

251

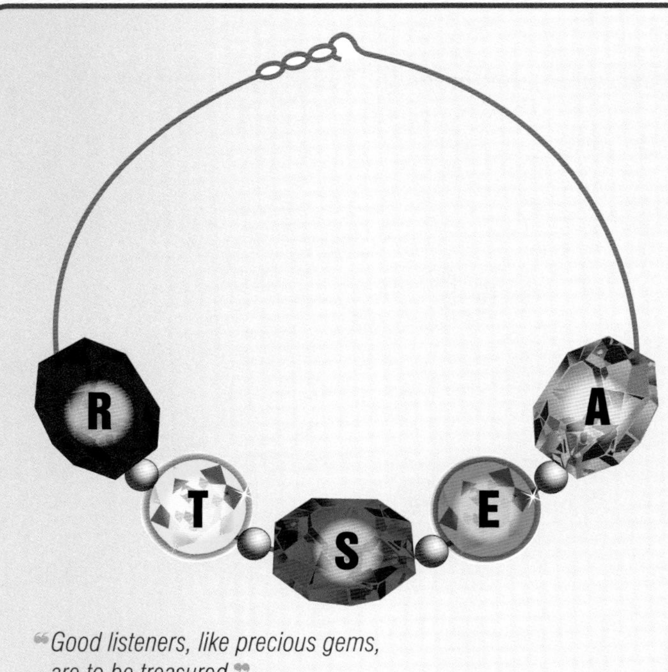

Puzzling Necklace

The gems in the necklace have been rearranged. Work out what the new sequence of the gems should be from the clues listed below?

- The position of the ruby has been changed.
- Neither the emerald nor the ruby is next to the sapphire.
- The topaz is only next to another gem and it isn't the ruby.
- The amber is two gems to the left of the topaz.

"Good listeners, like precious gems, are to be treasured."

Walter Anderson

252

Show the Shapes

The mathematical shapes below have been rearranged. Work out what the new sequence of the shapes should be from the clues listed below?

- The rectangle is three positions to the right of the circle.
- The circle is only next to another shape.
- The hexagon is two shapes to the left of the square.

"The thought you have now shapes your experience of the next moment. Practice shaping the moment."

Tom Barrett

Number Sorting

253

Fill the empty squares using the more or less signs. Every row, column and highlighted group should have the numbers 1–9 without repeating any number.

3	<		7	<		<		1
	4 ^					3	^ 5	
		5		4>		^		
^		8		v			<	v
7		v	1	6	9		8	5
			5>		>			9
>		9	3	<		2>		
^			>4	5	1	9		
		4		>2				

“No man acquires property without acquiring with it a little arithmetic also.”

Ralph Waldo Emerson

Look Out!

254

While driving, you notice a car in front of you that has an unusual number plate with different numbers and mathematical signs. Create an equation using each number only once to get the result 89. Use only the required mathematical signs in any combination and as many times as required.

178 + − = 94

89

/ 5 × ( )

Did you know that the first cars did not have steering wheels? Drivers steered with a lever.

255

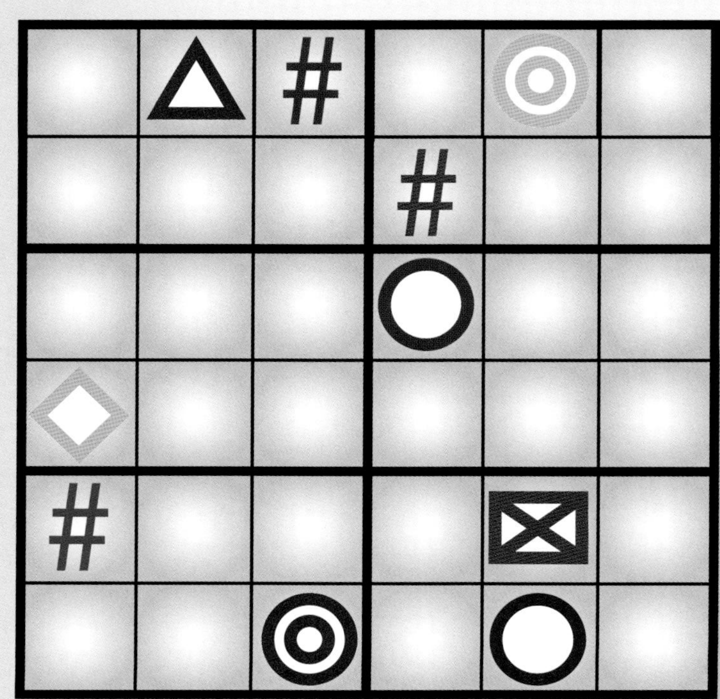

Flowchart Symbols

Complete the chart that has different symbols. Every row, column and group should have each symbol and color, without any repetition.

"Art is the symbol of the two noblest human efforts: to construct and to refrain from destruction."

Evelyn Waugh

256

Picture Perfect

The architect has drawn a plan for your new home. However, while building the home, you realize that one part of the sketch is different. Find the five difference between the sketch and your home.

"Houses are built to live in, not to look on."

Francis Bacon

257

Object Maze

Each object appears only once apart from one which appears twice. Can you find the odd one?

"No object is so beautiful that, under certain conditions, it will not look ugly."

Oscar Wilde

258

Puzzling Letters

	A	D	
C			A
D			

Fill the empty blocks in the puzzle using the letters A–D. Every row and column should have all 4 letters, without repeating any letter.

"Why is the alphabet in that order? Is it because of that song? The guy who wrote that song wrote everything."

Stephen Wright

259

Filling Squares

Help Andy fill the empty squares using the numbers and more or less signs available in the puzzle. Every row and every column should have numbers 1–4, without repeating any number.

	1^2	$(3\times2)-2$ $\vee$	
$\sqrt{4+1}$	$<$		$2-1$ $\wedge$
$(4\times3)-8$ $\vee$	$>$		
$<$		$<$	

"Writing is mentally stimulating; it's like a puzzle that makes you think all the time."

Stephanie Zimbalist

260

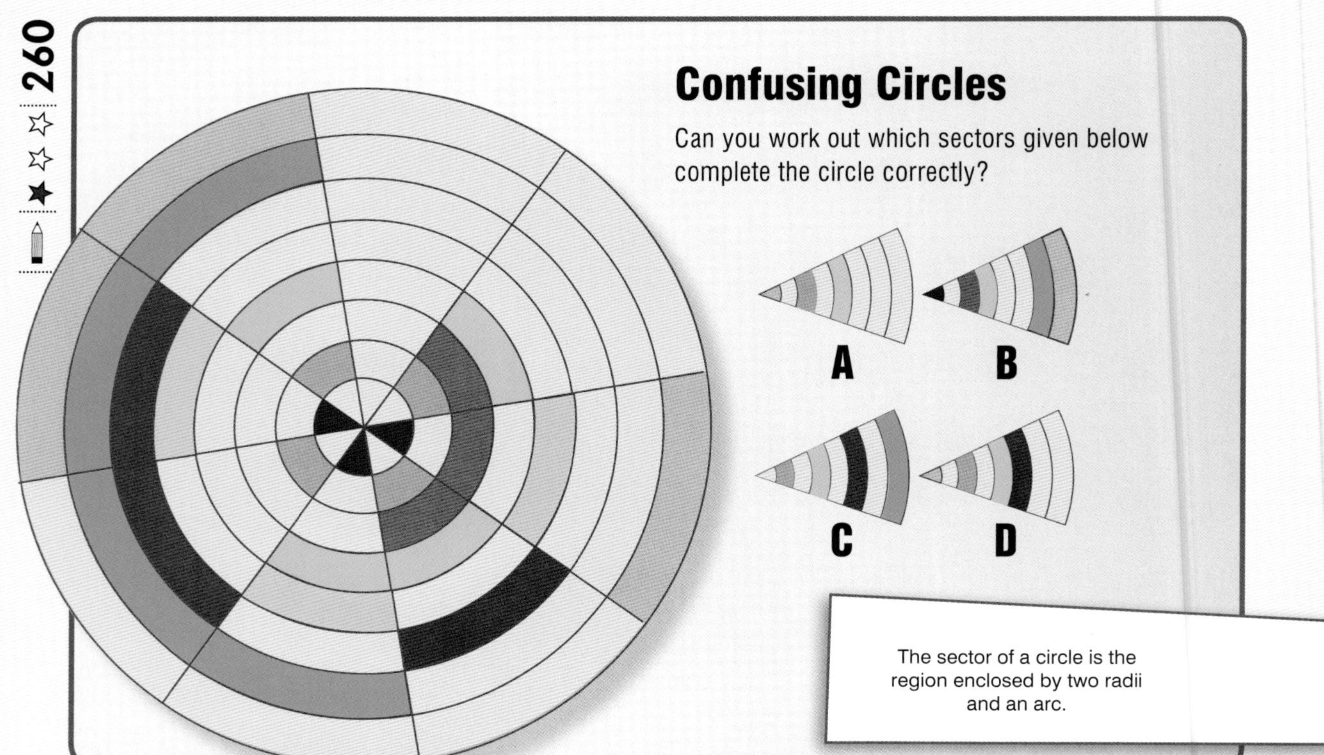

Confusing Circles

Can you work out which sectors given below complete the circle correctly?

The sector of a circle is the region enclosed by two radii and an arc.

261

Puzzling Square

Here's a unique square with different shapes and numbers. Divide each number inside the shape by the number of edges around it. Find 3 adjacent shapes that add up to 24.

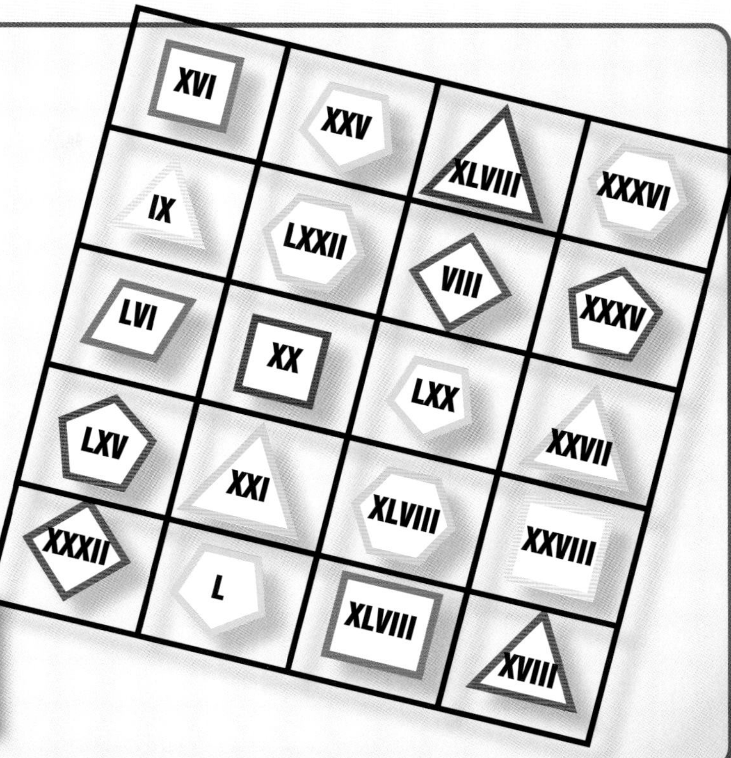

Roman numbers have their roots in ancient Rome and are based on letters of the alphabet where I=1, V=5, X=10, L=50, and so on.

262

Number the Balloons

Number the balloons 1–9 so that no number is repeated in a row, column, group and the balloons that are linked together. Also, each row, column, and group should have all nine balloons.

Did you know that the first rubber balloons were made by Professor Michael Faraday in 1824 to use in his experiments with hydrogen at the Royal Institution in London?

263

Color and Multiply

What percentage of the multiplication sign is red, green, and cream?

"Two percent of the people think; three percent of the people think they think; and ninety-five percent of the people would rather die than think."

George Bernard Shaw

264

Mystifying Mouse Pad

Here's an interesting mouse pad. Can you work out which shapes given below correctly complete the mouse pad?

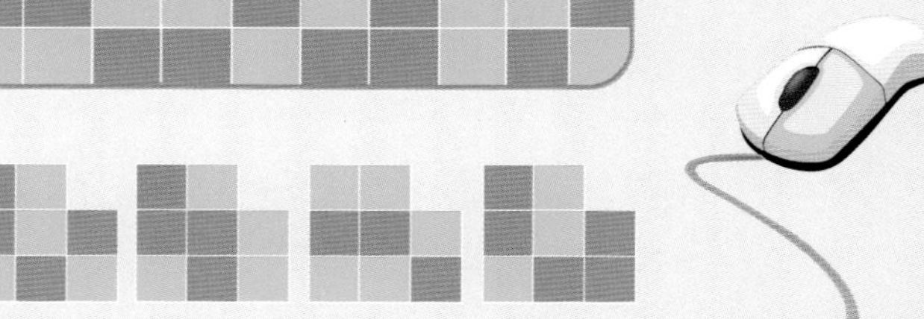

The computer mouse was invented in 1964 by Douglas Englebart.

265

Pie Chart

Each section has a number on it. Find the missing number on one of the sections.

"Small is the number of people who see with their eyes and think with their minds."

Albert Einstein

266

Time Setting

It's time for supper and you want to heat your food in the microwave. Create an equation using each number on the microwave only once to set the time to 72 seconds. Use only the required mathematical signs in any combination and as many times as required.

Did you know that boiling a cup of water in a microwave can cause it to explode?

267 ★★★

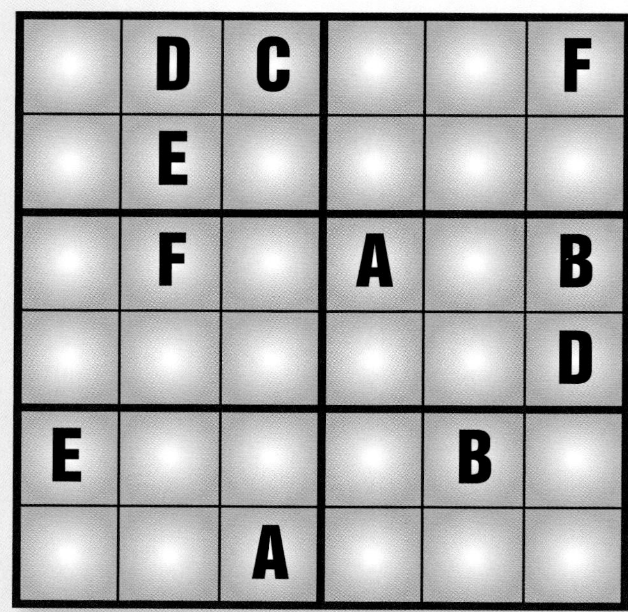

Game Time

Here's a tricky game that needs to be completed. Every row, column and group should have the letters A–F, without any repetition. Can you find the missing letters?

"The score never interested me, only the game."

Mae West

268 ☆★★

Number the Letters

Find the secret number in the last diamond. Use the numbers at the corner of the diamonds to form the central number in the same way in all three cases.

Diamonds are formed over a period of a more than billion years deep within Earth's crust and are pushed to the surface by volcanoes.

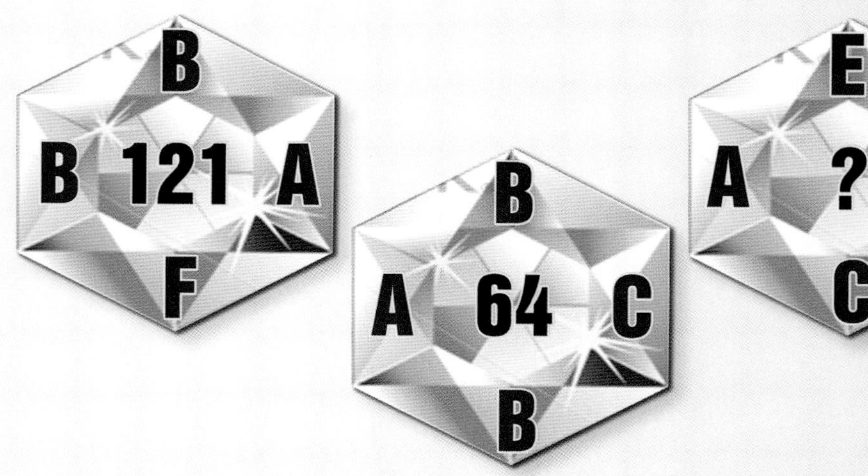

269

Four is the only number in the English language equal to the number of letters it is made of.

Number Game

The numbers on each row and column identify black squares and groups of black squares that are adjoining in that row or column. Color all the black squares to find a six number combination.

Column clues:

	1									1	
	1	5				1			5	1	
2	1	1	1		1	1	3		1	1	
3	1	1	1		3	1	1		1	1	5
1	1	1	3		1	1	5		1	1	5

Row clues:

		1	3	3
	2	1	1	1
1	1	3	1	1
	4	1	1	1
		1	3	3
		4	3	3
		1	1	1
		4	1	3
		1	1	1
		4	1	3

270 ★★★

Spider Web

Count the total number of insects in the web. The number specifies the adjacent (horizontally, vertically and diagonally) number of squares to be shaded. The shaded squares will tell you how many insects are in the web.

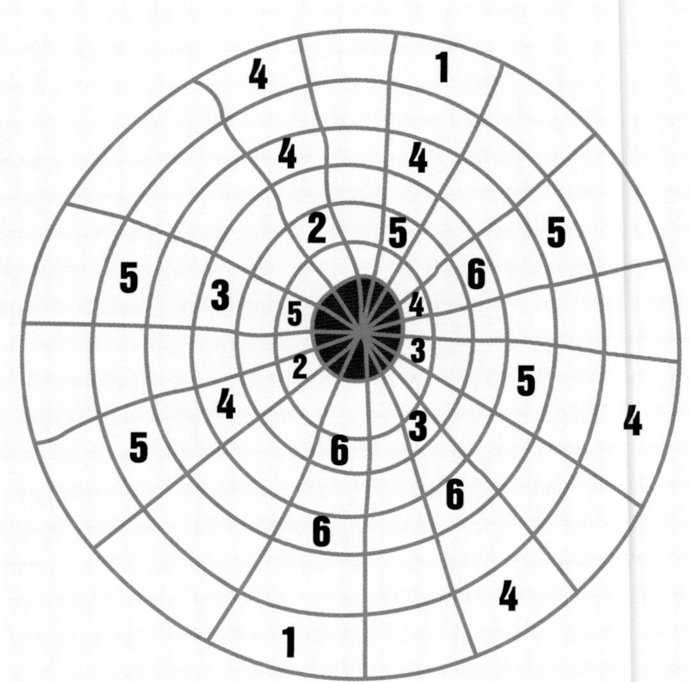

"In the spider-web of facts, many a truth is strangled."

Paul Eldridge

271 ★★☆

Colorful Wall

You need to describe how the tiles will be placed on a section of the wall to your architect. You need to find out what percentage of the wall is red, blue, green and cream to explain it correctly?

"Every wall is a door."

Ralph Waldo Emerson

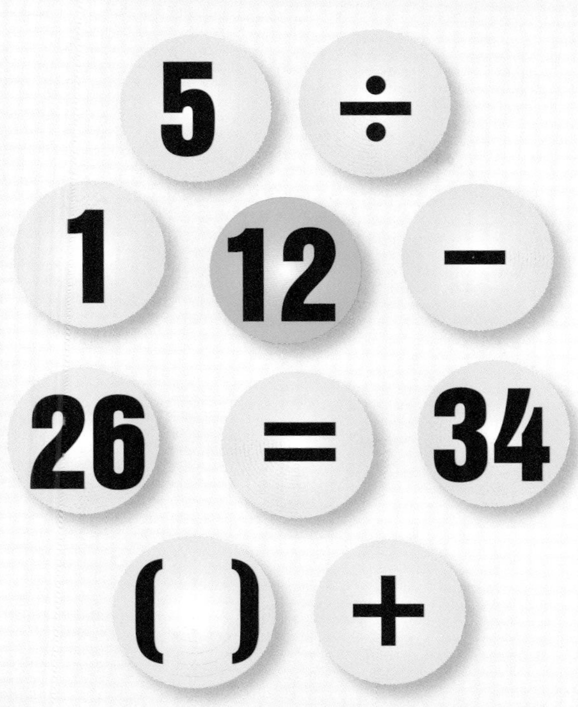

Equation Time 272

Create an equation using each number only once to get the result 12. Use only the required mathematical signs in any combination and as many times as required.

"Go down deep enough into anything and you will find mathematics."

Dean Schlicter

Looking from the Top 273

Identify which of the pictures below matches the overhead view shown.

"Happiness makes up in height what it lacks in length."

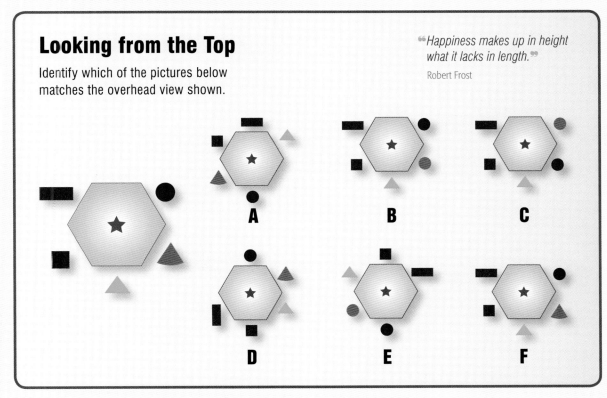

Robert Frost

A B C

D E F

274 ★☆☆

Dance Dance!

This group practices every evening. Compare the two pictures and find the five differences.

"Dancing is like dreaming with your feet!"

Constanze

275 ★★★

Number the Duckling

The farmer has a duck with four ducklings. He has numbered each one to make sure they don't get lost. The number on one duckling has been erased. Can you help the farmer find the missing number?

"Be like a duck. Calm on the surface, but always paddling like the dickens underneath."

Michael Caine

276 Number the Dartboard

Can you crack the dartboard code and work out what number belongs where the question marks are?

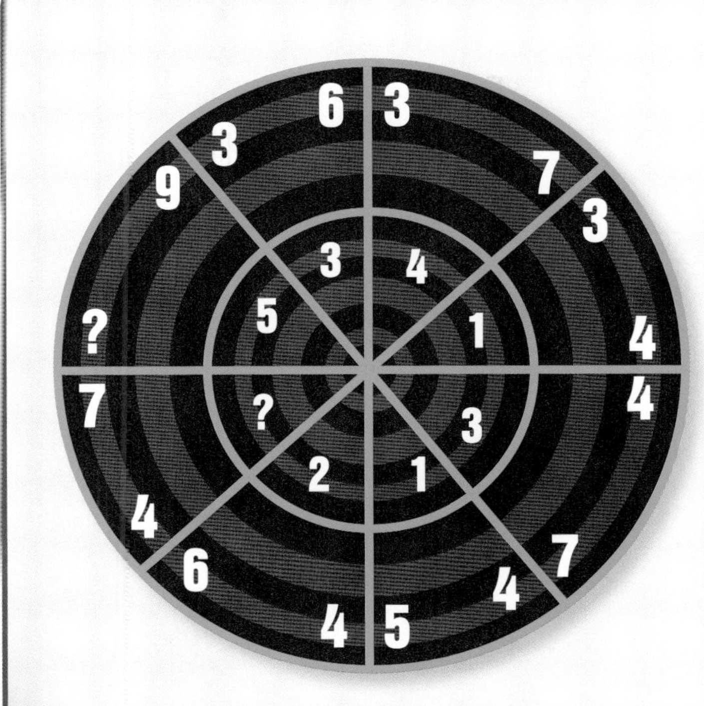

The standard diameter of a tournament dartboard is 15.5 inches (39.4 cm).

277 Show me the Honey!

It's time to collect some honey, but some bees have had a head start. Find out which honeycombs have been visited? The numbers in the cells indicate the exact number of visited cells around them. Shade these till all the numbers are surrounded by the correct number of visited cells.

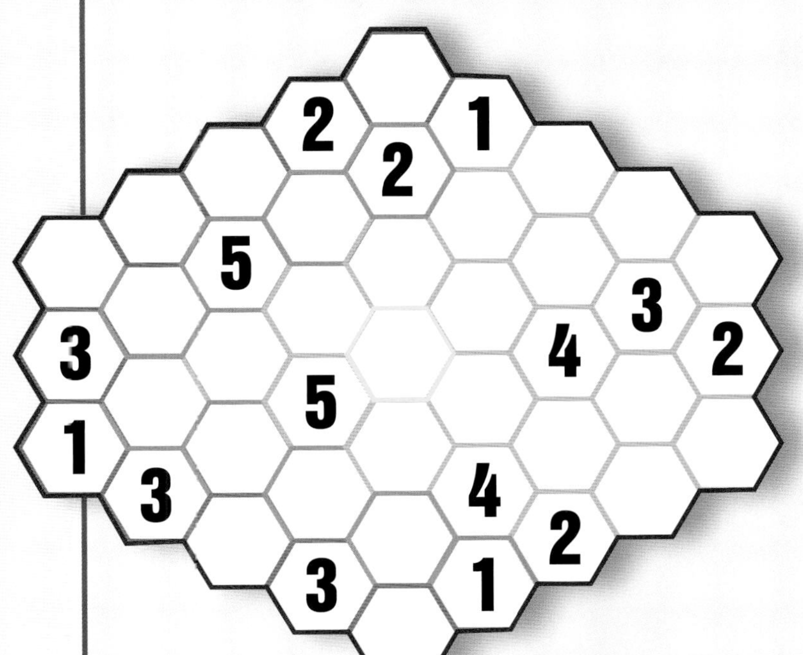

278 ☆☆★

Mug Maze

Out of these six mugs, one matches the unfolded pattern. Find the mug whose pattern matches the unfolded one.

"Art is pattern informed by sensibility."

Herbert Read

279 ☆☆★

Fall Leaves

Number the fall leaves so that each row and column has all five numbers, without repeating any number. Also, leaves that are linked together should have all five numbers.

"Fall is a second spring where every leaf is a flower."

Albert Camus

280

Fruit Frolic

Each fruit in the box below represents a number. The numbers at the end of each row and the bottom of each column are the totals of the numbers that row or column added together. Find out which number each fruit represents and find the number to replace the question mark.

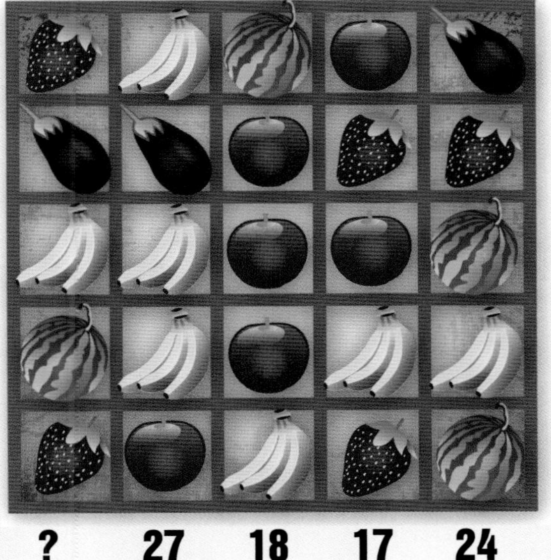

A banana ripens quickly (overnight), when you put it into a brown paper bag with an apple or tomato.

281

Color the Ball

The ball needs to be painted black and white. The numbers in the octagon specify the number of octagons around it that need to be colored black.

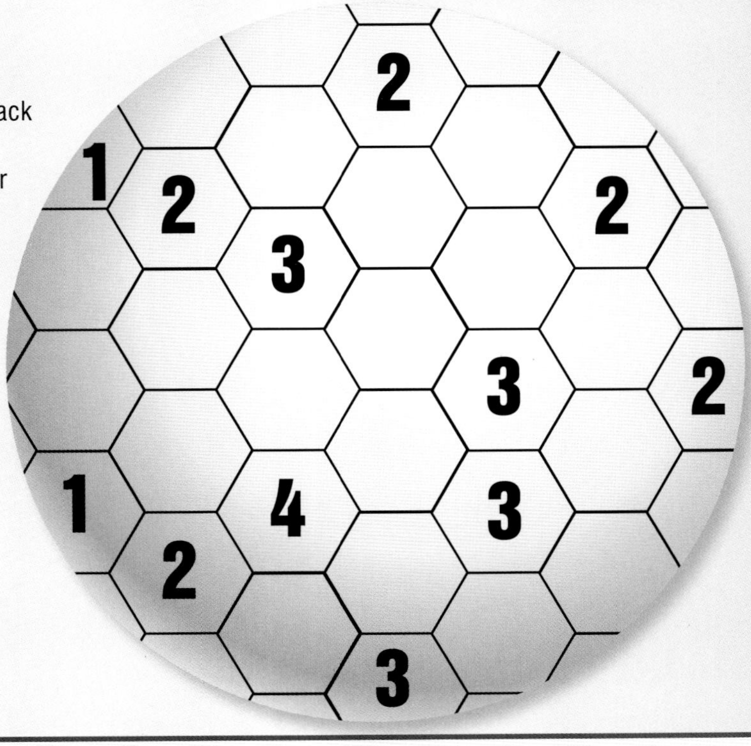

282

Counting Money

It's time to count the amount of money saved. Complete the grid using the using the more or less signs. Every row and column should have numbers 1–5, without repeating any number.

5^2-4^2 -8		30/6	$>$	
	$<$		$<$	
(2×2) -2 $<$			$\sqrt{36}$ -1	
	27–24			$\wedge$ 1^2+1^2
$\vee$	$\wedge$	$<$	$<$	$(1+1)^2$

"A penny saved is a dollar earned."

B. Franklin

283

Number Juggler

The juggler is juggling 9 balls with different numbers and mathematical signs. Create an equation using each number only once to get the result 54. Use only the required mathematical signs in any combination and as many times as required.

4 + ( ) 6 = × 3 − 7

54

"The world cannot be governed without juggling."

John Selden

284

A B C

Tea Cup Set

Keith has ordered nine tea cups, but has received 11. He knows eight of the tea cups that were definitely ordered. Can you help him to identify the missing cup from the three below.

A cup of black tea has half the amount of caffeine than a cup of coffee.

285

Helping Hands

Compare the two pictures to find five differences.

"Tis not enough to help the feeble up, but to support them after."

William Shakespeare

286

Fix the Screen

The computer has an interesting game where you need to color the number of squares specified. The numbers in the squares specify the number of squares around it (horizontally, vertically, or diagonally) that need to be colored.

"Games lubricate the body and the mind."

Benjamin Franklin

287

Puzzling Patterns

Only one of the patterns below is unique, the other 14 all have an exact double. Can you find the one-off?

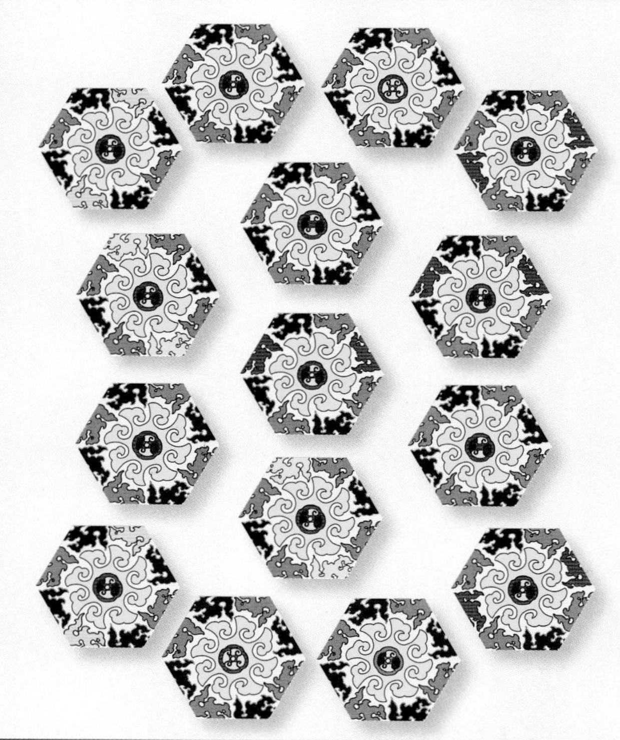

"Art is pattern informed by sensibility."

Herbert Read

288

Money, Money, Money

Can you identify the currency note that is not part of a pair?

"If you want to feel rich, just count the things you have that money can't buy."

289

Pyramid Puzzle

The pyramids have been arranged in four rows and four columns. Each row and column should have pyramids that are numbered 1–4. The ones that are linked together should have all the numbers.

The Egyptians didn't have accurate measuring tape. They used fiber-cords that could shrink or stretch.

290

Gem Search

This crown is studded with stones that have different shapes and letters. Find the corresponding number for each letter. Multiply the number you found with the total number of edges of the shape around it. For example, D=4, and 4X4=16. The rubies have been placed in 3 adjacent blocks whose average is 36. Can you find them?

"A crown, golden in show is but a wreath of thorns."

John Milton

291

Flower Placement

Can you work out which of the alternatives, A, B, C, or D, should replace the question mark?

The Cutleaf Evening Primrose flower has only four petals. It is also a wild host for clouded and tarnished plant bugs.

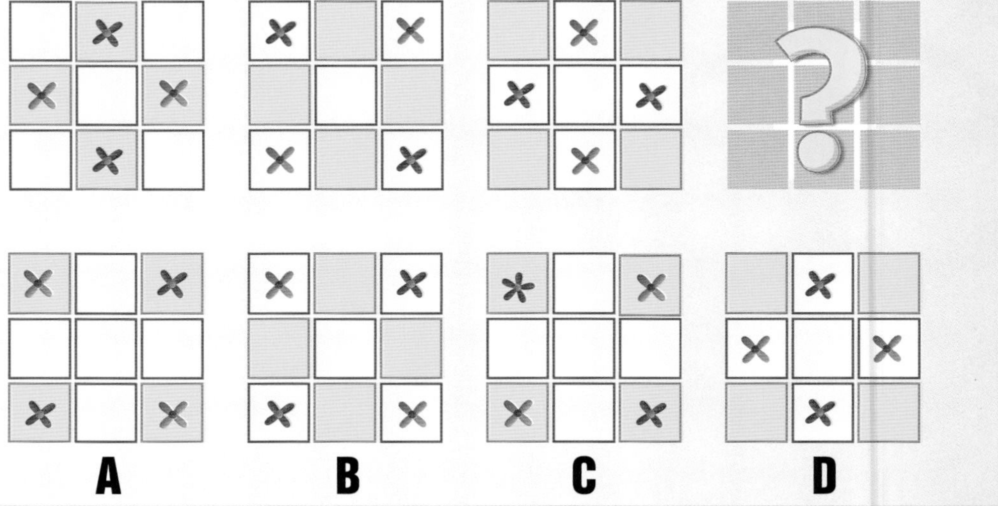

292

"Every flower is a soul blossoming in nature."

Gerard De Nerval

Mysterious Board

The flower board contains pairs of numbers. Join each pair of numbers with a line without crossing lines for any other connections. Your lines cannot pass through the flowers.

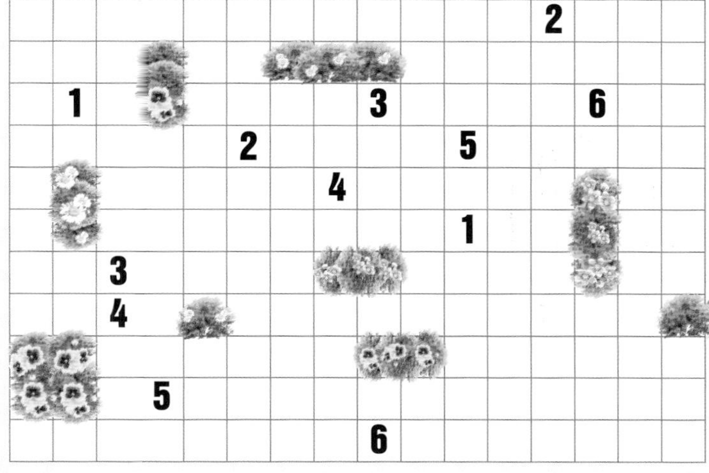

293

Horse Race

Create an equation using each number only once to get 20 as the result and get a free entry to the horse race. Use only the required mathematical signs in any combination and as many times as required.

7 + = × 20 − 13 49 ( ) ÷

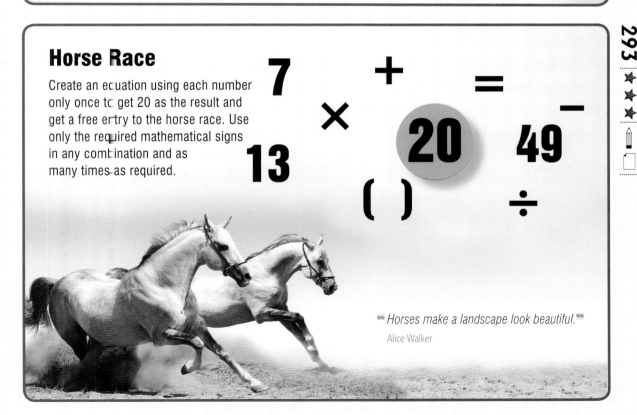

"Horses make a landscape look beautiful."

Alice Walker

294

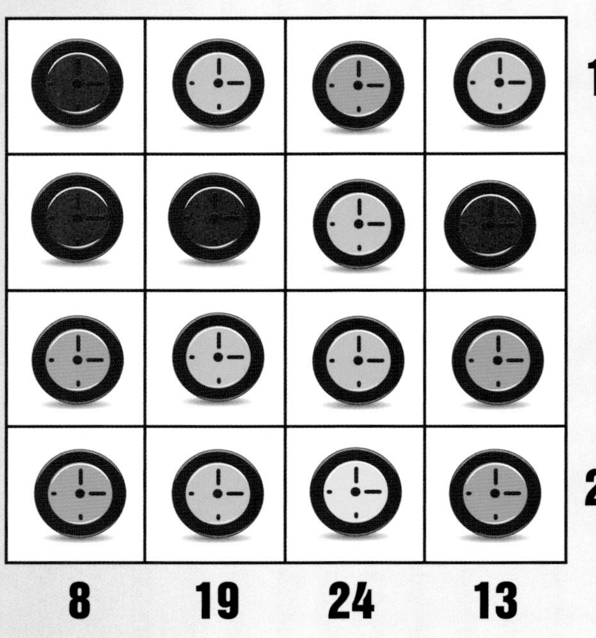

Unfold the Numbers

Each clock in the box below represents a number. The numbers at the end of each row and the bottom of each column are the totals of the numbers in that row or column added together. Find out which number each clock represents and find the number to replace the question mark.

The word clock comes from the French word "cloche" that means bell.

295

Boggling Boxes

Can you work out which cube from A, B, C and D will fill the empty box?

5	2	7
7	6	13
3	6	9

2	1	3
7	8	15
11	8	19

3	2	5
8	9	17
1	6	7

A

2	1	3
4	2	7
3	4	5

B

6	5	11
2	1	3
1	1	2

C

3	1	4
4	3	7
4	4	8

D

4	5	9
1	2	3
4	7	11

296

Sharing Happiness

You need to join each pair of numbers with a line without crossing lines for any other connection. Your lines cannot pass through the shaded blocks.

"Happiness is nothing more than good health and a bad memory."

Albert Schweitzer

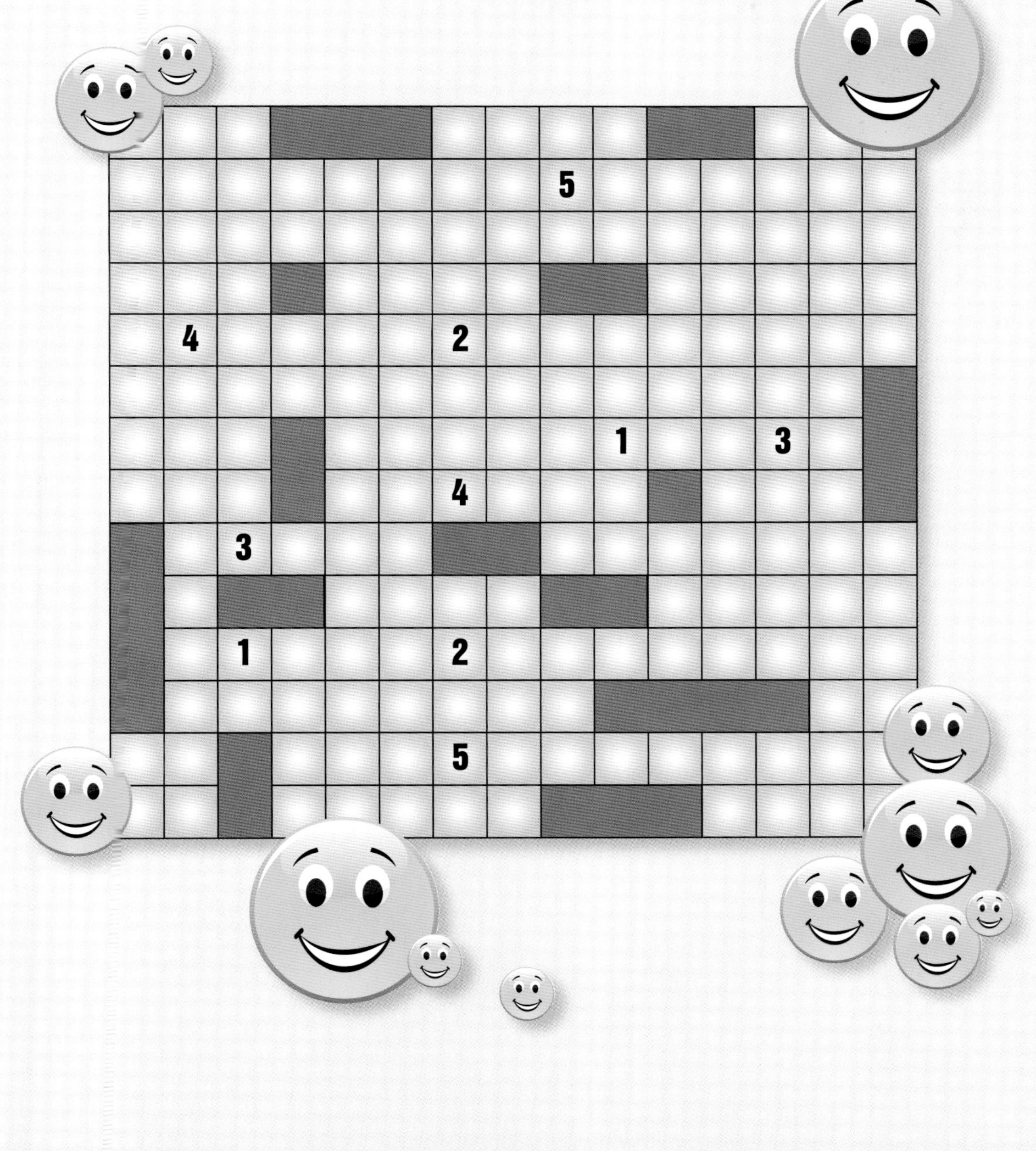

297

Missing Books

You have borrowed some books from the library. When you go to return the books, you realize that you have left one book back at home. Compare the two pictures to identify the missing book.

"We may sit in our library and yet be in all quarters of the earth."

John Lubbock

298

Tricky Triangles

Which of the pictures below represents the correct overhead view of this scene?

"Let your hopes, not your hurts, shape your future."

Robert H. Schuller

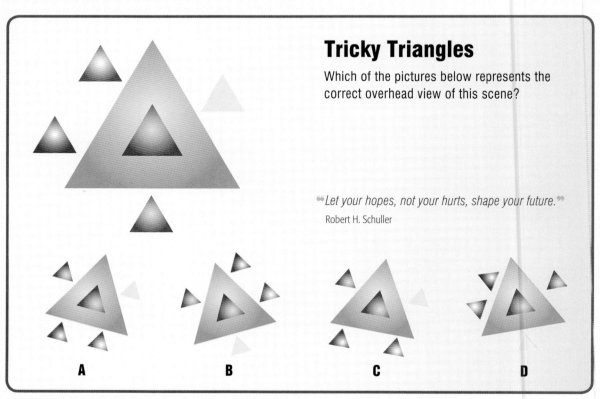

A B C D

299

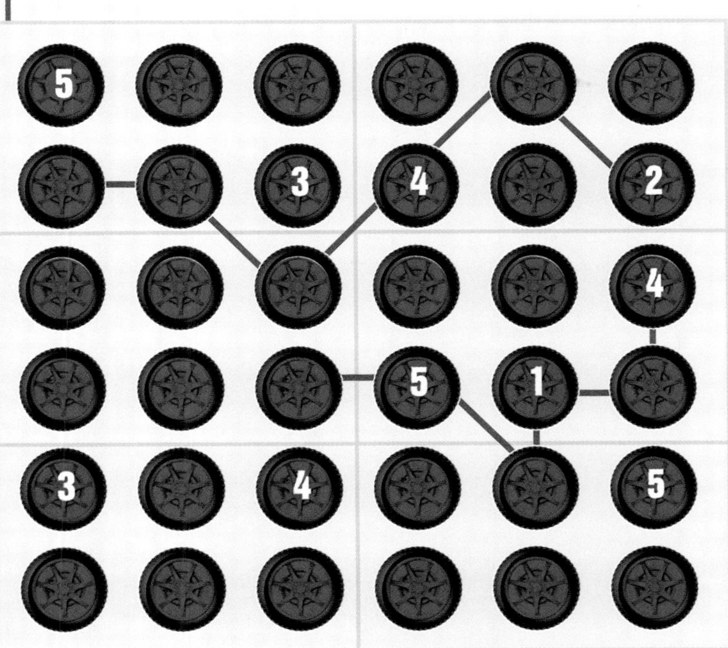

Tire Numbers

Fill the numbers 1–6 on the blank tires. Each row, column, group and linked tire should have all six numbers. No number should be repeated in a row, column, group, and the tires that are linked together.

A tire can lose up to half of its air pressure and not appear to be flat.

300

Flower Pot Mystery

Find the missing numbers so that the total of each pairs of flower pots forms the flower pot directly below them.

"How does the Meadow flower its bloom unfold? Because the lovely little flower is free down to its root, and in that freedom bold."

William Wordsworth

301

Tricky Truck

"As men get older, the toys get more expensive."
Marvin Davis

In a toy shop, you find a truck with a puzzle printed on it. Each block on the truck has different shapes with numbers. Multiply the digits inside shape and add the result to the number of edges. Find 5 adjacent blocks that add up to 68.

302

Free Coffee

You walk into a coffee shop and order a cup of coffee. The cup has multiple oval shapes on it, with numbers in some. The numbers specify the number of ovals around it that need to be shaded. Shade the cup to get your coffee free.

Did you know that coffee is actually a fruit? It's a cherry.

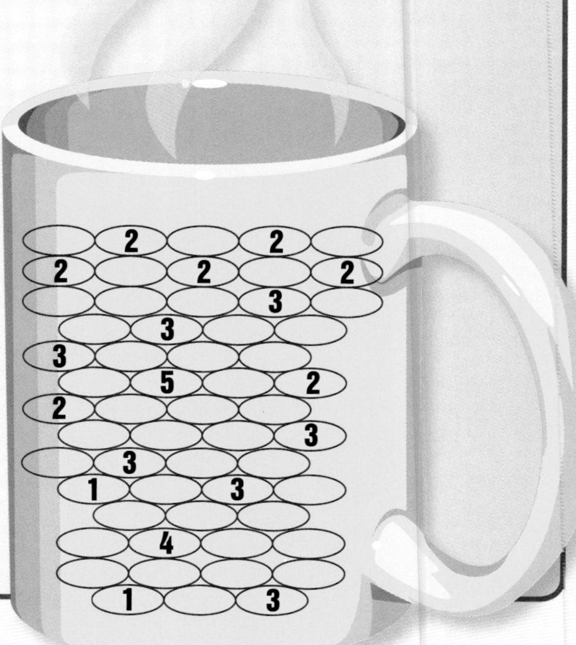

Number Stumper

303 ★★★

Fill the missing numbers on the puzzle using the more or less signs. Every row, column and highlighted group should have the numbers 1–6, without any repetition.

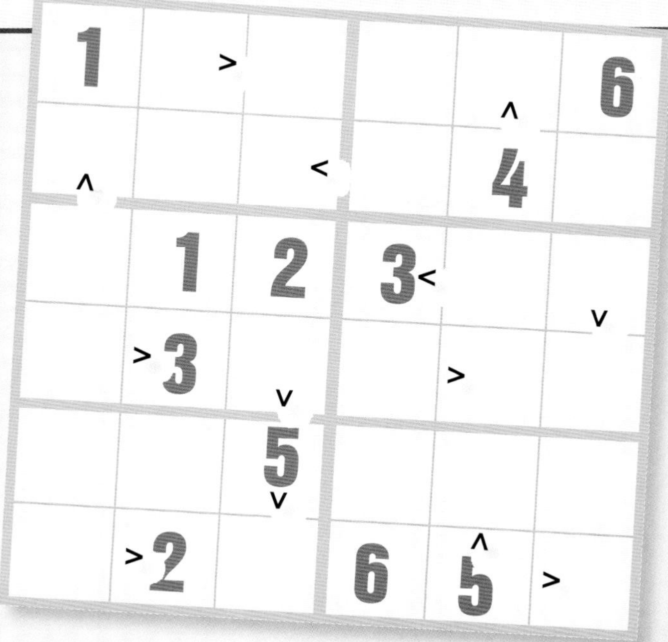

Tulip Teaser

304 ☆★★

Create an equation using every number on the tulip only once to get 128 as the result. Use only the required mathematical signs in any combination and as many times as required.

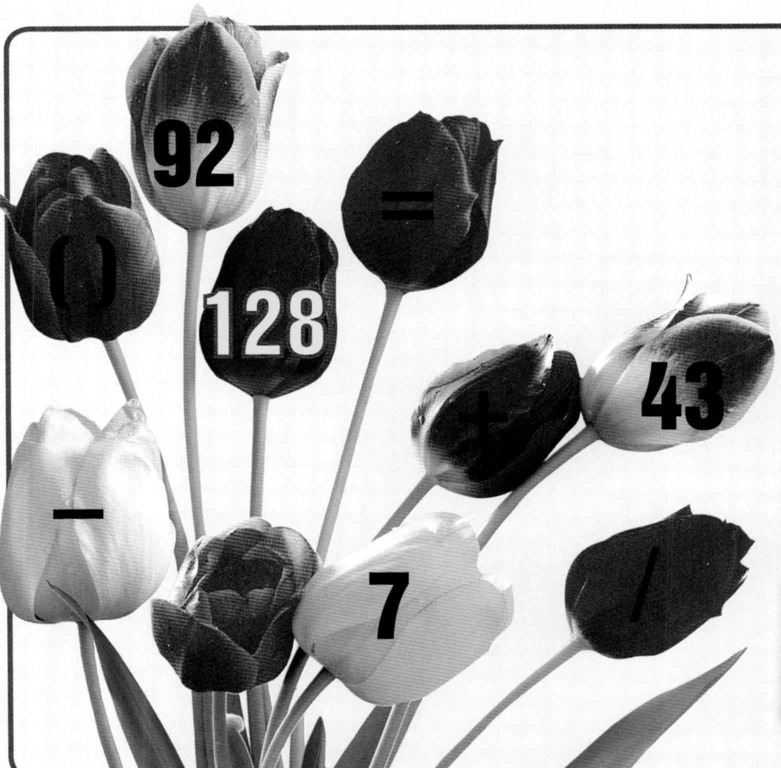

Tulip bulbs can be used in place of onions for cooking.

305

"They that mistake life's accessories for life itself are like them that go too fast in a maze: their very haste confuses them."

Seneca

Hexagon Maze

In the sequence below, which of the alternatives, A, B, C, or D, should replace the question mark?

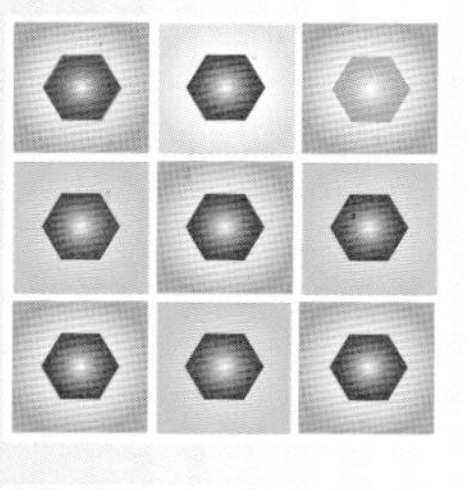 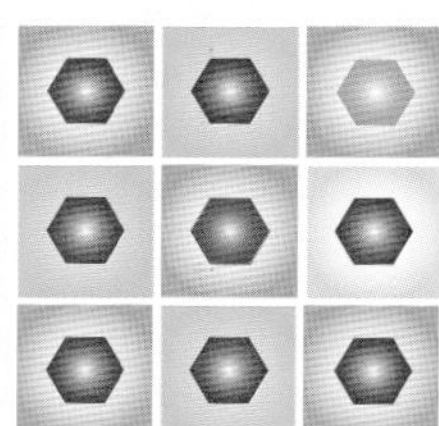  

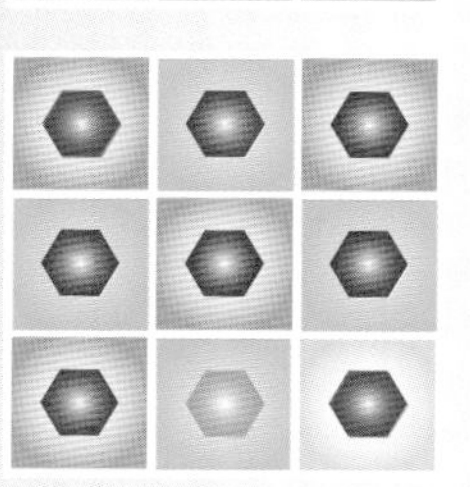

A

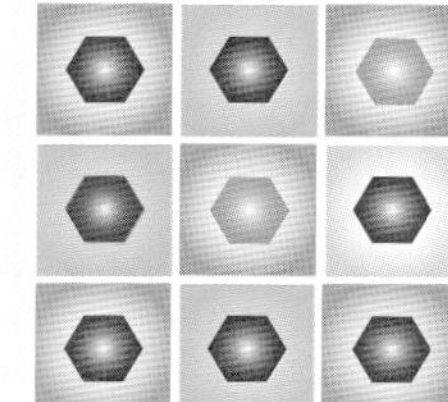

B

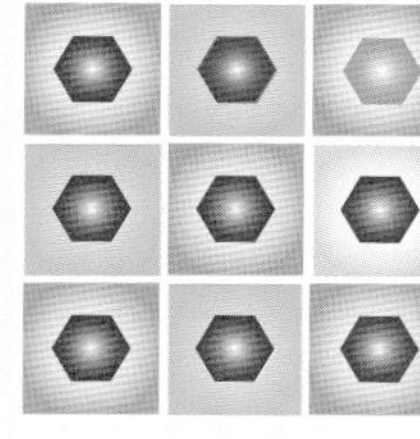

C

D

306

Number Relation

Find the missing numbers so that the total of each pair of apples forms the apple total directly above them.

?

? 23

11 ? ?

? 7 ? ?

? 2 ? 1 ?

Did you know that apple trees take four to five years to produce their first fruit?

307

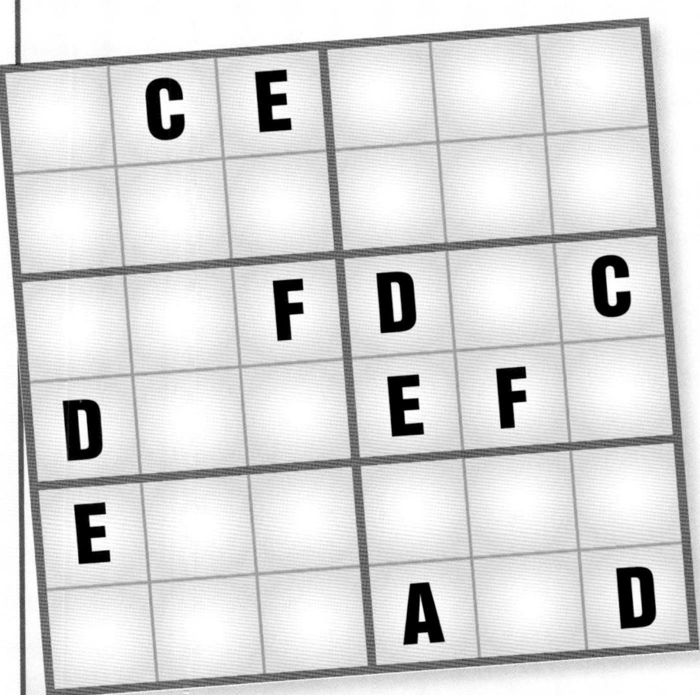

Zoo Entry Discount

The zoo has a big board with some missing letters at the entrance. Fill the missing letters to get a discount. Every row, column and group should have the letters A–F, without any repetition.

"I love acting, but it's much more fun taking the kids to the zoo."

Nicole Kidman

308

Find the Flag!

Each flag appears twice apart from the one that appears only once. Can you find the odd one?

The Study of the flags is called Vexillology.

309

Whistle Blowing

There are multiple games arranged for Mike's birthday party. Number the whistles so that each row and column will have all 1–4 numbers. No number should be repeated in a row, column or the whistles that are linked together.

310

Shade the Blocks

The office table has multiple blocks with different shapes and letters. Find the corresponding number for each letter. Add the number you find with the total number of edges of the shape around it. For example, D=4 and 4+3=7. Shade 3 adjacent block that add up to 22.

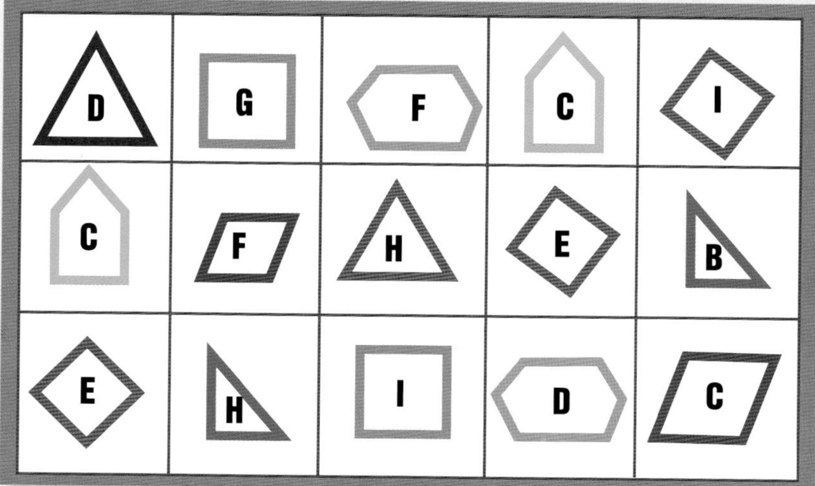

"A table, a chair, a bowl of fruit and a violin; what else does a man need to be happy."
Albert Einstein

311 ☆☆★

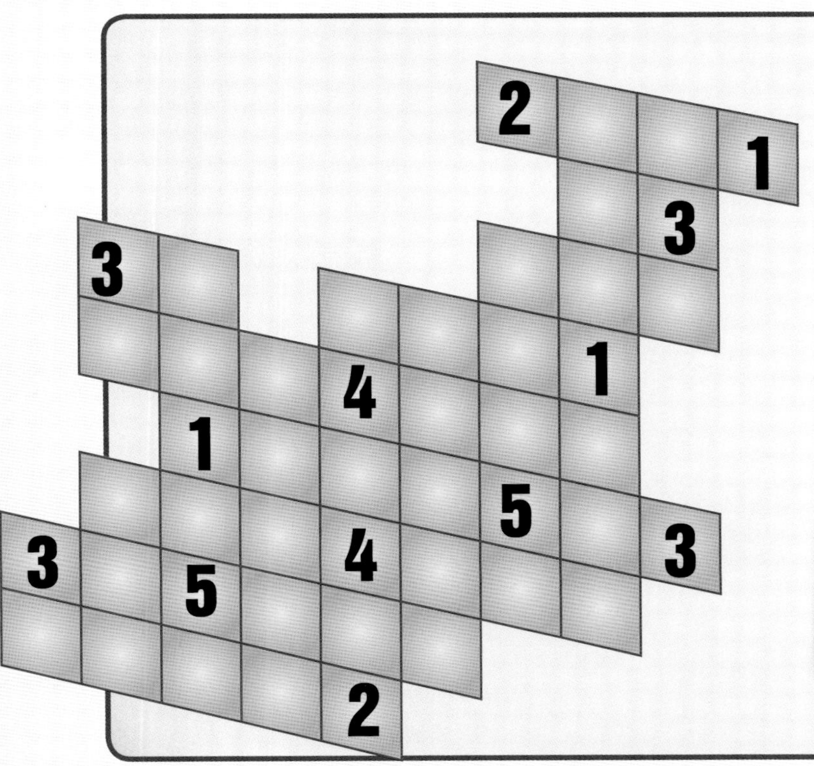

Shading Time

The puzzles have squares with numbers that specify the number of squares around them (horizontally, vertically or diagonally) that need to be shaded. Start coloring!

The first jigsaw puzzle was produced by John Spilsbury in 1760.

312 ★★★

Sudoku Stumper

Complete the puzzle using the more or less signs. Every row, column and highlighted group should have the numbers I–VIII, without any repetition.

		V	II	III		v	
VII	>				<	II	VIII
	I	>		VIII	^	v	
			VI <			III	I
		< IV			<		
VIII	VI ^			IV	<		
		I		II		>	^ V
>		VI	VIII			VII	>

The first World Sudoku championship was held in Lucca, Italy in 2006.

313 ☆☆★

The Drugstore

While working at a drugstore, you need to arrange the capsule and syrup bottles. Ensure that no two syrups and consecutive numbers are placed together horizontally or vertically. Some of the bottles have already been placed. Complete the puzzle by arranging the remaining bottles.

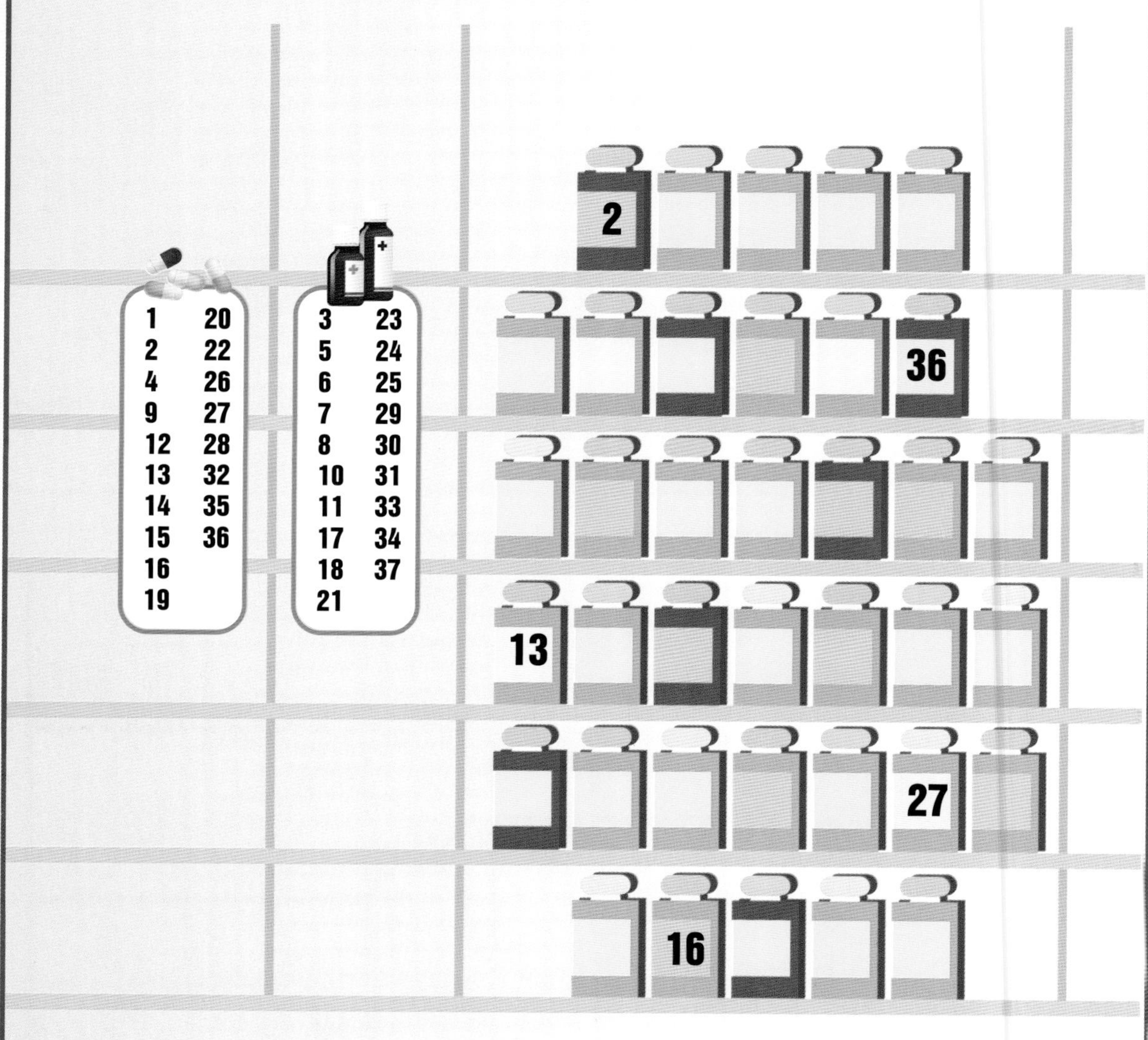

314

Leaves and Numbers

Find the number on the last leaf. Use the numbers at the edge of the leaves to form the central number in the same way in all three cases.

Did you know that olive leaf extract lowers blood pressure and improves your immune system?

315

Missing Stationery

Help the administration department at your office find the missing stationery. Arrange the items so that the rows and columns have every stationery item and color, without any repetition.

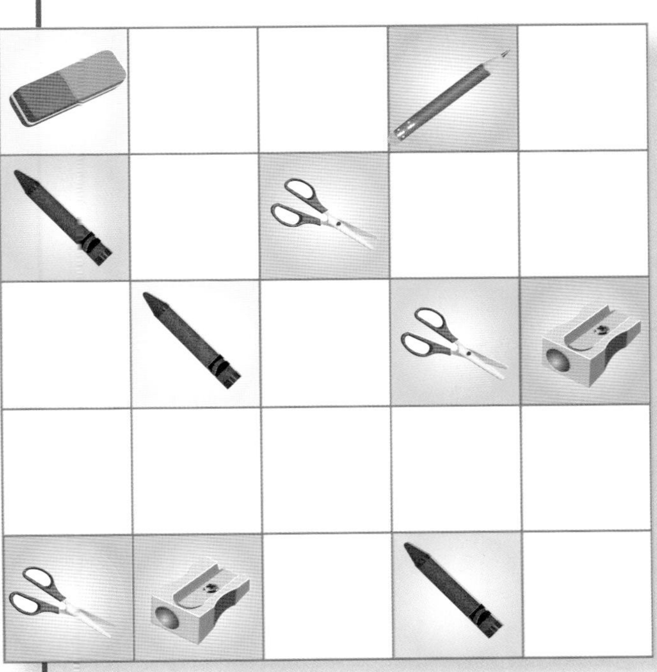

Did you know that prior to the invention of the eraser, tablets of wax were used to erase lead/charcoal marks from paper?

316 ★★★

Brain Boggle

Can you work out which cube from A, B, C and D will fill the empty box?

"Mathematics–the unshaken Foundation of Sciences, and the plentiful Fountain of Advantage to human affairs."

Isaac Barrow

21	5	34
3	55	1
89	13	8

2	144	3
1	5	89
55	8	21

233	3	21
5	89	34
2	13	1

A

28	8	13
34	21	5
3	144	1

B

1	17	21
13	2	34
5	55	3

C

34	3	13
1	377	55
21	3	5

D

317	28	34
1	2	3
4	5	13

317 ★★★

Flower Power

The numbers on the first two flowers can help you number the sixth flower. Can you find the missing number on the sixth flower?

"The caterpillar does all the work but the butterfly gets all the publicity."

George Carlin

Roaring Races

318 ☆☆★

The tickets on the racing car have a puzzle with six rows and six columns. Every row, column and group should have the letters A–F, without any repetition. Complete the puzzle to meet the winner of the race.

				E	
		F	B		
	E	C			
A					D
	C				
				B	A

"Finishing races is important, but racing is more important."
Dale Earnhardt

Bird Watching

319 ☆★★

Find the missing numbers so that the total of each pair of birds forms the total on the bird directly in front of them.

?
? ?
? ? ?
? ? 30
? 9 17 ?
? ? 30
1 ?
?

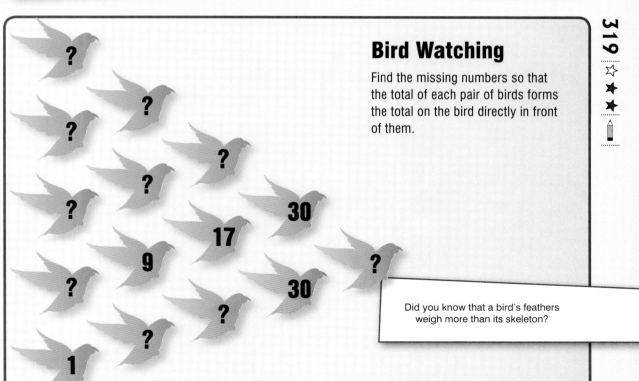

Did you know that a bird's feathers weigh more than its skeleton?

320 ★★☆

Boat Logic

The boats are arranged in five rows and five columns. Fill the numbers on the blank boats so that every row, column and linked boats have all 1–5 numbers, without any repetition.

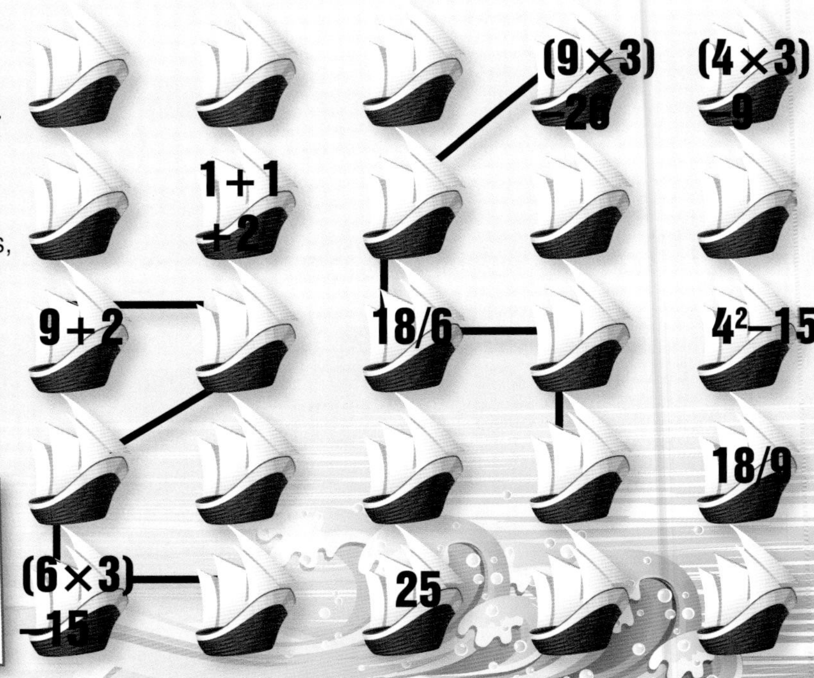

In 1906, the Germans launched the 1st U boat (undersea boat) that is like a submarine.

321 ★★☆

=

×

( )

4

16

3

/

+

12

Equation Time

Create an equation using each number only once to get the number 16 as the result. Use only the required mathematical signs in any combination and as many times as required.

“Politics is for the present, but an equation is for eternity.”

Albert Einstein

322

All Packed Up

There is a suitcase with multiple blocks and different shapes and numbers. Add the number inside the shape with the number of edges around it. Color five adjacent blocks whose average is nine.

"The towels were so thick there I could hardly close my suitcase."

Yogi Berra

323

Coloring Fun

There are numbers on the petals of a flower. Each number specifies the adjacent petals to be shaded. Shade the petals.

324

Dolphin Frolic

Fill the empty squares using the more or less signs. Every row and column should have the numbers 1–5, without any repetition. Find the corresponding number for each letter to identify which number is greater than the other. For example, C=3, so the number in the second cell of the first column needs to be less than 3.

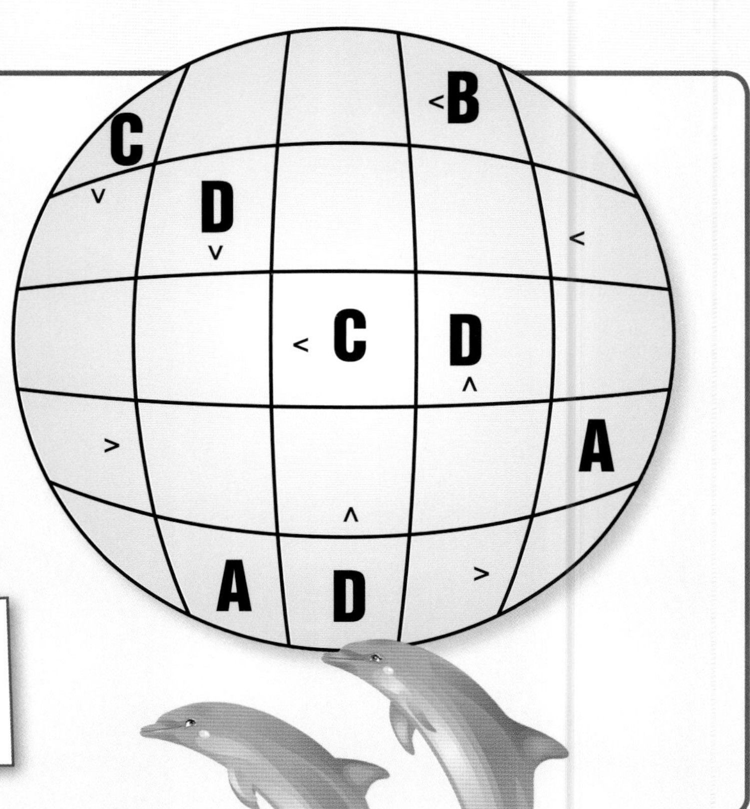

Dolphins do not have prominent external ear openings. Their ear openings are small slits located behind their eyes?

325

Remote Equation

Create an equation using any of the numbers 1–9 on the remote only once to get 56 as the channel. Use only the required mathematical signs in any combination and as many times as required.

Did you know that the TV remote control was invented in 1956 by Robert Adler?

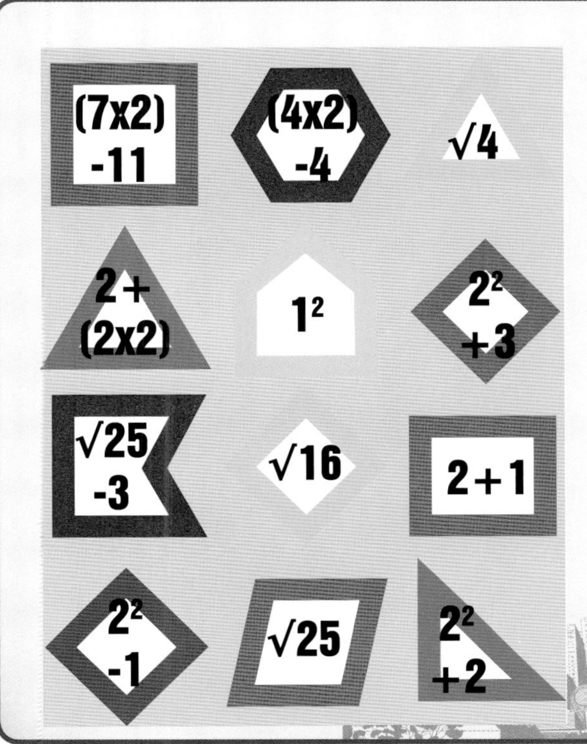

Skyscraper Teaser

326 ☆★★

The new skyscraper has different shapes and calculations on it. Add the result of every calculation with the number of edges around it. Find 3 adjacent blocks that add up to 26.

The first skyscraper was built in 1885.

Dog House

327 ☆☆★

Arrange the numbers on the dog house so that no consecutive and even number comes together vertically, horizontally, and diagonally.

"Man is a dog's idea of what God should be."

Holbrook Jackson

328

Fruit Confusion

At a fruit store, you find a poster with a puzzle on it. Fill the empty blocks using the letters A–H so that all eight letters appear in each row, column and group without repeating any letter.

F	B			A		C	
	H	A		F			E
A		D			E	F	B
G							
	G	B		C	A		F
	A		F			H	
			A				H
B			E	D		A	C

Did you know that Guava is the most nutritious fruit?

329

Shape Shuffle

Each shape appears twice apart from the one that appears only once. Can you find the odd one?

"A round man cannot be expected to fit in a square hole right away. He must have time to modify his shape."

Mark Twain

330 ★★★

Action!

Fill the missing numbers so that every row, column and group has all I–IX numbers, without any repetition. The blocks that are linked together should have all nine numbers without any repetition.

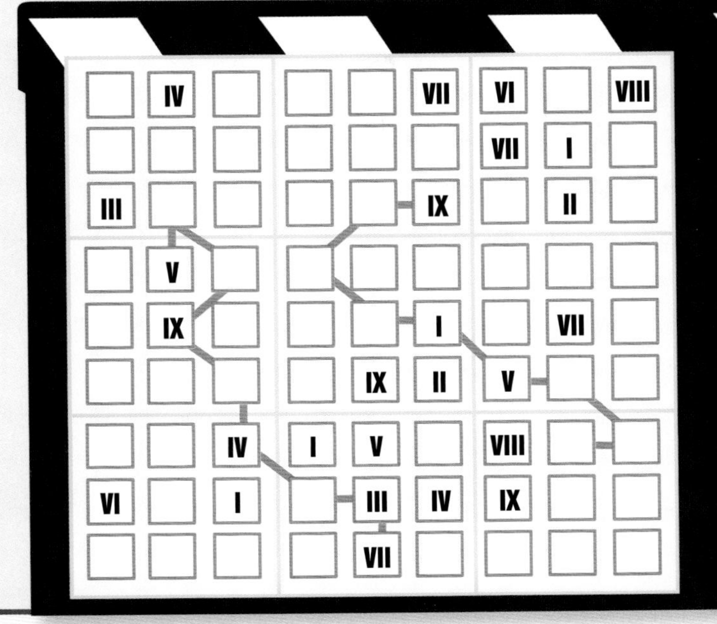

"Every great film should seem new every time you see it."

Roger Ebert

331 ☆★★

Plate Jumble

You have been given a plate that has blocks containing shapes and letters. Find the corresponding number for each letter. Add each number found to the number of edges. Find six adjacent blocks whose average is eight.

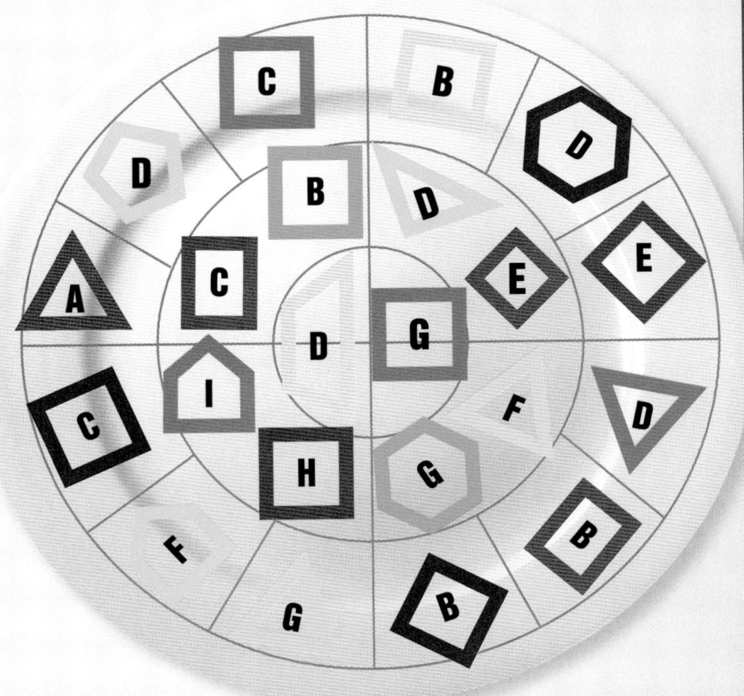

"To give and then not feel that one has given is the very best of all ways of giving."

Max Beerbohm

332

Find the Crack

The flower pot has some cracks in it. The numbers on the pot indicate the number of adjacent circles that need to be shaded. The circles that are not shaded indicate the cracks in the pot.

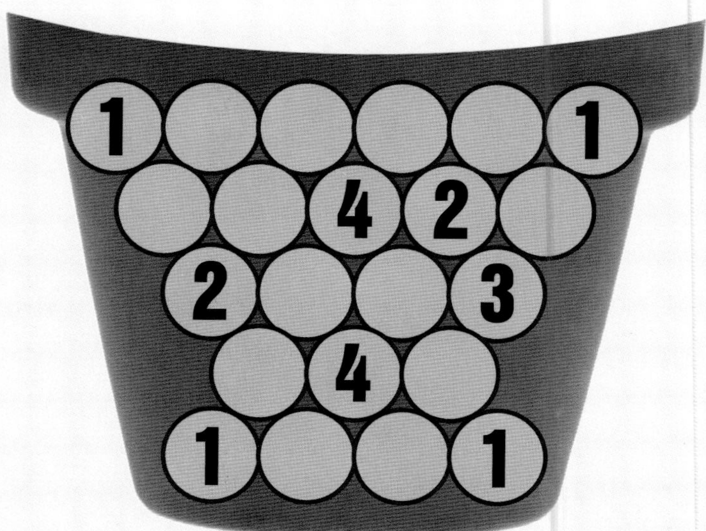

"Flowers seem intended for the solace of ordinary humanity."

John Ruskin

333

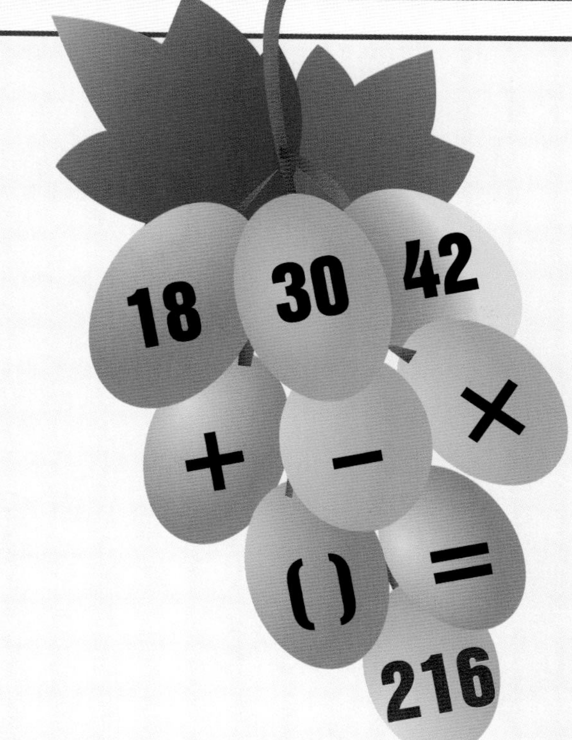

Grape Count

Create an equation using each number only once to get 216 as the result. Use only the required mathematical signs in any combination and as many times as required.

One grape cluster has on an average 75 grapes.

Spot the Difference

Compare the pictures and find the five differences.

"Life is painting a picture, not doing a sum."
Oliver Wendell Holmes

334

335 ★★★

Discount Delights!

"A ring is a halo on your finger."
Doug Coupland

The jewelry shop has six ring boxes on display. Find the missing number on the sixth box.

336 ☆☆★

Circle Dilemma

Which of the pictures below represents the correct overhead view of this scene?

"In helping others, we shall help ourselves, for whatever good we give out completes the circle and comes back to us."
Flora Edwards

A

B

C

D

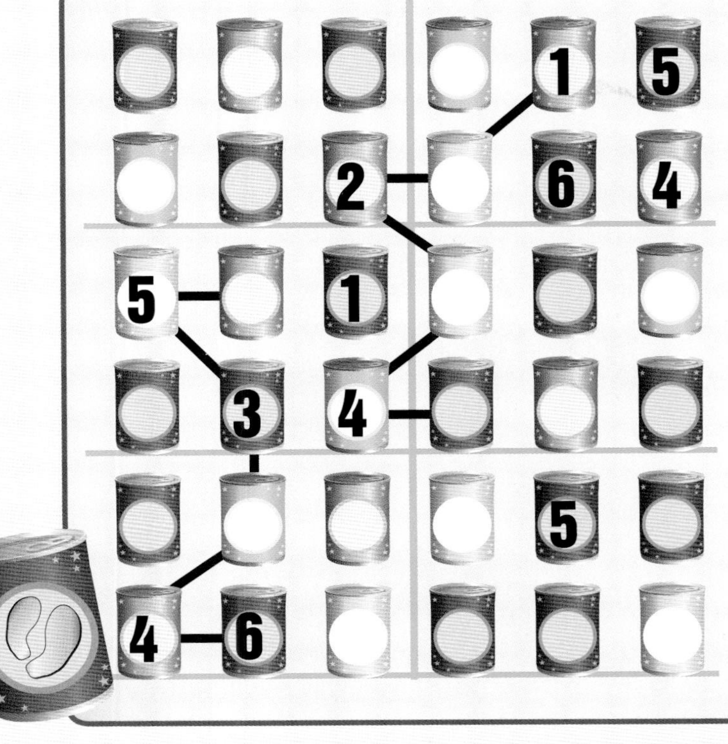

Can Craze

337 ★★★

Fill the missing numbers on the cashew nut cans so that each row, column, group and linked cans have all 1–6 numbers, without any repetition.

Cashew nuts do have a relatively high fat content, but it is considered "good fat" with zero percent cholesterol.

Heart Search

338 ☆★★

This heart contains diamonds and numbers. The numbers specify the number of diamonds (horizontally, vertically and diagonally) that need to be shaded.

"One of the hardest things in life is having words in your heart that you can't utter."

James Earl Jones

339 ☆☆★

Totaling Shapes

The puzzle is divided into multiple cells with shapes and numbers. You need to divide each number by the number of sides. Find 4 adjacent cells that add up to 16.

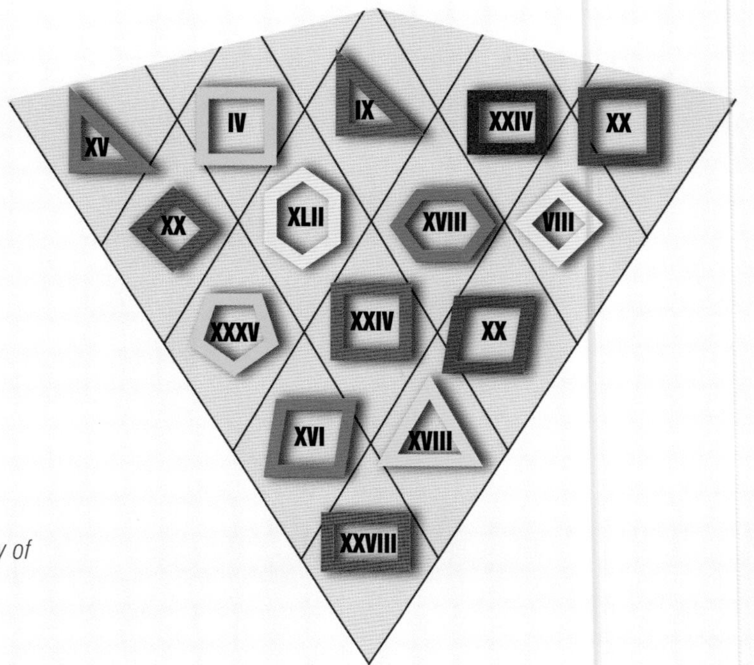

"Education is a progressive discovery of our own ignorance."

Will Durant

340 ★★★

Free the Giraffe

The giraffe is caged in with a lock code. Create an equation using each number only once to get 242 as the result. Use only the required mathematical signs in any combination and as many times as required.

Giraffes are vegetarians and live on the leaves of the baobab tree.

Baffling Boxes

341 ★★★

Find the secret number in the last box. Use the numbers at the corner of the boxes to form the central number in the same way in all three cases. Find the number that should replace the question mark for the third box.

"Still more astonishing is that world of rigorous fantasy we call mathematics."

Gregory Bateson

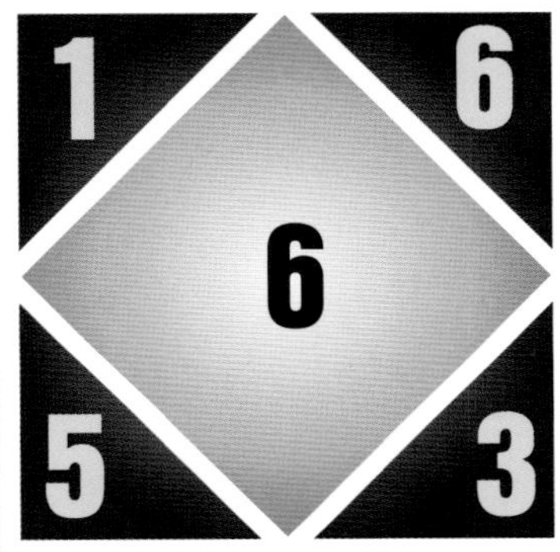

Four by Four

342 ☆☆★

Fill in the missing numbers in such a way that every row, column and linked squares have all 1–4 numbers, without any repetition.

The Number Four is the first non-prime number.

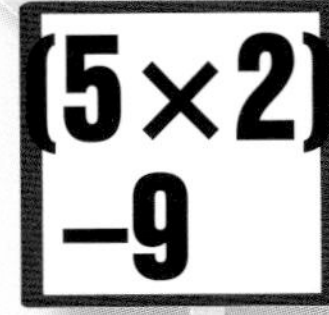

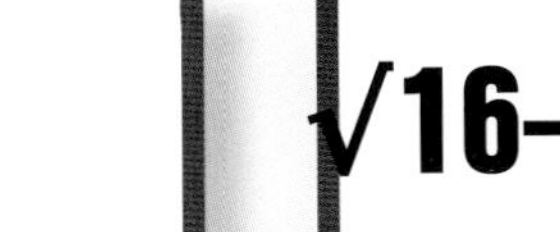

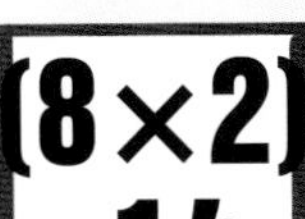

343

Shining Star

The star has multiple triangles with some numbers on it. The numbers specify the number of triangles around it, sharing common sides, which need to be shaded. Make the star shine by shading the triangles.

"He who is fixed to a star does not change his mind."

Leonardo da Vinci

344

Beaker Seeker

The beaker has multiple blocks on it with shapes and letters. Find the corresponding number for each letter. You need to multiply the number found with the number of edges of the shape. Find 3 adjacent blocks whose total is 35.

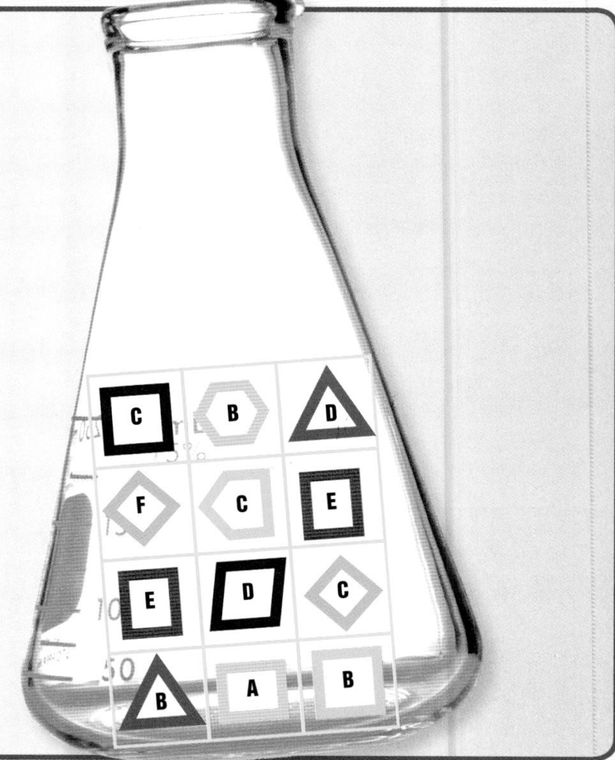

The word beaker is derived from the Latin word *bicarium*, which means "drinking vessel".

345

Elephant Equation

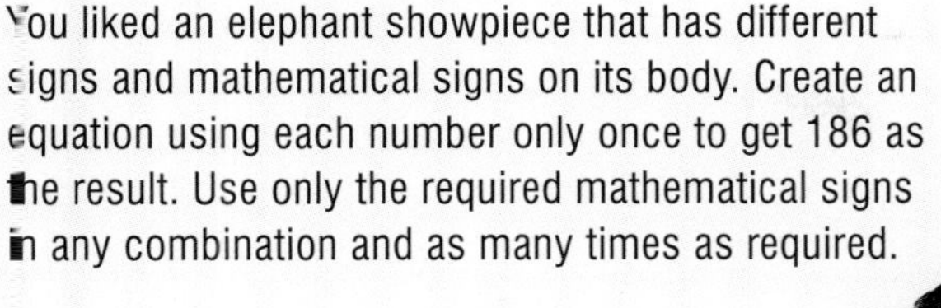

You liked an elephant showpiece that has different signs and mathematical signs on its body. Create an equation using each number only once to get 186 as the result. Use only the required mathematical signs in any combination and as many times as required.

Elephant skin is wrinkled as it helps them regulate their temperature and keep cool.

346

Unfold the Picture

The camera has a picture that has the numbers I–VI. Enter the missing numbers in such a way that every row, column, group and linked squares have all six numbers without any repetition.

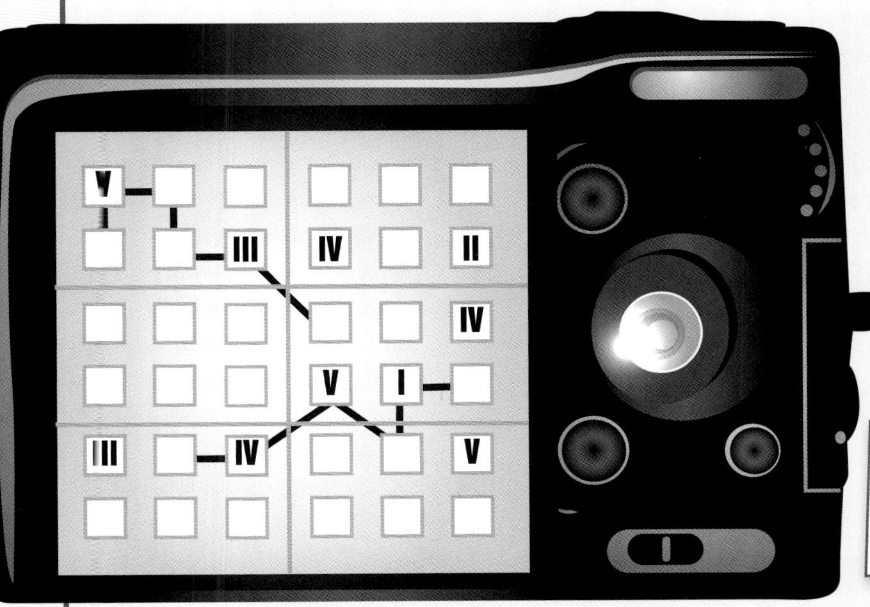

Kodak engineer Steven Sasson developed the first digital camera prototype in 1975.

347

Compound Clouds

Find the missing numbers so that each pair of clouds forms the cloud directly above them.

270

18 ?

6 ? ?

? ? ? 5

348

Color the Pattern

The pattern has numbers specifying the number of scales around it that need to be colored.

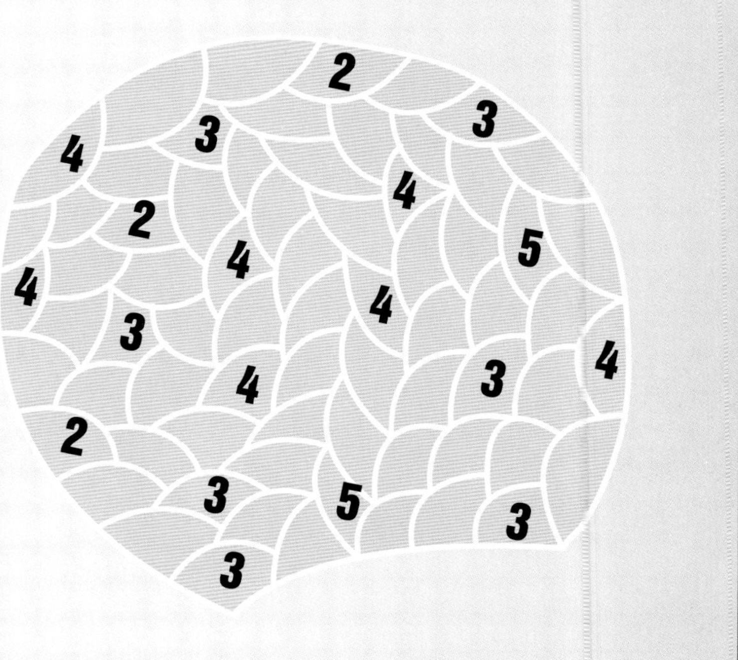

Art Decor 349

You have decorated your home with flower bowls. Each bowl has the number of flowers to be placed in them. You need to find the number for the bowl with a question mark.

"I like flowers, I also like children, but I do not chop their heads and keep them in bowls of water around the house."

George Bernard Shaw

Addition and Subtraction 350

This cell phone cover has different shapes and numbers. Subtract the number of sides of the shape from the number inside the shape. Find two adjacent blocks that add up to five.

351

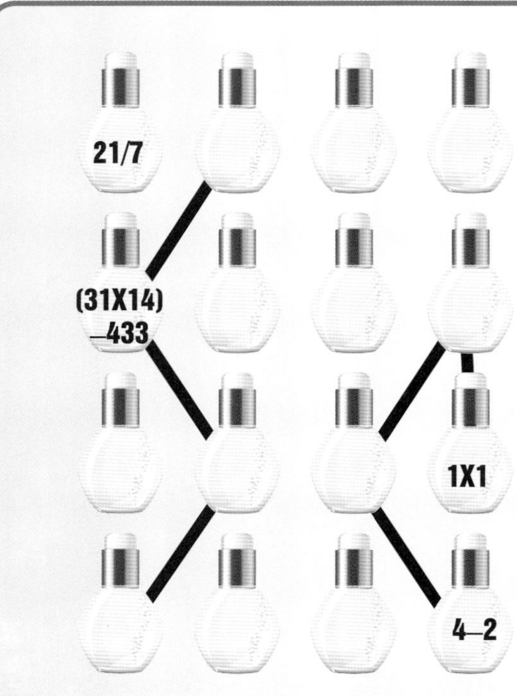

Number Game

Number the perfume bottles in such a way that every row, column and linked bottles are labelled 1 to 4 without any repetition.

Did you know that perfume is made up of alcohol, water and perfume (fragrance) oil?

352

Number Calculations

This calculator has numbers in blue and black. Create an equation using each black number only once to get one as the result. Use the required mathematical signs in any combination as many times as required.

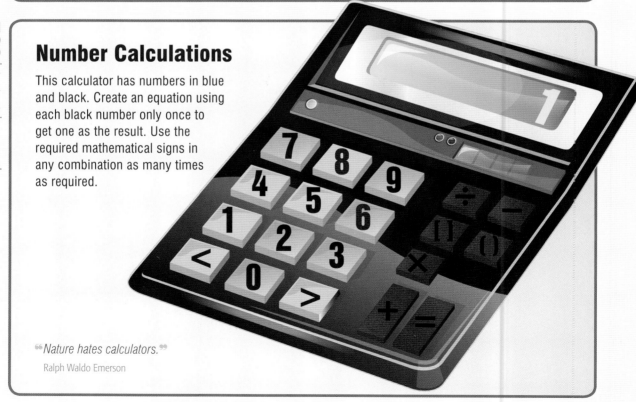

"Nature hates calculators."

Ralph Waldo Emerson

Picture Comparison

Here are two pictures of a village. The second picture has some differences when compared to the first picture. Find the ten differences.

"A village is a hive of glass, where nothing unobserved can pass."

Charles H. Spurgeon

354

Unfold the Sum

The puzzle has different shapes and letters. Find the corresponding number for each letter. Add the number found with the number of edges around it. Find 4 adjacent blocks that add up to 35.

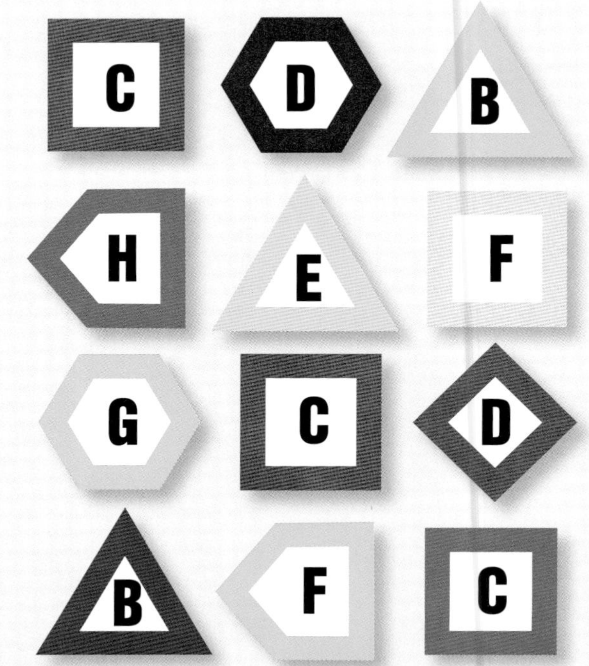

"A man is the sum of his actions, of what he has done, of what he can do, Nothing else."

John Galsworthy

355

Number the Tomatoes

The tomatoes are numbered from I–V. Fill the missing numbers in such a way that each row, column and linked tomatoes have all five numbers, without any repetition.

Did you know that washing your hair with tomatoes after swimming removes chlorine from your hair?

Fix It! 356 ☆☆★

The chair in your office is broken in various places. The numbers in each square mention the number of broken pieces around (horizontally, vertically and diagonally) the numbered square. Find the broken parts by shading the appropriate squares.

					3
	4		5		
					2
3		5			
				6	
2		6			
					4
3		4		2	

"A house that does not have one warm, comfy chair in it is soulless."

May Sarton

Mind Twister 357 ☆★★

Can you work out which cube from A, B, C and D will fill the empty box?

"There are things which seem incredible to most men who have not studied mathematics."

Aristotle

36	45	81
27	9	3
9	5	4

7	42	49
12	7	84
7	6	1

36	8	9
15	3	5
3	24	12

A

12	16	10
9	2	18
5	8	6

B

8	24	16
32	4	9
4	6	2

C

15	20	25
30	5	5
5	4	3

D

36	8	18
2	6	12
3	48	6

358

Television Game

The television screen has different numbers and mathematical signs on it. Create an equation using every number only once to get 54 as the result. Use only the required mathematical signs in any combination and as many times as required.

"I'm always amazed that people will actually choose to sit in front of the television and just be savaged by stuff that belittles their intelligence."

Alice Walker

359

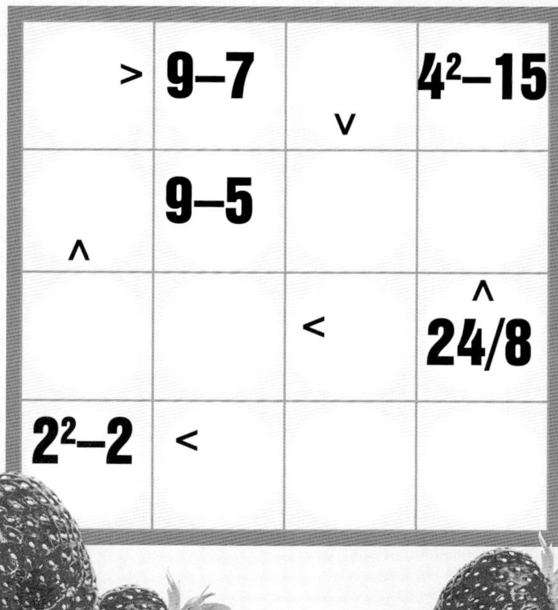

Strawberry Teaser

The cover of the strawberry box has a puzzle with some calculations and more or less signs. Fill the empty squares using the more or less signs. Every row and column should have the numbers 1–4, without any repetition. Complete the puzzle to get a box of strawberries free.

Did you know that strawberries contain a special substance called ellagic acid which can help fight some cancers?

360

Parking Conundrum

The squares on the ambulance are numbered for parking. Fill the missing numbers so that each row, column, and linked squares have all 1–5 numbers, without any repetition.

"We must be part of the general staff at the inception, rather than the ambulance drivers at the bitter end."

Lane Kirkland

361

On the Bus

The bus has a few empty seats left. The numbers in the rectangle specify the number of rectangles around (horizontally, vertically and diagonally) that need to be shaded. The shaded rectangles are the seats that are occupied. Find the number of passengers in the bus.

	2		3	
3		4		
				2
3		6		
				3
4		5		

Sandra's Shoe Challenge

Sandra wants to arrange her shoe collection in the closet so that no type of shoe is repeated in any row, column, group, or connected hexagons. Every row, column, group, and connected hexagons contain all the numbers 1–9. Can you help Sandra?

> "I did not have three thousand pairs of shoes. I had one thousand and sixty."
>
> Imelda Marcos

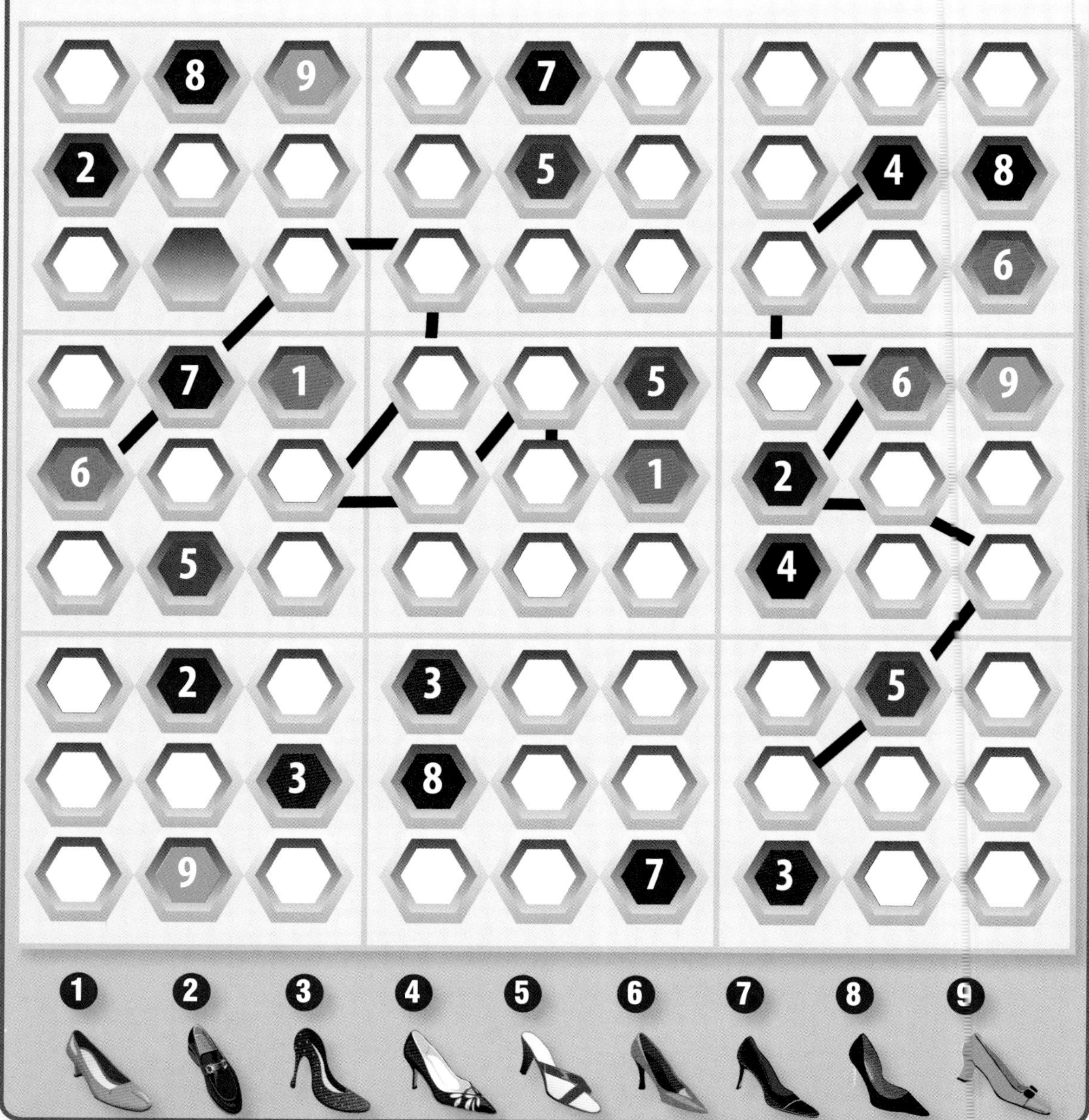

Fruit Placement 363

The puzzle has four different fruits. Every row and column should have each fruit in it, without repeating any fruit.

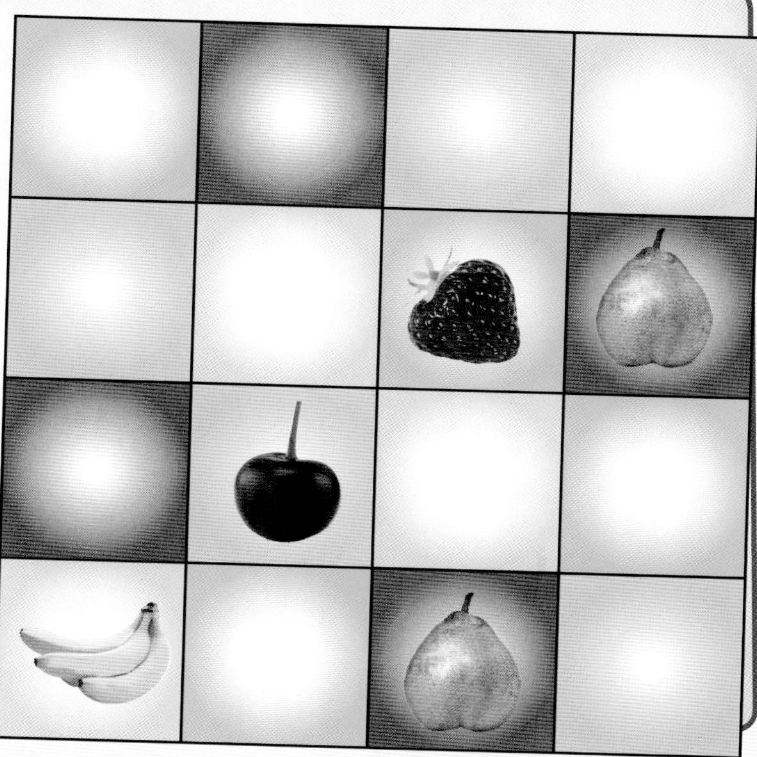

Letter Hunt 364

The table mat has a hidden letter on it. Multiply each number inside the shape with the number of edges around it. Find seven adjacent blocks that add up to 150 and reveal a hidden letter. What is the hidden letter?

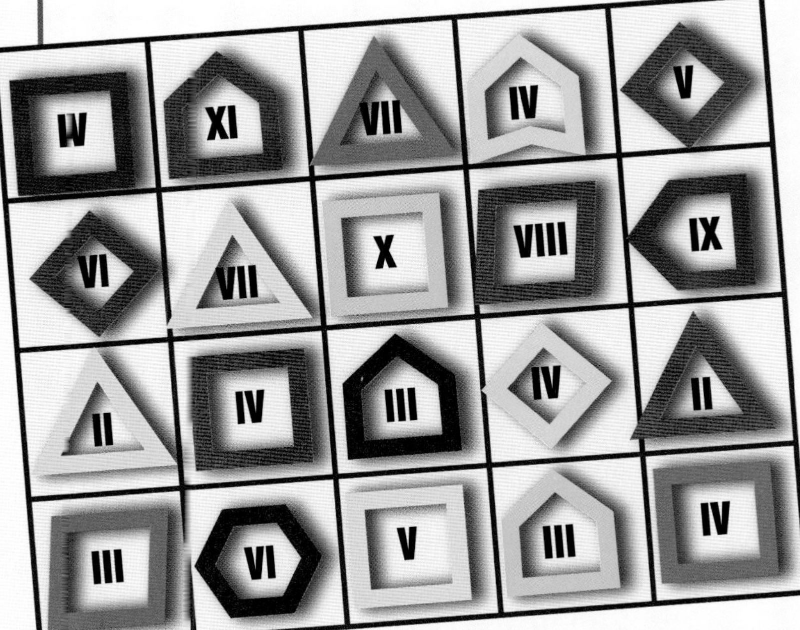

Did you know that most letters in the alphabet began as a simplified version of ancient drawings of animals, objects or signs?

365 ☆★★

Wildlife Differences

Compare the pictures. Can you find five differences?

"An animal's eyes have the power to speak a great language."

Martin Buber

SOLUTIONS

1. Disco Light

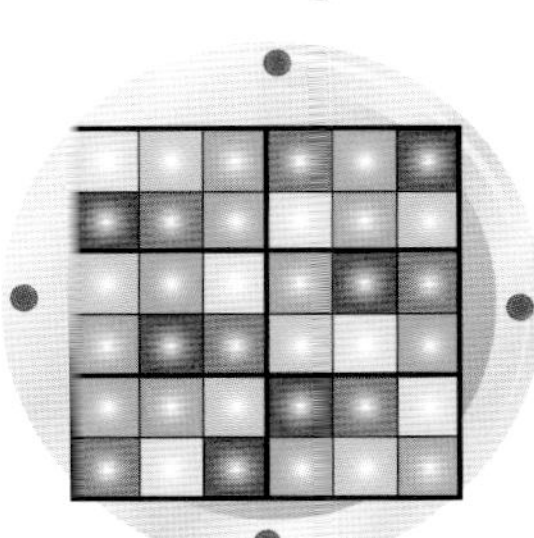

2. Flower Power

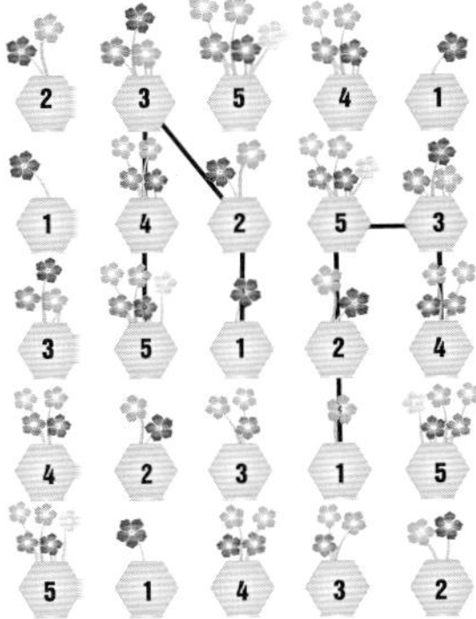

3. Find the Missing Block

Answer: C

Logic: The two numbers from each corner sum up to the number 15.

9+6=15
7+8=15
2+13=15
14+1=15

4. Odd Shape Out

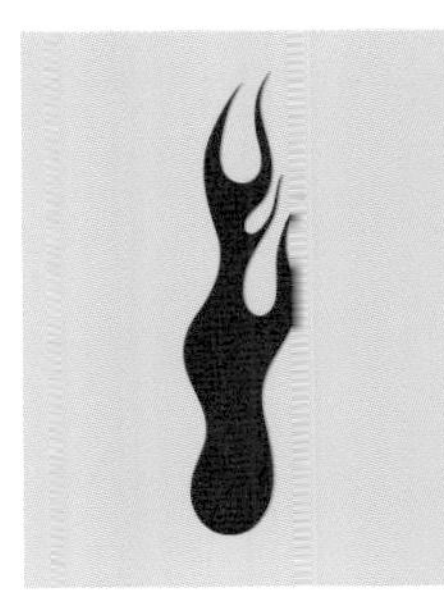

5. Train Passkey

Logic:

3+5=8; 2+1=3;
9+1=10; 7+2=9

6. Score Card

2	1	6	5	4	3
4	3	5	6	1	2
1	5	2	3	6	4
6	4	3	2	5	1
5	2	1	4	3	6
3	6	4	1	2	5

7. Kite Flying

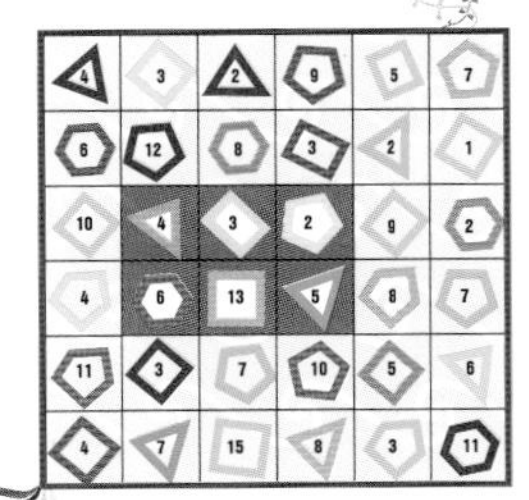

Logic:
(4+3)+(6+6)+
(3+4)+(13+4)+
(2+5)+(5+3)=58

8. Alpha Add

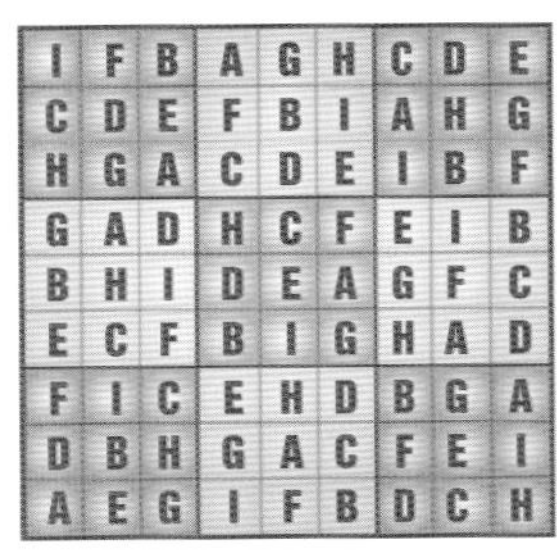

I	F	B	A	G	H	C	D	E
C	D	E	F	B	I	A	H	G
H	G	A	C	D	E	I	B	F
G	A	D	H	C	F	E	I	B
B	H	I	D	E	A	G	F	C
E	C	F	B	I	G	H	A	D
F	I	C	E	H	D	B	G	A
D	B	H	G	A	C	F	E	I
A	E	G	I	F	B	D	C	H

9. Tricky Triad

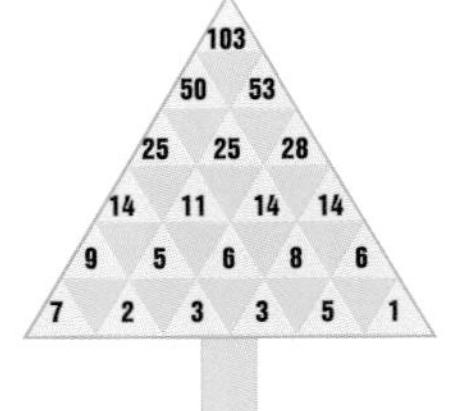

10. Aptitude Test

(7×3) – (28/4)=14

11. Smile Please

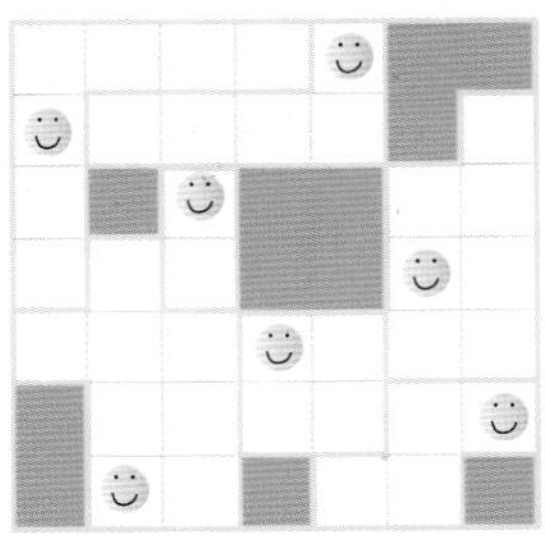

12. Paired Patterns

13. Complete the Flower

Answer: 5

Logic:

4+3–5+1=3
8+1–5+2=6
5+2–3+1=5

14. Number Connection

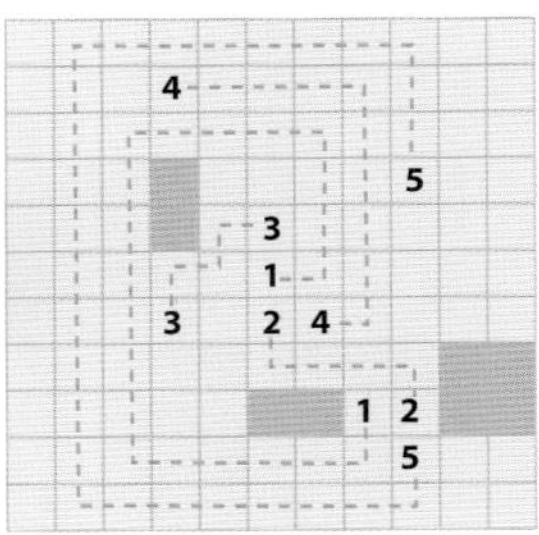

15. Egg Equation

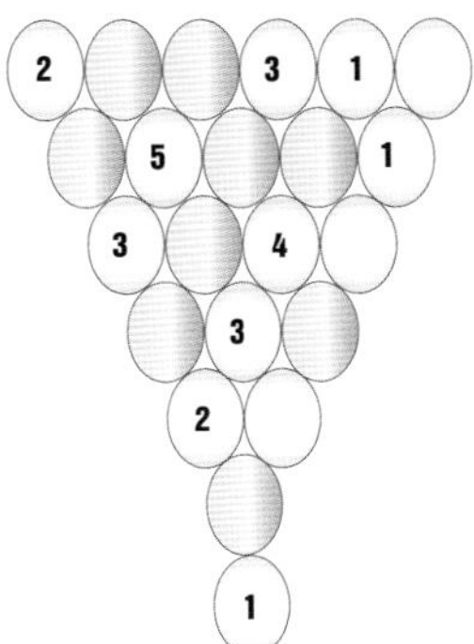

16. Chain Relation

Answer: 12

Logic:

13, 14

12, 13

11, 12

10, 11

17. Circuit Connection

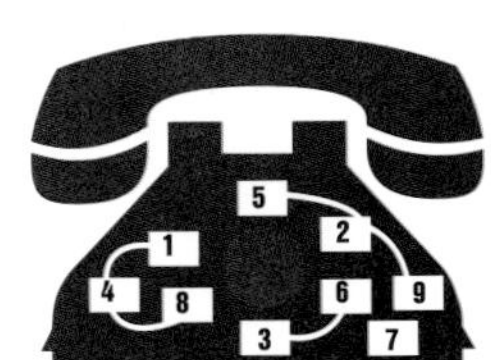

SOLUTIONS

18. Number Connection

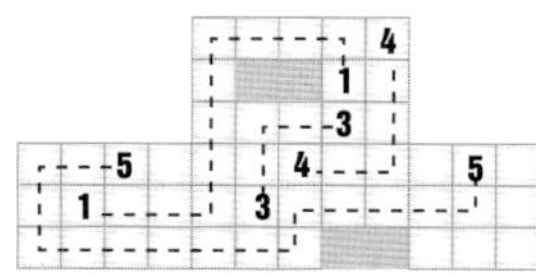

19. Shape and Color Shuffle

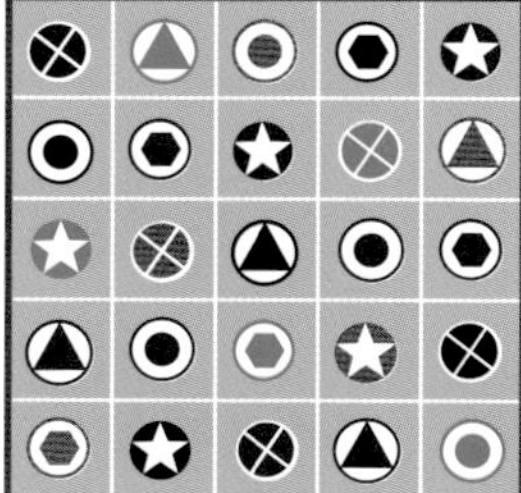

20. Drawer Code

Answer: 77

Logic: Multiplication of consecutive prime numbers.

3×5=15

5×7=35

7×11=77

11×13=143

21. Photo Frame

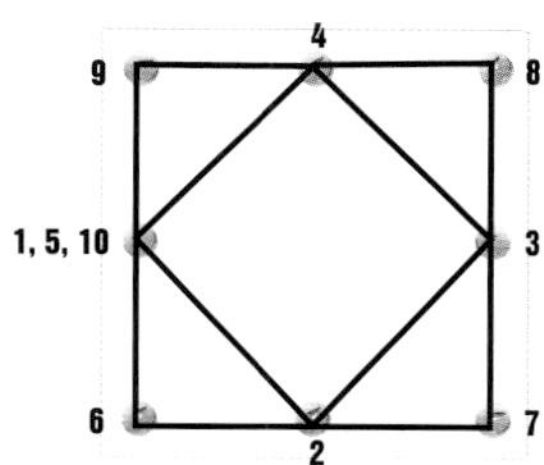

22. Charity Drive

Answer: 145

Logic:
3+5=8;
and 8+**3**=11

11+7=18;
and 18+**11**=29

29+9=38;
and 38+**29**=67

67+11=78;
and 78+**67**=145

Where 5, 7, 9, 11 are all prime numbers

23. Find the Missing Fruits and Vegetables

24. Prism Pairs

25. Secret Star

Answer: 31
Logic: Total of the product of the top and bottom corners is the central number.

For the last star:
7×3=21
5×2=10
21+10=31

26. Baffling Bricks

27. Dream Land

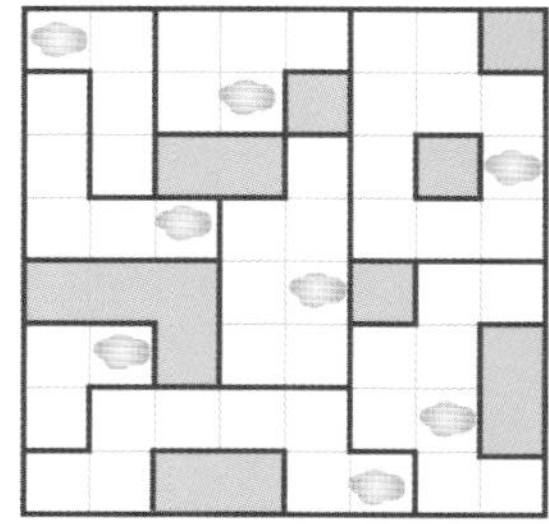

28. Match the Swimming Rings

29. Candy Confusion

3 4 2 1
1 2 4 3
2 1 3 4
4 3 1 2

30. Ice Cream Equations

Answer: ((6×2) + (3×3) +9) / 3=10

31. Ball Game

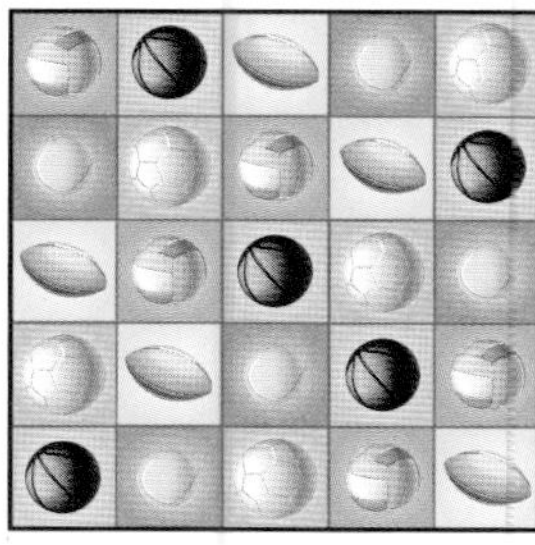

32. Birthday Buzz

Logic: Number in the 10th ? is 21. Every alternate number starting from number 13 is more by 2 and is an odd number.

Number in the 11th ? is 31. Every alternate number starting from number 11 is more by 4 and is an odd number.

33. Complete the Sequence

Answer: D

Logic: Each row and each column totals to form the same number. Example for first cube:
Total of row 1=25
Total of row 2=25
Total of row 3=25
Total of all columns=25

34. Unfold the Scroll

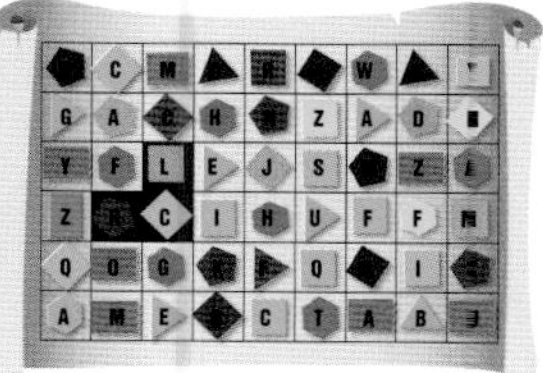

Logic:
(12×4)+(3×4)+(8×5)=100

SOLUTIONS

35. Crack the Fireworks

Answer: 7

Logic:
9+3+4=16. √16=4
4+3+2=9. √9=3
21+18+10=49. √49=7

36. Wrack your Brains!

3<	8	2	7<	9	5	6	4	1
3	4	6	8	1	2	<3	5	7
1	7	>5	6	4>	3	8	<9	2
5<	9	8	2	<7	4>	1	3	6
7	2	3	1	6	9	4	8	5
4	6	1	<5	3	8	7	2	9
6>	5	9	3<	8	7	2	1	4
2	3	<7	4	5	1	9	6	<8
8	1	<4	9	2<	6	5	<7	3

37. Complete the Pyramid

90
52 38
37 15 23
31 6 9 14
27 4 2 7 7
24 3 1 1 6 1

38. Snowflakes

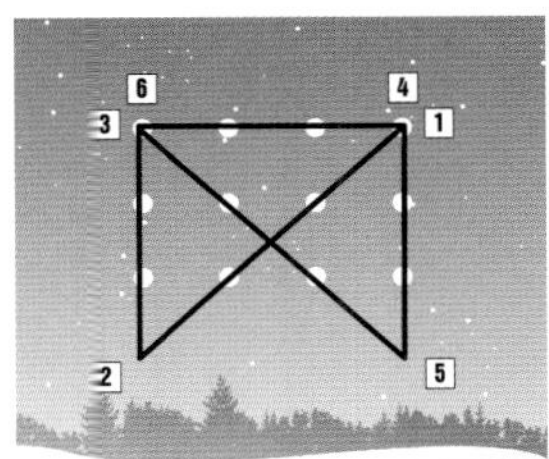

39. Identify the Pen Stand

40. Number the Cup Cakes

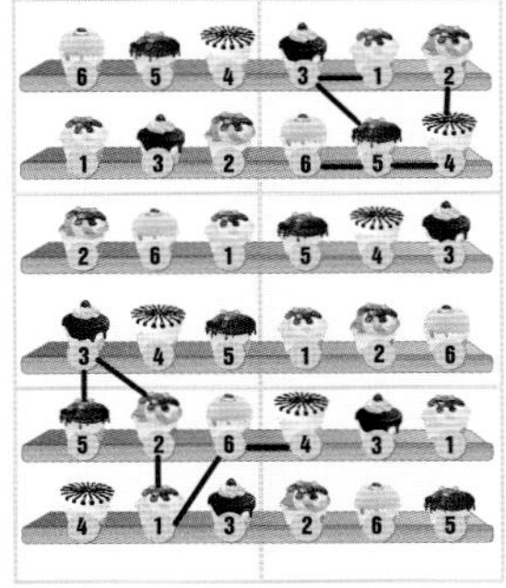

41. Alpha Addle

D	E	B	G	I	C	H	F	A
H	F	C	D	A	E	G	I	B
A	I	G	F	B	H	D	C	E
E	A	F	H	C	I	B	D	G
C	D	I	A	G	B	E	H	F
B	G	H	E	F	D	C	A	I
F	B	D	I	H	G	A	E	C
I	C	E	B	D	A	F	G	H
G	H	A	C	E	F	I	B	D

42. Create a Spring

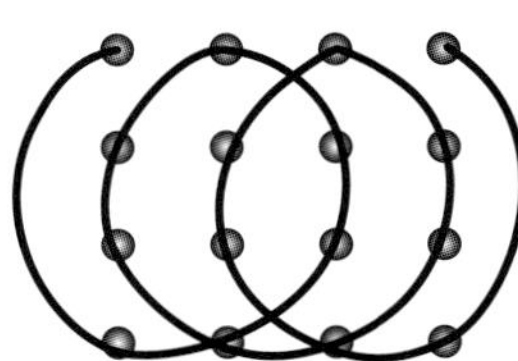

43. Book Management

44. Colorful Cubes

Answer: C

Each star is moving one step forward.

45. Puzzling Hot Air Balloon

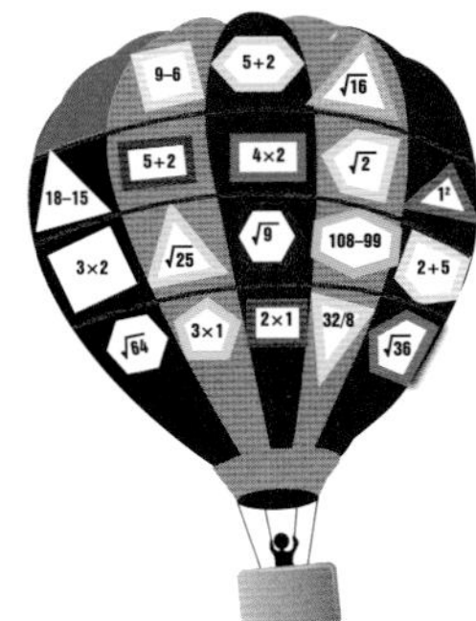

Logic: (3+3)+(6+4)+(8+6)=30

46. Geometric Chart

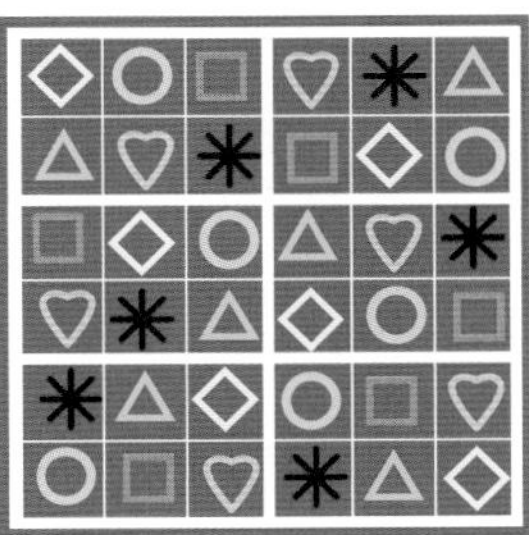

47. Power Failure

Answer:
(2×5) + (4×8) = 42

48. Music Maze

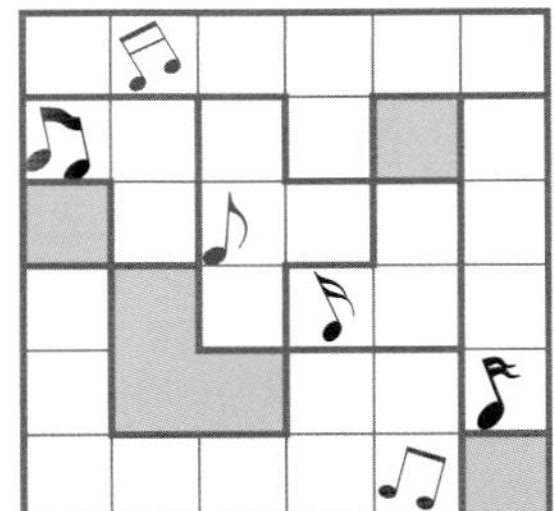

49. Find the Numbers

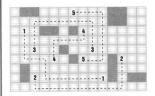

50. Over the Top

Answer: B

51. Spot the Man

52. Computer Count

Answer: 80

Logic: 12+17=29;
29+17=46;
46+17=63;
63+17=80;
80+17=97

SOLUTIONS

53. Closed Circuit

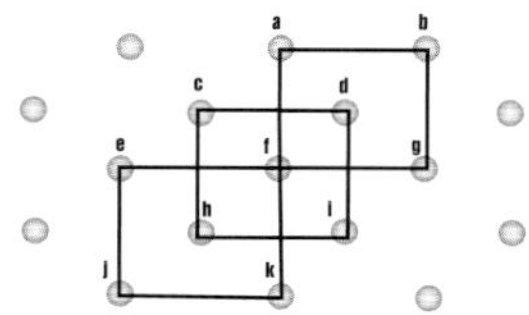

54. Alpha Painting

G	B	C	H	E	F	A	D	I
H	I	E	D	G	A	F	C	B
D	A	F	I	C	B	H	E	G
B	D	A	C	F	G	I	H	E
E	F	G	A	I	H	D	B	C
I	C	H	B	D	E	G	F	A
C	E	D	F	A	I	B	G	H
F	H	I	G	B	C	E	A	D
A	G	B	E	H	D	C	I	F

55. Bucket Pairing

56. Find the Only Pair

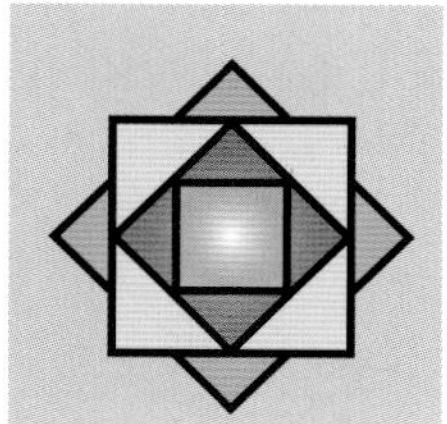

57. Cups and Glasses

58. Book Bafflement

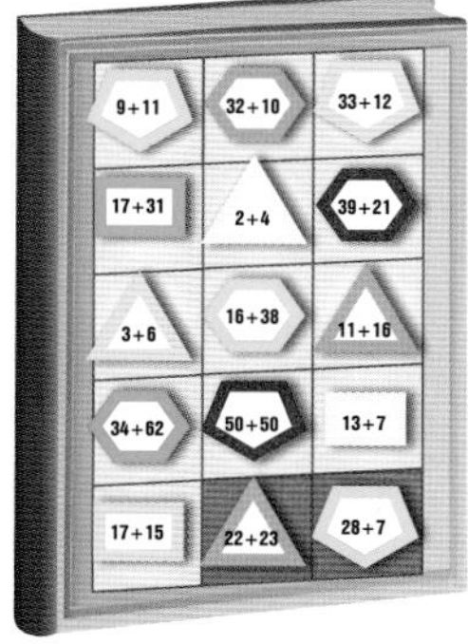

Logic: (45+3)+(35+5)=88

59. The Dog and the Bone Mystery

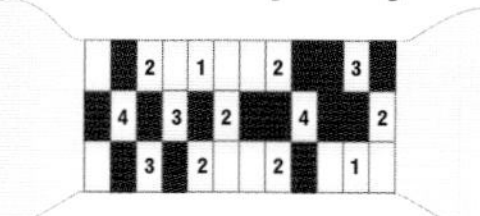

60. Win a Medal

I	V >	IV	II	III	< VI
II	VI	III	V	IV	I
IV >	I	II	III	VI	> V
V	III	< VI	IV >	I	< II
VI	> IV	V	I	II	III
III	II	I	VI	V	IV

61. Math Maze

[3×(7+(18/6))]–8=22

62. Candle Confusion

Logic:
(13–5) + (18–4) + (24–4) + (13–5) = 50

63. Currency Chart

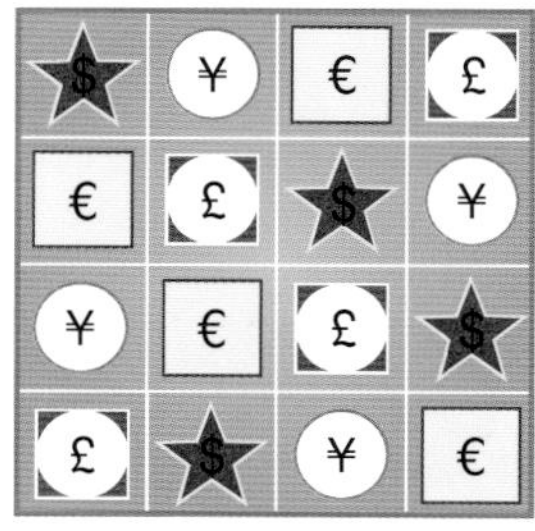

64. Population Analysis

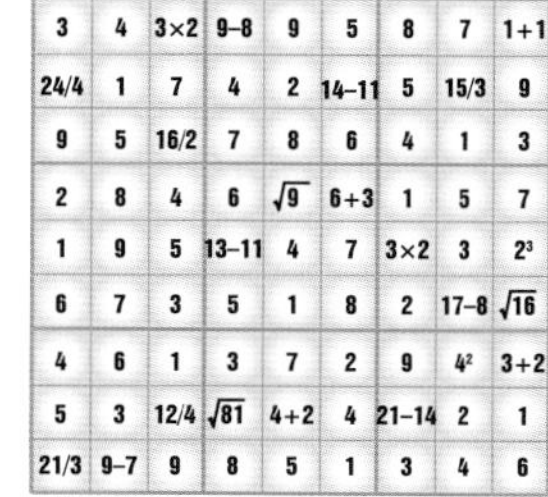

3	4	3×2	9–8	9	5	8	7	1+1
24/4	1	7	4	2	14–11	5	15/3	9
9	5	16/2	7	8	6	4	1	3
2	8	4	6	$\sqrt{9}$	6+3	1	5	7
1	9	5	13–11	4	7	3×2	3	2^3
6	7	3	5	1	8	2	17–8	$\sqrt{16}$
4	6	1	3	7	2	9	4^2	3+2
5	3	12/4	$\sqrt{81}$	4+2	4	21–14	2	1
21/3	9–7	9	8	5	1	3	4	6

65. Number Board

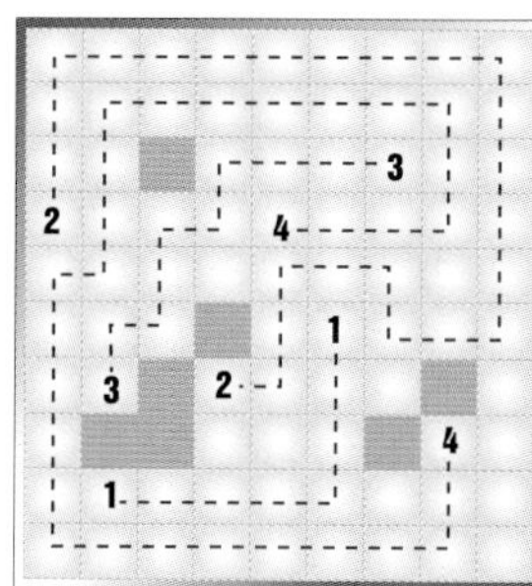

66. Tally the Tile

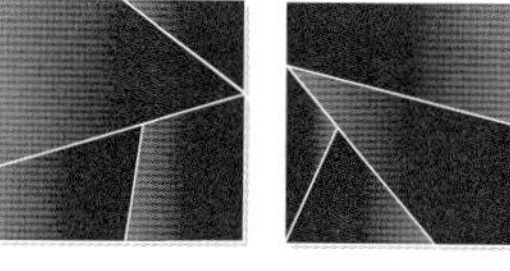

67. Triangle Trouble

Answer: D

Logic: The box background opposite (horizontally, vertically, or diagonally) to the pink background box has to be yellow. Also, the black triangle is positioned in the same square for all options.

68. Join the Oranges

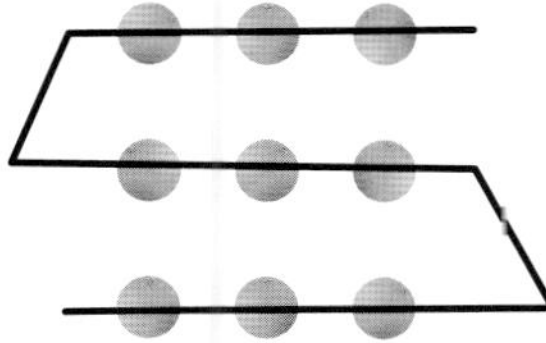

69. Cup Conundrum

Answer: 20

Logic: The second number being added or subtracted are all even numbers.

2+4=6 or
56–14=42

6+6=12 or
42–12=30

12+8=20 or
30–10=20

20+10=30 or
20–8=12

30+12=42 or
12–6=6

42+14=56 or
6–4=2

70. Let's do Alpha Doku!

F	E	B	A	C	D
D	A	C	B	E	F
C	F	D	E	B	A
E	B	A	F	D	C
A	D	E	C	F	B
B	C	F	D	A	E

SOLUTIONS

71. Mirror Image?

72. Diamond Décor

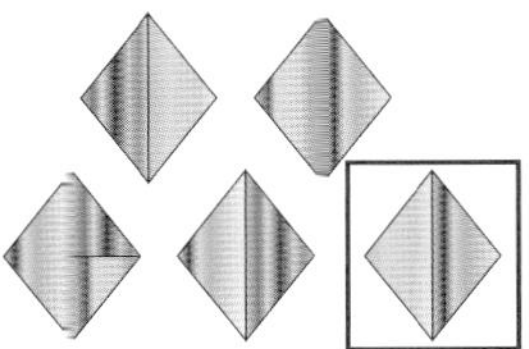

73. Shade the Triangles

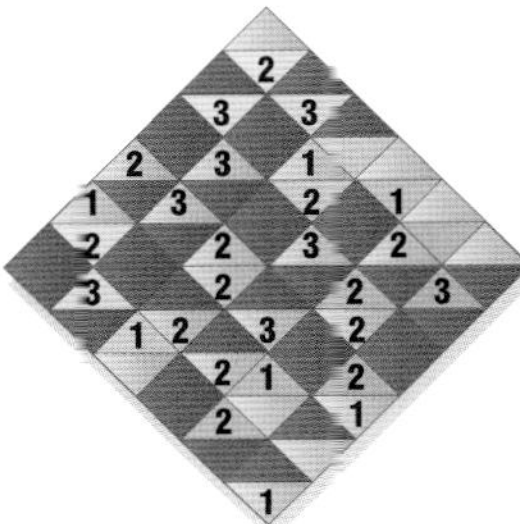

74. Aerial Shapes

Answer: C

75. Tournament Arrangement

76. Computer Conundrum

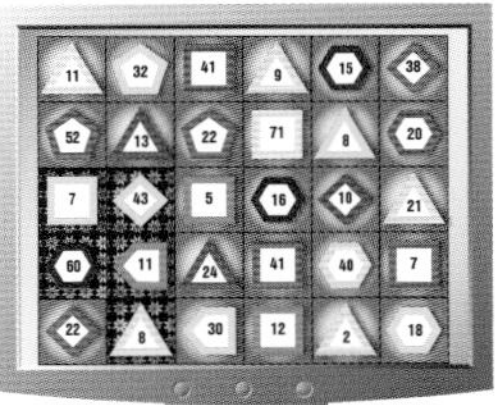

Answer:
(7×4) + [(4+3) × 4] + (6×6) + [(1+1) × 5] + (8×3) = 126

77. Shirt Stumper

78. Greater than or Less?

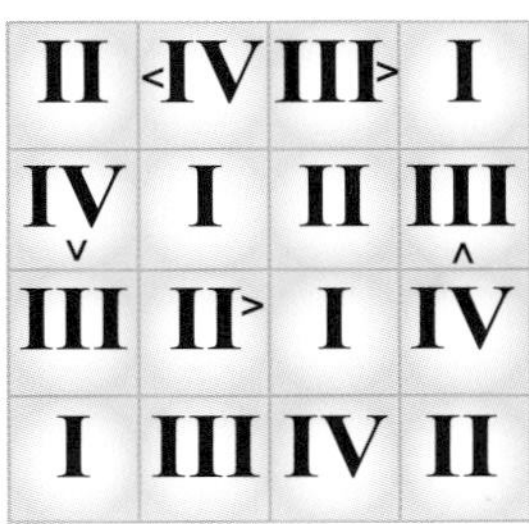

79. Flower Fun

(8–(7/2)) × 6 = 27

80. Look for the Answer

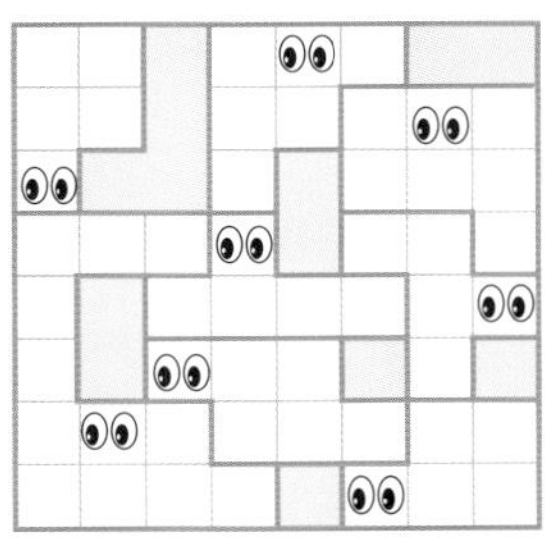

81. Roll the Dice

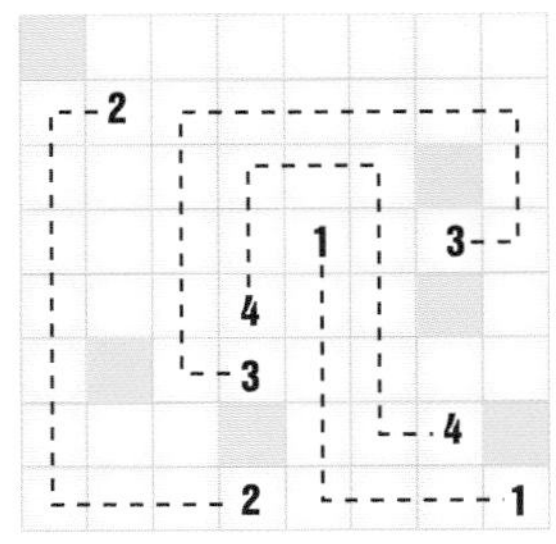

82. Missing Fruits and Vegetables

83. Coloring Board

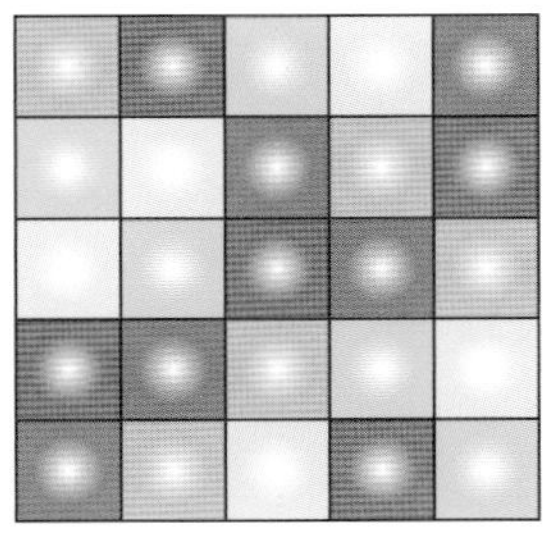

84. Complete the Necklace

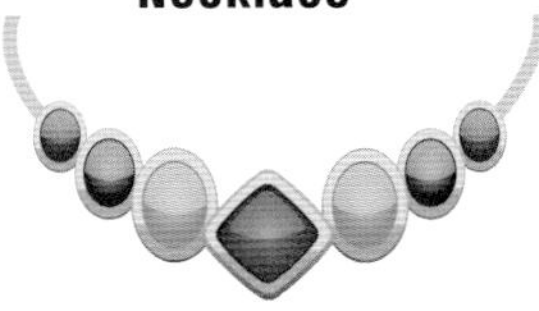

Answer: 24

Logic: The second number being added or deleted are all prime numbers.

3+5=8 or 63–15=48

8+7=15 or 48–13=35

15+9=24 or 35–11=24

Where 5, 7, 9, 11, 13, 15 are all prime numbers.

85. Bird Spotting

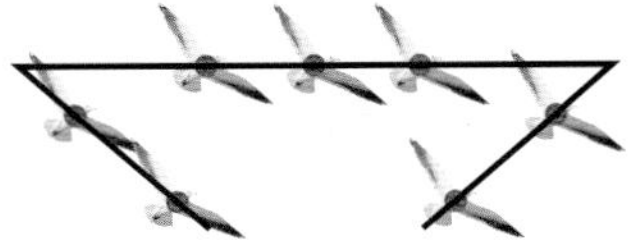

86. Alpha Ado

F	E	B	A	C	D
D	A	C	B	E	F
C	F	D	E	B	A
E	B	A	F	D	C
A	D	E	C	F	B
B	C	F	D	A	E

SOLUTIONS

87. Music Mania

88. The Secret Code

4	5 >	2	7	3^2	3	24/3	6	1 ^
8	6	3	3+1	1	5	< 49	9	17-15
1^2	9	^ 7	6 >	2	8	4	3	5
5 v	1 ^	6	8	3 ^	< 9	2	4	3+4 v
3	2^2	3^2	1	7	2	25	8	6
2	7	3+5 v	13-8	3×2	> 4	3	1^2	9
6	2	4	9	8	49 >	1	5	3
9	9 <	5	2	4	12-11	6	15-8	8
7	64	1	3	10-5	6	3^2	2	4

89. Help the DJ

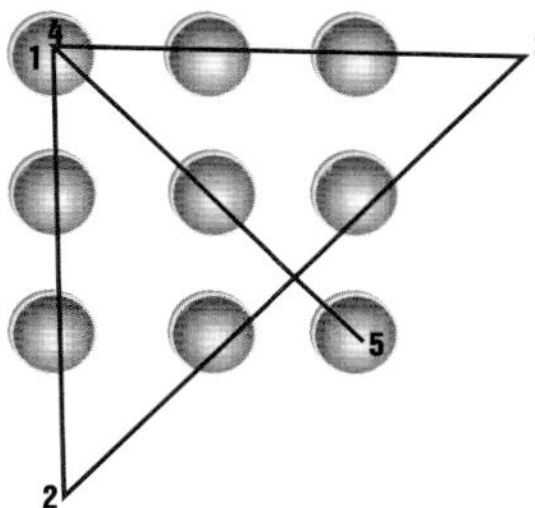

90. Gift Placement

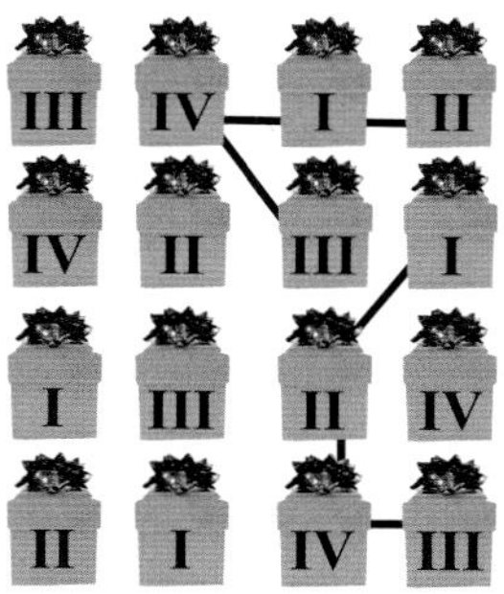

91. Lunch Party

(5+4)+(7+3)+(7+4)=30

92. Circuit Confusion

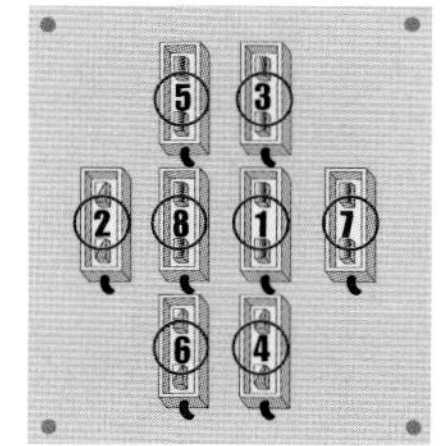

93. No Can Do!

D >	C	A	E >	B	F v
F	B	E >	D	C	A
A	^ D	F	C	< E	B
^ B	E	C v	F	A	D v
E	F	B	A	D	C
C	> A	D >	B	F	E

94. Puzzling Purse

There is a total of 8 diamonds in the purse.

95. Rocket Launch

(15×3)+(6/2)+7=55

96. Computer Code

97. Aim for the Solution

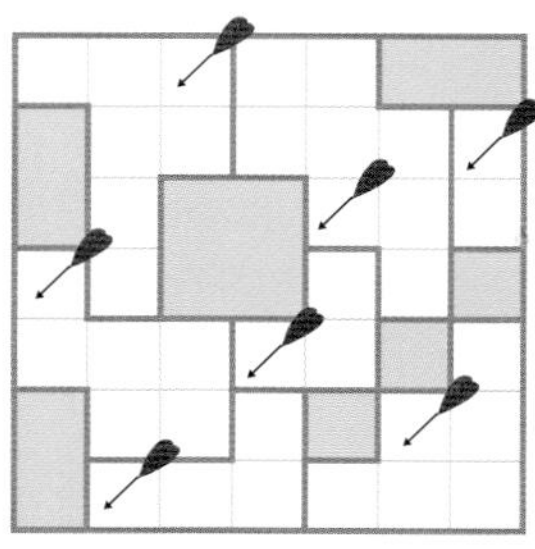

98. Table Tops

99. Kitchen Arrangement

100. Unfold the Colors

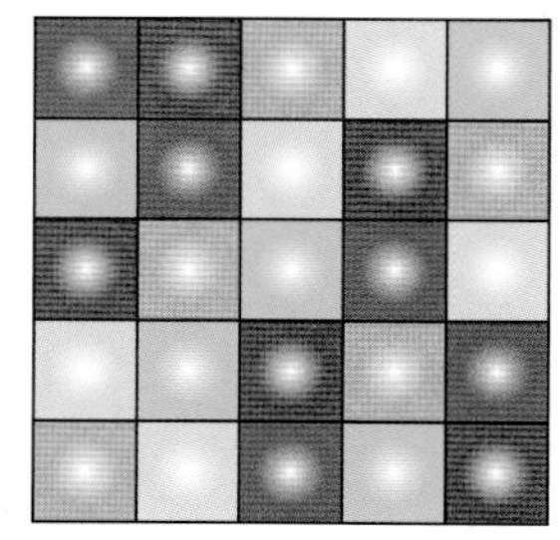

101. Box Brain-Teaser

Answer: C

Logic: All the numbers in each cube are prime numbers only.

In Cube A – 4 is not a prime number

In Cube B – 6 is not a prime number

In Cube D – 21 is not a prime number

102. Balloons

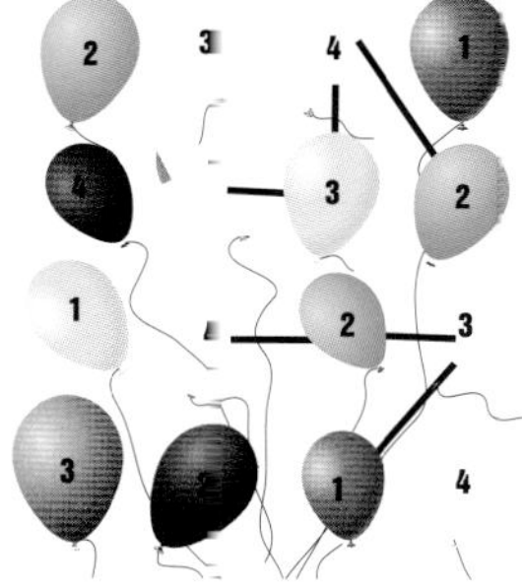

103. Slippery Problem

Answer: 22

Logic:

7+5=12

12+5=17

17+5=22

22+5=27

27+5=32

104. Tea Set

D A C B
C B D A
A D B C
B C A D

105. Puzzle Gift

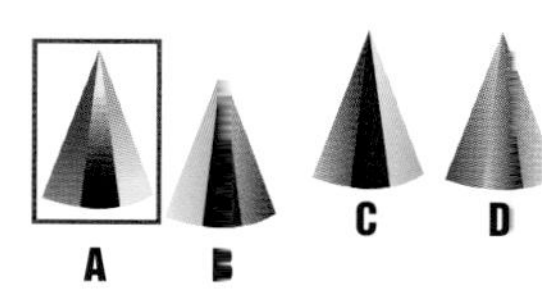

SOLUTIONS

106. Tic Tac Toe Trouble

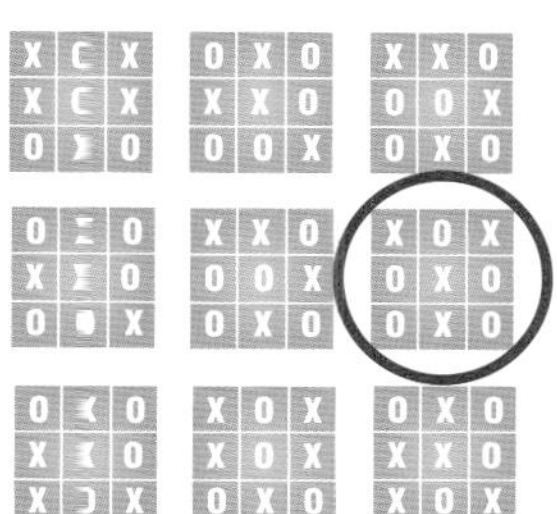

107. Fireworks Fun

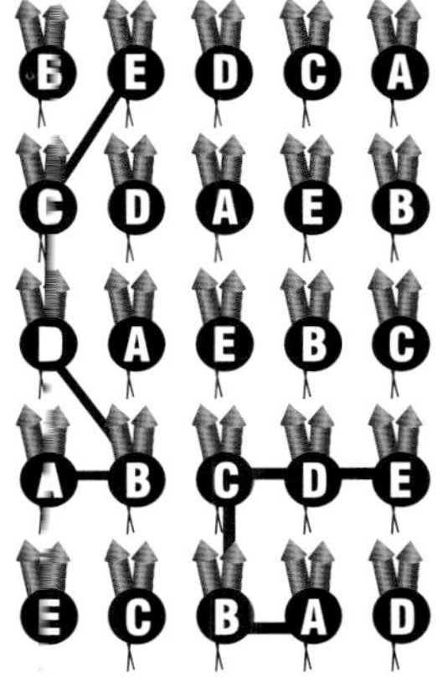

108. Test your Eyes

109. Find the Clock

110. Flower Color

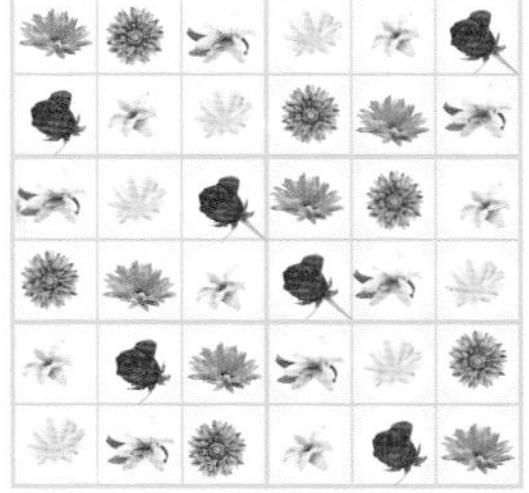

111. Repair the Guitar

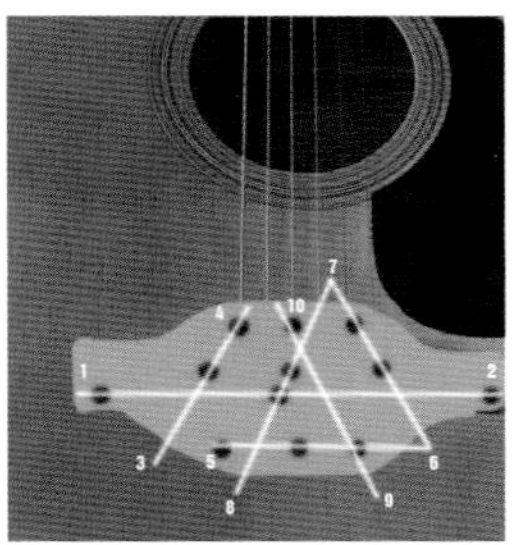

112. Baffled Baker

Answer: 12

Logic:

$2 \rightarrow 2+2^2=6$
$5 \rightarrow 5+5^2=30$
$3 \rightarrow 3+3^2=12$
$4 \rightarrow 4+4^2=20$

113. Gigantic Grid

E	C	A	D	F	B
D	F	B	A	E	C
A	E	D	B	C	F
C	B	F	E	A	D
F	D	E	C	B	A
B	A	C	F	D	E

114. Match the Bucket

115. Identify the Pack of Cards

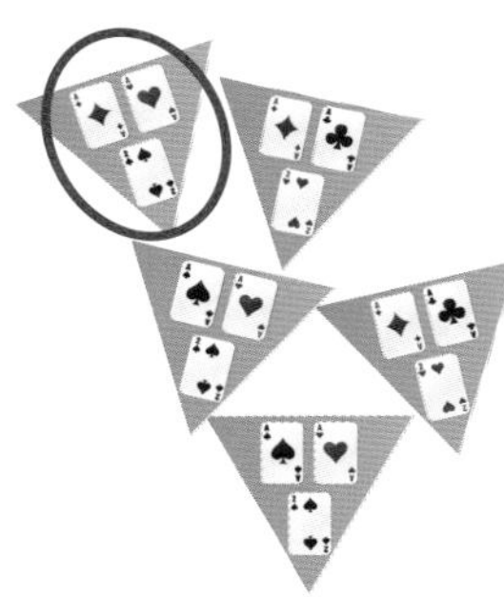

116. Struggling with Certificates

4	2	1	3	5
1	5	3	2	4
2	3	5	4	1
5	4	2	1	3
3	1	4	5	2

117. Food Fest

118. Rug Puzzle

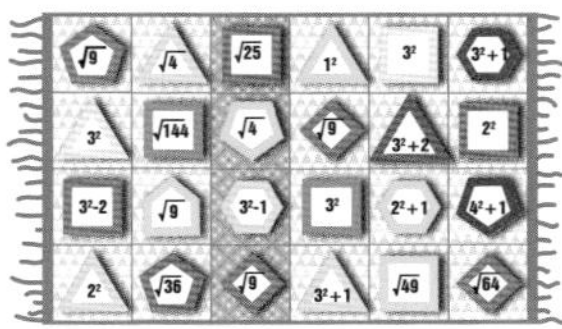

Logic:
$(5\times4)+(2\times5)+(8\times6)+(3\times4)=90$

119. Count the Eggs

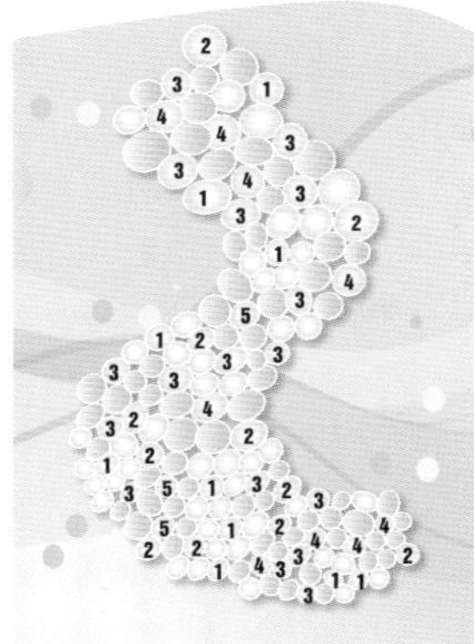

120. Letter Equation

C >	A <	B	E >	D
D v	C	E	A	B
A	D >	C >	B	E
E v	B	A	D v	C
B	E	D	C	A

121. Paint the Equation

Answer:
$[(4\times8) / (6–2)] + 5=13$

SOLUTIONS

122. Laws of Nature

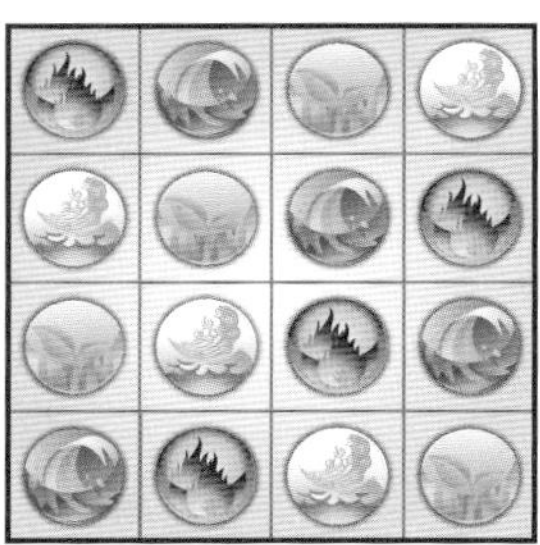

123. Find the Hidden Smiley

124. Join the Pairs

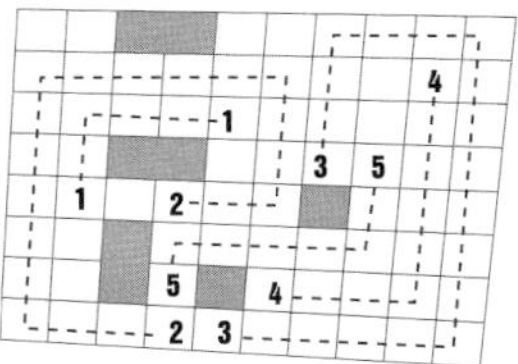

125. Jigsaw Puzzle

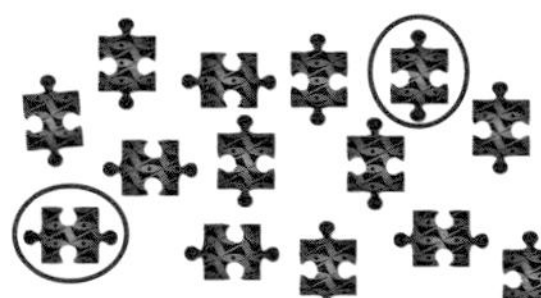

126. Place the Flags

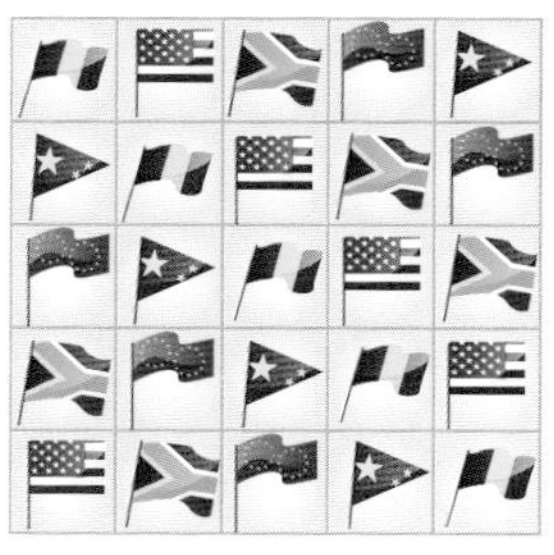

127. Achieve the Impossible

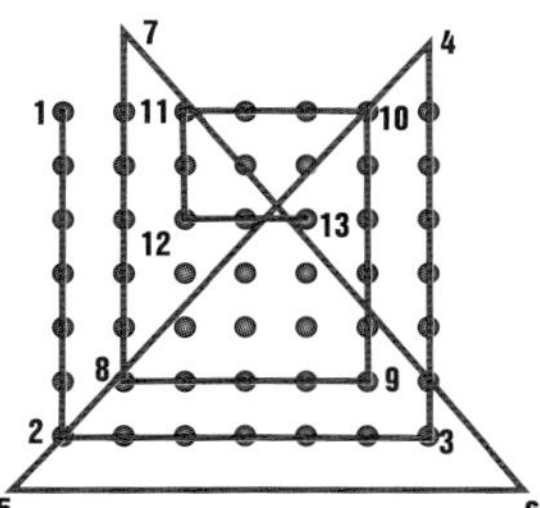

128. Let's Play Baseball

Answer: 36

41 → $(4\times1)^2=16$

72 → $(7\times2)^2=196$

23 → $(2\times3)^2=36$

129. Complete the Name Game

130. Match the Box

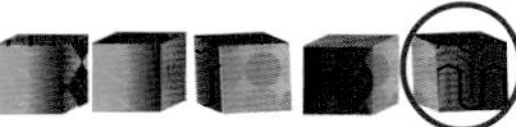

131. Animal Search

132. Flower Numbering

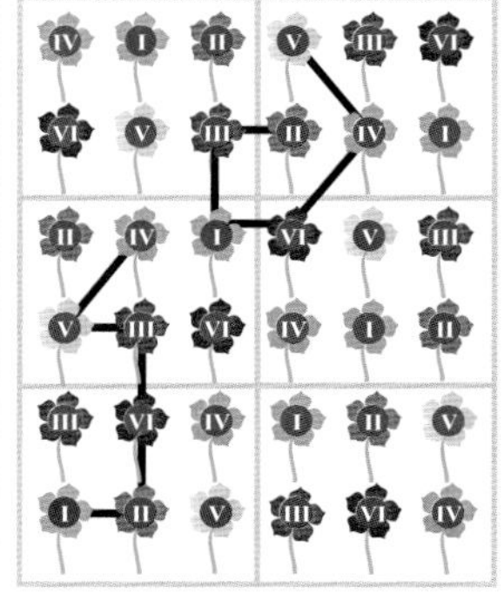

133. Jewel Jumble

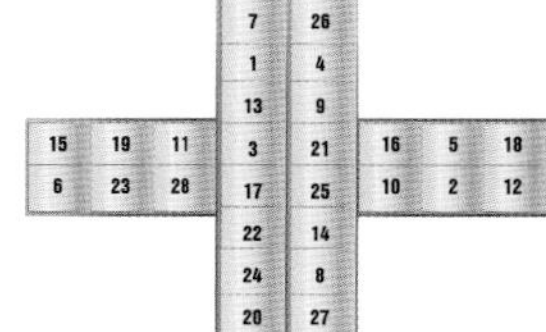

134. Unfold the Laptop

Logic:
(2+4)+(11+6)+(5+3)=31

135. Open the Safe

5	2×2 ˅	1	< 2	3	6 ˅
18/3	3	2	5	˄ 4	1
4	1	< 7−4	6 >	3+2	12/6
˅ 2	4+1 ˅	6 >	4	1 ˄	3
1×1	2	< 4	3	6	15/3
3	6 >	5	1 <	12/6	2×2

136. Flower Maze

Answer:
(6/2) + (5–4)=4

137. Place the Shapes

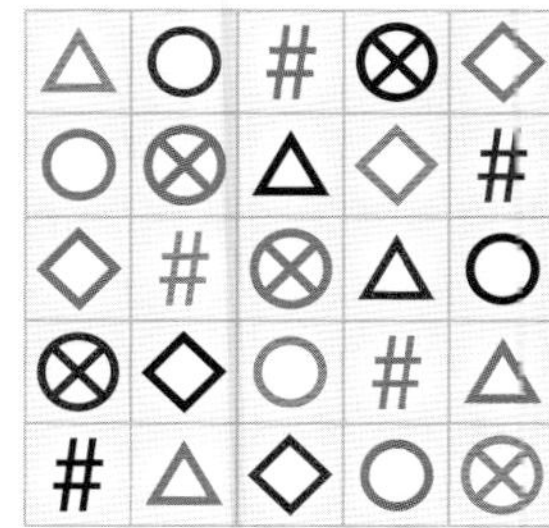

138. Spot the Difference

139. Egg Connection

2
7 10 5 14
12 6 1 8
4 9 11 13

140. Cookie Puzzle

4 1
3
2 1 2
3
4

141. Seeing Stars

Answer: D

SOLUTIONS

142. Arrange the Bottles

143. Join the Dots

Answer: A Lampshade

144. Lock and Key

Answer: 5

Logic: 111 → 1+3=4; where (1 is the digit used to form 111 and 3 is the number of times the digit is used in the number)

So:
5555 → 5+4=9;
444 → 4+3=7;
33 → 3+2=5;
88 → 8+2=10

145. Matching Mirrors

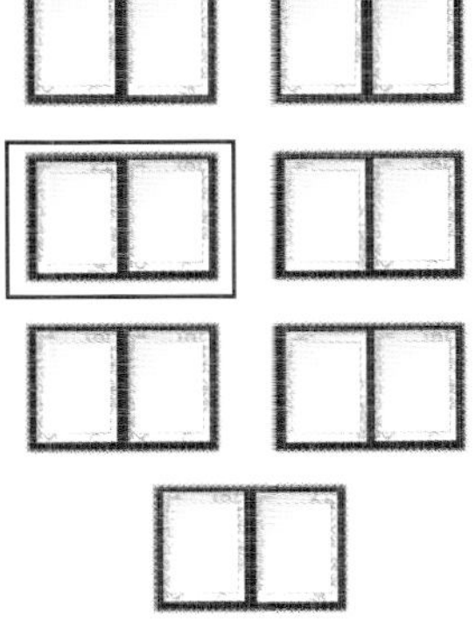

146. Calculate the Profit

B	D	A	C	E
C	A	B	E	D
E	C	D	A	B
A	B	E	D	C
D	E	C	B	A

147. Match the Skirt

148. Number the Homes

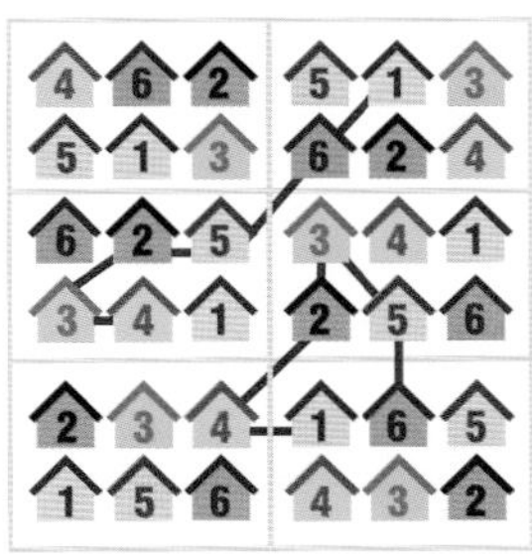

149. Arrange the Cans

26	9	32	17	2	31
19	30	35	6	15	18
4	1	10	21	28	5
11	22	27	16	13	34
14	3	8	33	24	29
25	36	23	12	7	20

150. Bag Confusion

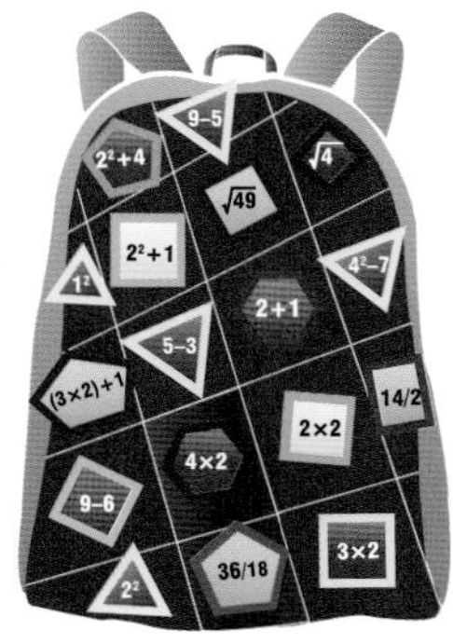

Answer:
(8+6)+(2+5) = 21

151. Paint the Flower Pyramid

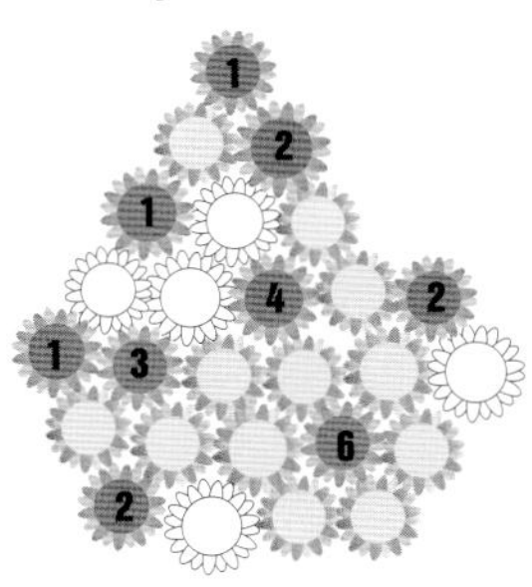

152. Count the Cattle

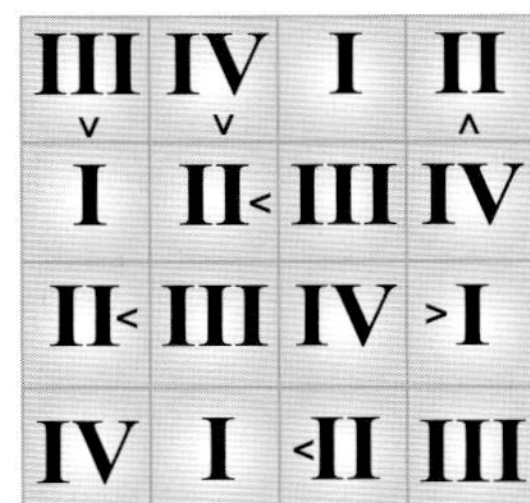

III	IV	I	II
∨	∨		∧
I	II<	III	IV
II<	III	IV	>I
IV	I	<II	III

153. Egg Equation

Answer:
[(7−3) × 4] + 8=24

154. Spot the Tree

155. Spring Confusion

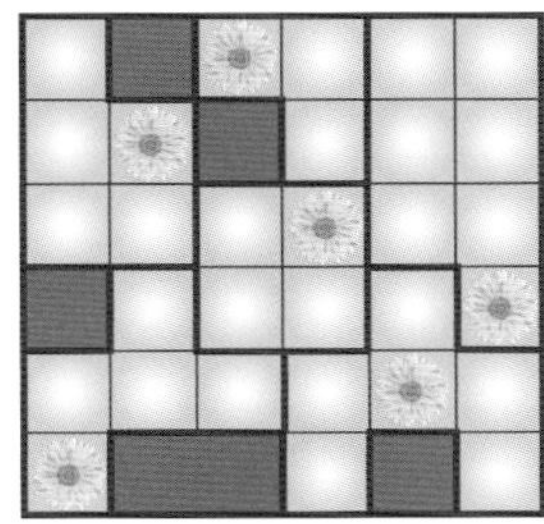

156. Doughnut Store

1	3	6	2
5	7	4	8
9	11	14	10
13	15	12	16
17	19	22	18
21	23	20	24
25	27	30	26
29	31	28	32

SOLUTIONS

157. Mysterious Ship

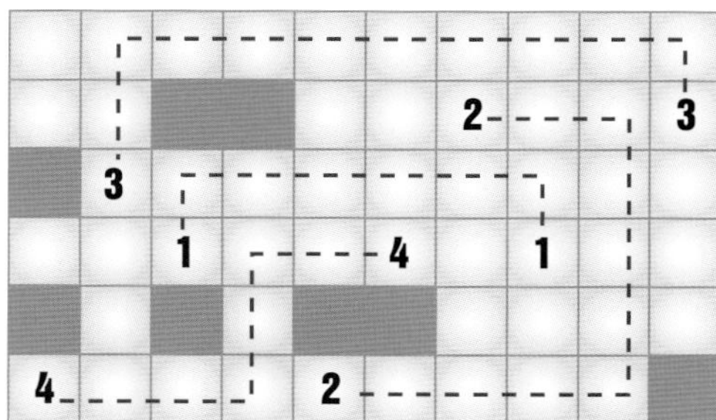

158. Balloon Maze

Answer: 3

Logic: Total of alternate numbers is same.
For the last balloon:
2+5=7
4+3=7

159. Complete the Vegetable Chart

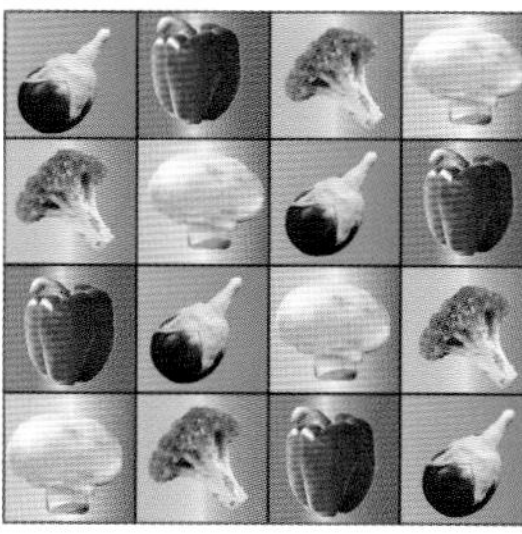

160. Draw the Boat

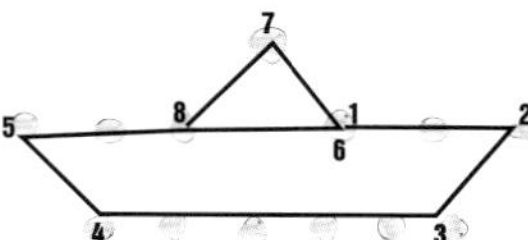

161. Make the Star Glow

Answer: 16

Logic: All are prime numbers+3:
2+3=5; 3+3=6;
5+3=8; 7+3=10;
11+3=14; 13+3=16

162. Dazzling Diamonds

Answer: B

Logic: The diamond to the right of the blue shaded square has to be blue in color. Also, the third diamond in the same row needs to be red in color.

163. Find the Watch

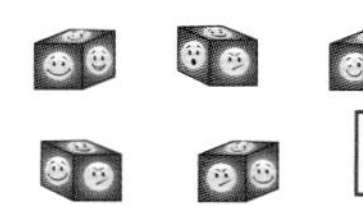

164. Find the Odd One Out

165. Arrange the Display

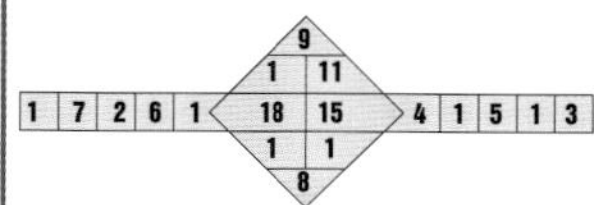

166. Number the Balls

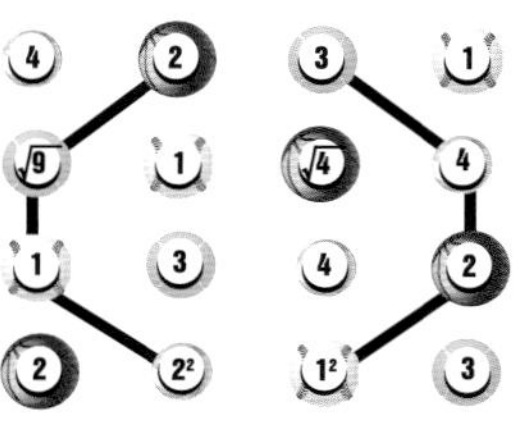

167. Bottle Game

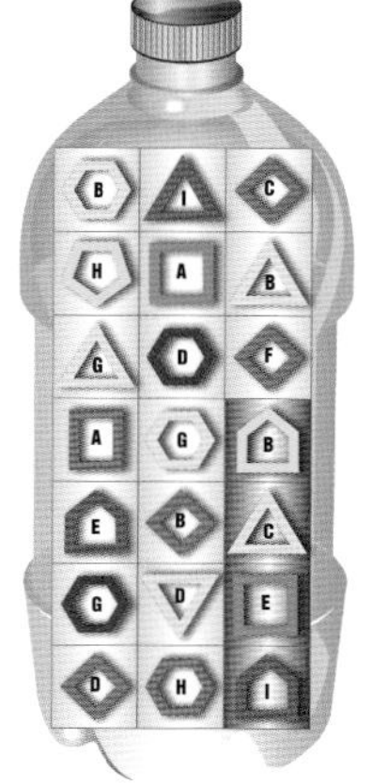

Logic:
$(2\times5)+(3\times3)+(5\times4)+(9\times5)=84$

168. Color the Fish

There are 20 yellow colored fishes in the fish bowl.

169. Star Sticker

Answer:
$(9-3)\times(7+5)=72$

170. Number Logic

4	6	9	5	2	1	3	8	7
8	7	2	3	4	6	1	5	9
1	3	5	9	8	7	4	6	2
2	4	8	7	6	9	5	1	3
7	5	1	8	3	2	9	4	6
6	9	3	1	5	4	2	7	8
3	2	4	6	7	5	8	9	1
9	8	6	4	1	3	7	2	5
5	1	7	2	9	8	6	3	4

171. Find the Missing Signs

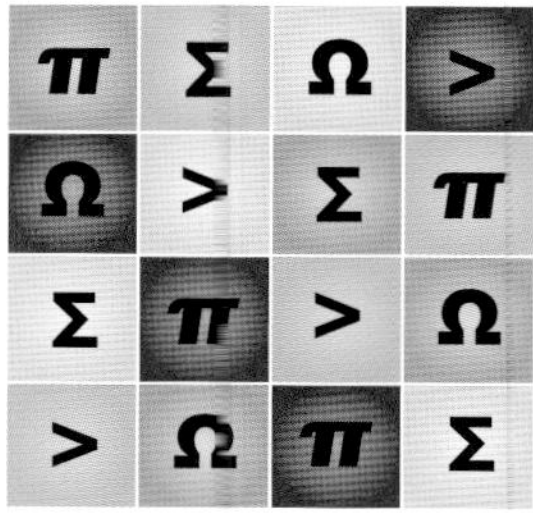

172. Decorate the Stage

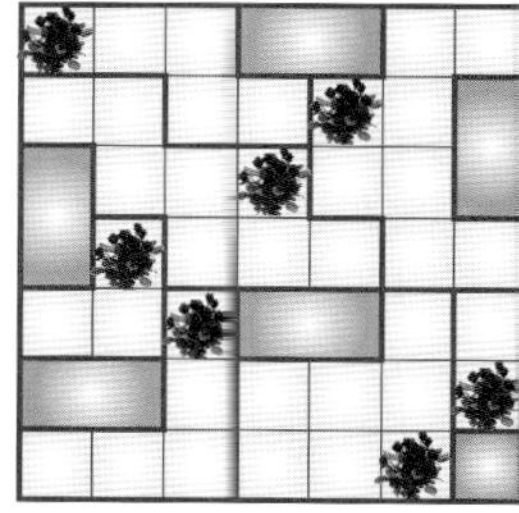

173. Join the Pairs

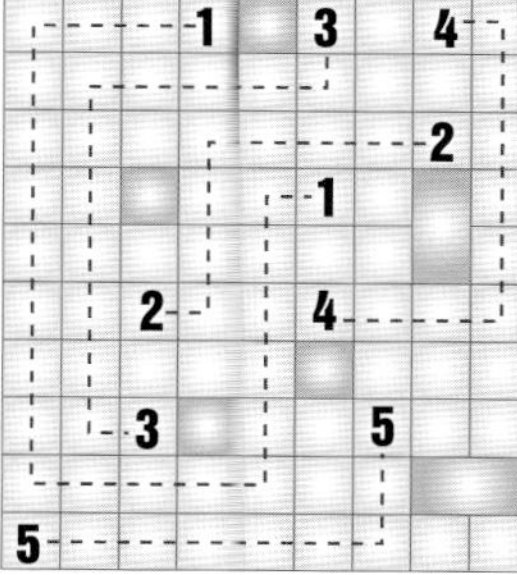

SOLUTIONS

174. Reuniting the Bricks

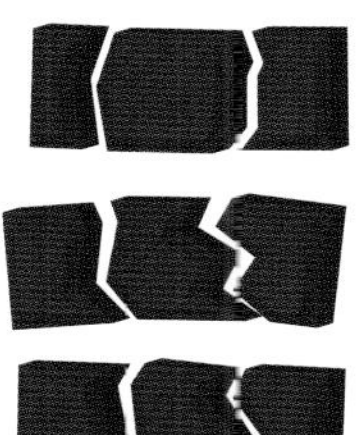

175. Fill the Tank

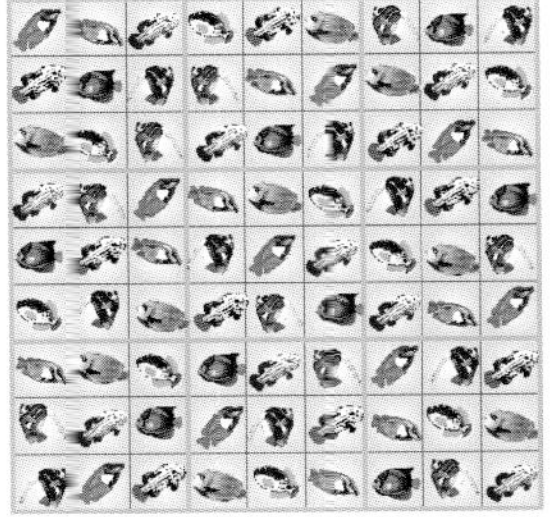

176. Join the Musical Notes

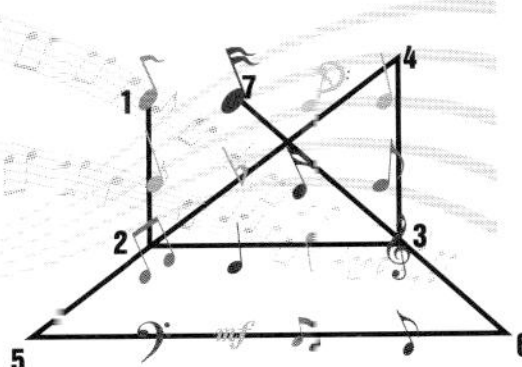

177. Logic and Calculations

Answer: 13

Logic:
1st, 3rd and 5th numbers → 8, 9 and 10

2nd, 4th and 6th numbers → 12, 13 and 14

178. Fun with Letters

F	A	C	D	E	B
D	E	B	C	F	A
E	B	D	F	A	C
A	C	F	B	D	E
B	F	E	A	C	D
C	D	A	E	B	F

179. Find the Right One

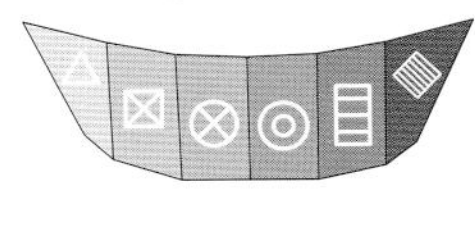

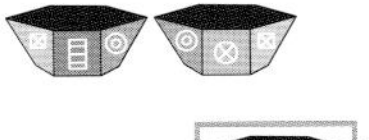

180. Number the Umbrellas

181. Music Store

	11	6	
9	14	3	16
2	17	7	1
13	4	10	5
18	8	15	12

182. Tray Mystery

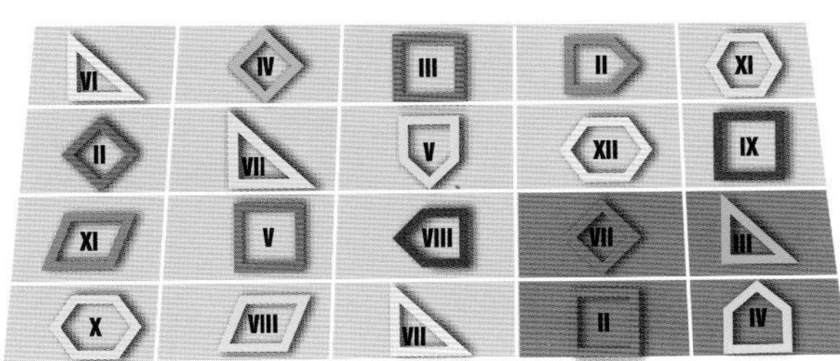

Logic:
$(7\times4)+(3\times3)+(4\times5)+(2\times4)=65$

183. Aqua Plants

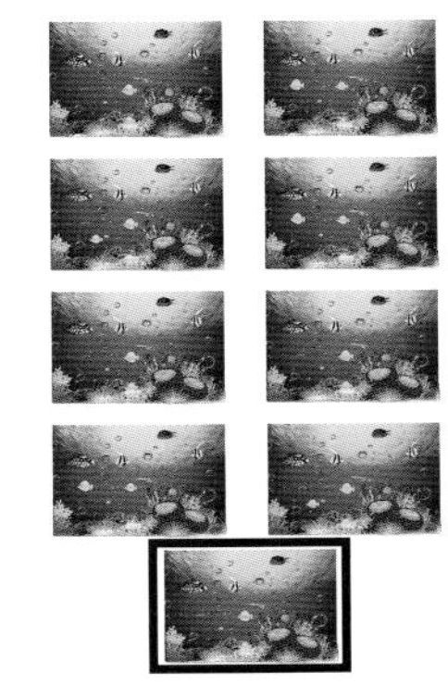

184. Pyramid Trick

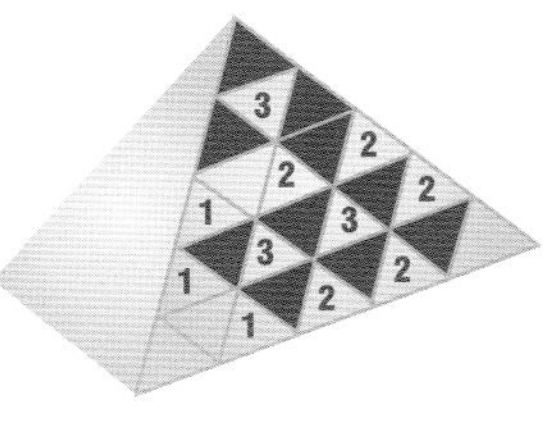

185. Fill it up

6 >	3	5	2 ∧	4 >	1
1	2 <	4	6	3	5
2	5	6	4	1 <	3
4 >	1	3	5 ∨	6	2
5	4 >	1	3	2	6
3 <	6	2	1	5 >	4

186. Circles and Squares

Answer:
$(12\times5)-38=22$

187. Elements of the Universe

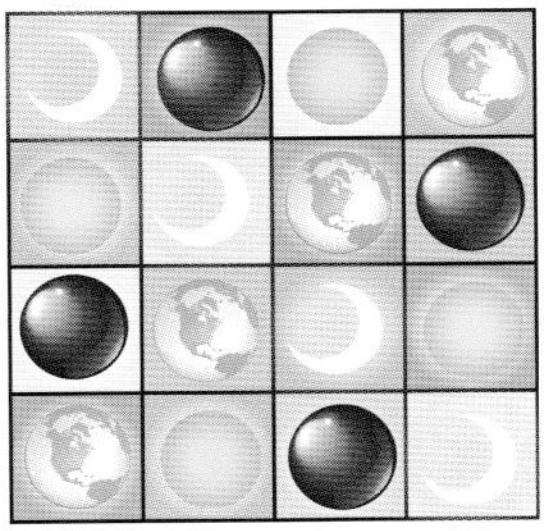

188. Design the T-Shirt

E	D	F	A	H	G	B	C
H	B	G	C	A	E	F	D
A	H	E	F	B	C	D	G
C	G	B	D	E	F	H	A
G	F	C	H	D	A	E	B
B	A	D	E	C	H	G	F
D	E	A	G	F	B	C	H
F	C	H	B	G	D	A	E

189. Complex Counts

Answer: B

Logic: The total of all the numbers in a cube equals 40.

190. Puzzling Puzzle

Answer: C

Logic: The circle placed in the square diagonally to the bottom left of the purple shaded square is purple in color.

SOLUTIONS

191. Crack a Smile

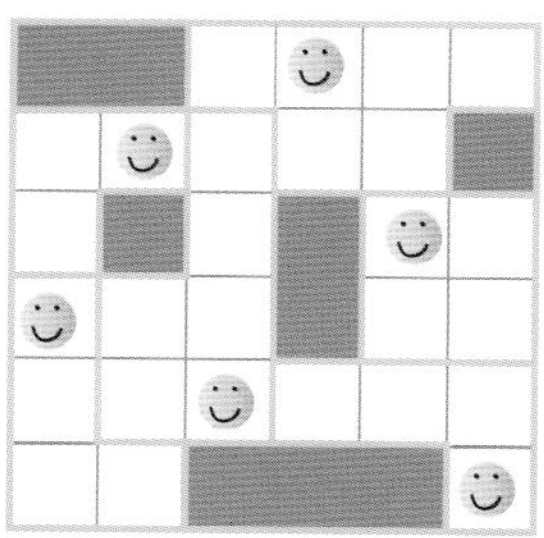

192. Complete the Puzzle

Answer: 42

Logic: The difference between the adjacent numbers is 12.

78–12=66

66–12=54

54–12=42

42–12=30

193. Logical Letters

D	B	C	A
C	A	B	D
A	C	D	B
B	D	A	C

194. Road Maze

195. Find the Correct Bangle

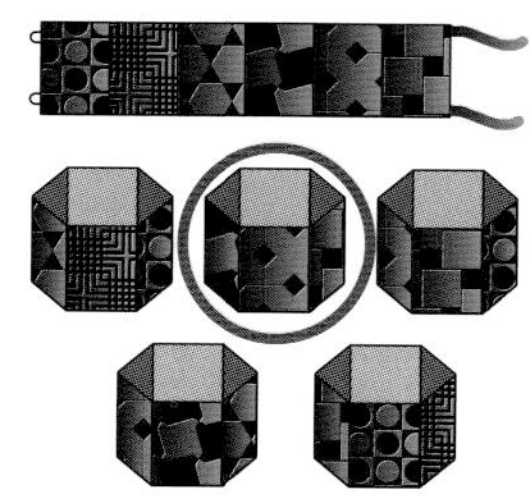

196. Find the Odd Dish

197. Number the Fruit Bowls

198. Coin Puzzle

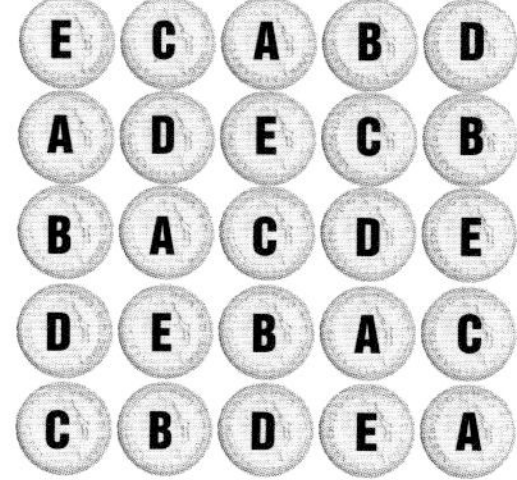

199. Follow the Arrow

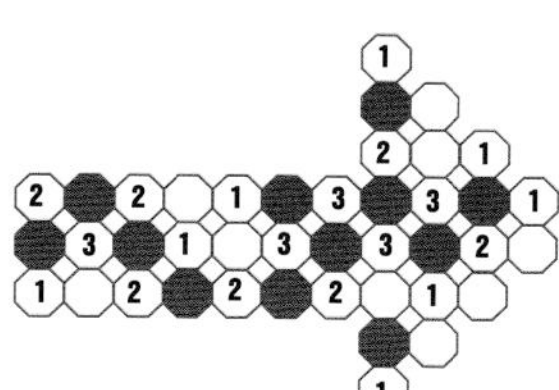

200. Look for the Star

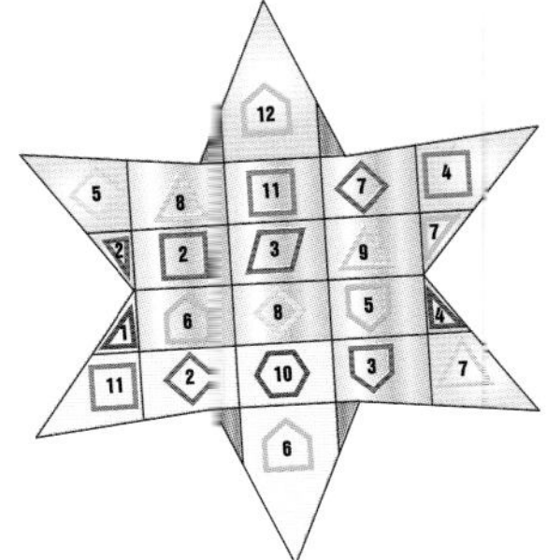

Logic: (1+3)+(11+4)+(2+4)+(10+6)+(6+5)=52

201. Challenge your Intelligence

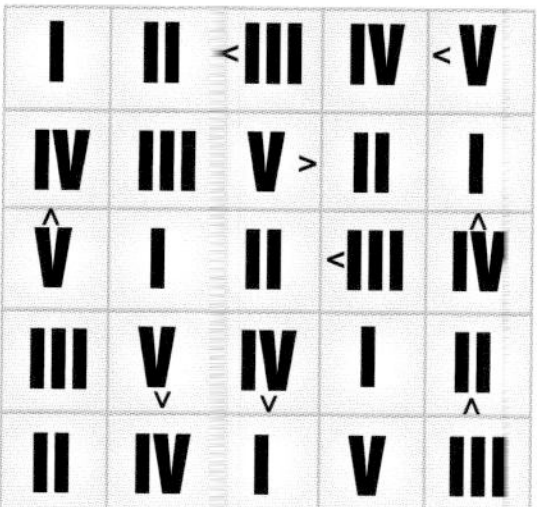

202. Equation Time

Answer: 51+8–24=35

203. Crack the Answer

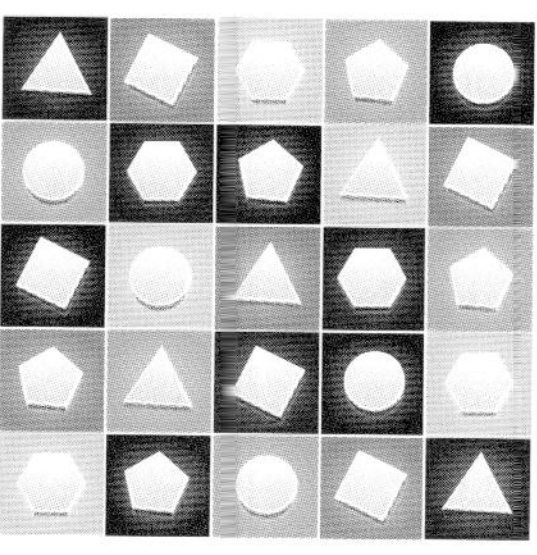

SOLUTIONS

204. Fashion Show

205. Colorful Bricks

Answer: A

Logic: Two green bricks have to be placed next to each other in any direction and the third brick in the row needs to be brown in color.

206. A Helping Hand

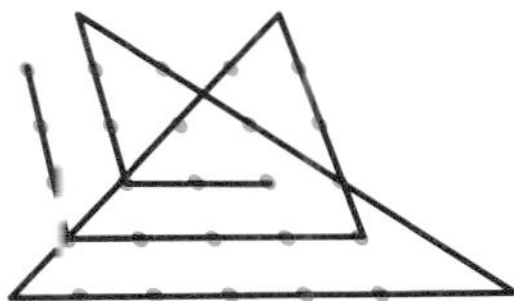

207. Switch on the Lamp

Answer: 20

12 → 12/4=3

20 → 20/4=5

28 → 28/4=7

36 → 36/4=9

208. Word Twister

B	D	E	C	A	F
F	A	C	D	B	E
E	C	F	B	D	A
D	B	A	F	E	C
A	F	B	E	C	D
C	E	D	A	F	B

209. Find the Pairs

210. Find the Mat

211. Fix the Flower

Answer: A, C and E

212. Letter Time

E	D	F	A	I	H	G	B	C
C	B	H	F	G	D	I	E	A
I	A	G	B	C	E	F	D	H
B	E	A	I	M	G	D	C	F
D	H	C	E	F	B	A	G	I
G	F	I	C	D	A	E	H	B
F	C	D	G	B	I	H	A	E
A	G	B	H	E	F	C	I	D
H	I	E	D	A	C	B	F	G

213. What's your Score?

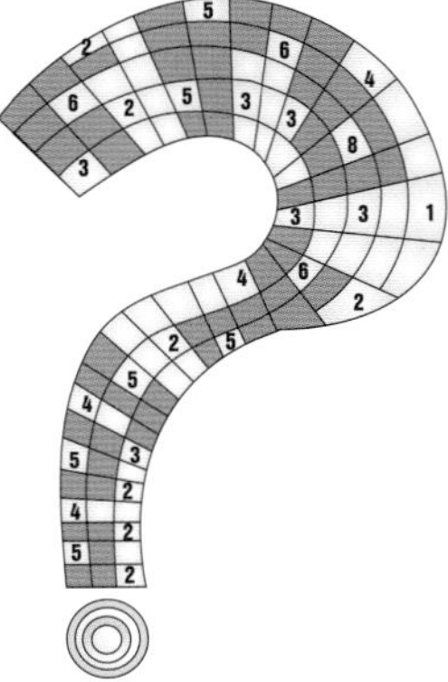

Answer: 34

Logic: Squares counted are the ones that have no numbers on them and are not shaded.

214. Chocolate Grid

H>	D	<G	C	E	F	A<	B
E	B	A	F	G>	C	D	H
B	F>	D	G	C	E	H	A
C	A	H	E	>B	D	G	F
G	E	F	<H	A	B<	C	D
A	C>	B	D	H	G>	F	E
D<	G	E	A	F	H	B	C
F	H	C>	B	D	A	E<	G

215. Pool Decoration

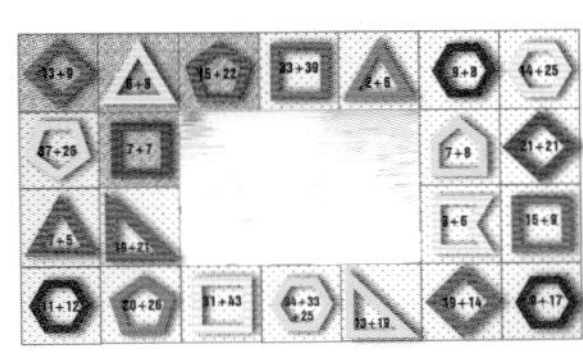

Logic:
[(2×2)+4] + [(1×1)+3)+[(3×7)+5] + [(1×4)+4]=46

216. Sandwich Hunger

Answer: 13

8+5=13

13+5=18

18+5=23

23+5=28

217. Home Sweet Home

Answer: (12×3)/4=9

218. Arrange the Signs

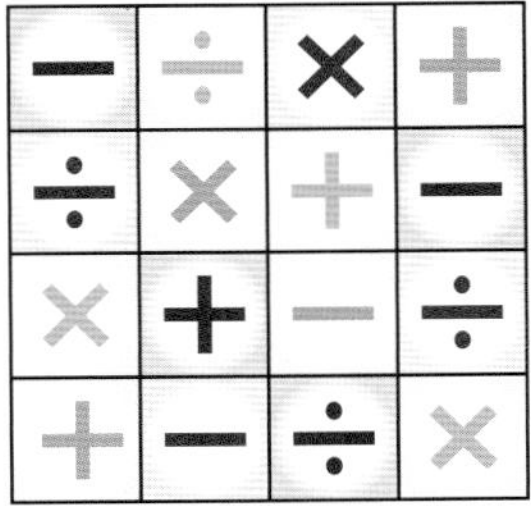

−	÷	×	+
÷	×	+	−
×	+	−	÷
+	−	÷	×

219. Air Show

220. Open the Door

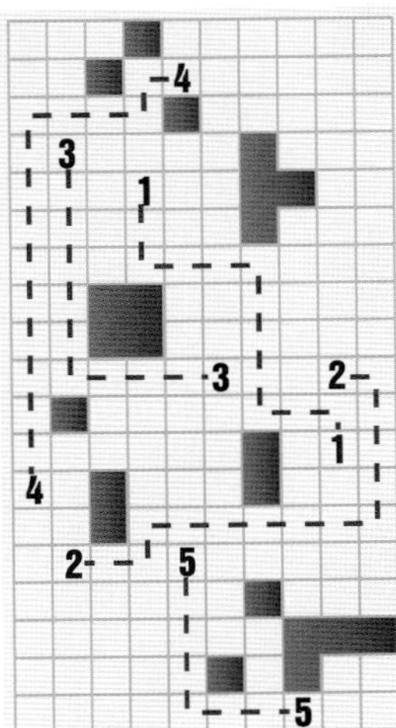

SOLUTIONS

221. Find the Marker Pens

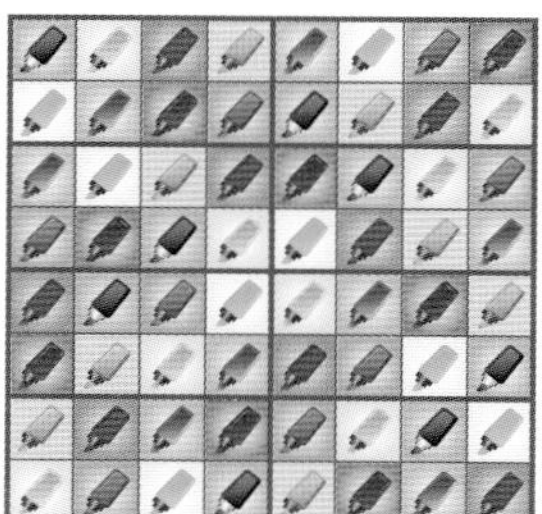

222. Join the Bricks

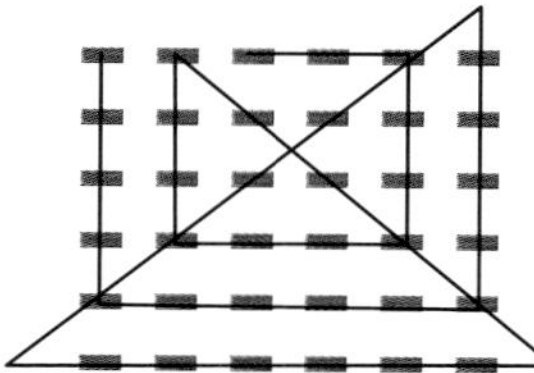

223. Number the Tin

Answer: 143

Logic:

$2^2-1=3$

$4^2-1=15$

$6^2-1=35$

$8^2-1=63$

$10^2-1=99$

$12^2-1=143$

224. Classroom Puzzle

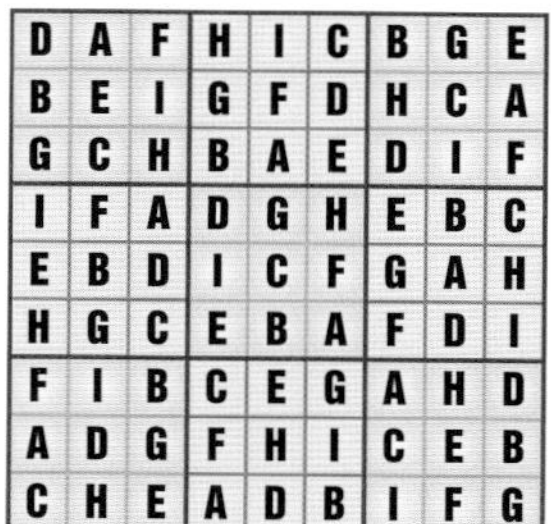

D	A	F	H	I	C	B	G	E
B	E	I	G	F	D	H	C	A
G	C	H	B	A	E	D	I	F
I	F	A	D	G	H	E	B	C
E	B	D	I	C	F	G	A	H
H	G	C	E	B	A	F	D	I
F	I	B	C	E	G	A	H	D
A	D	G	F	H	I	C	E	B
C	H	E	A	D	B	I	F	G

225. Find the Correct Cube

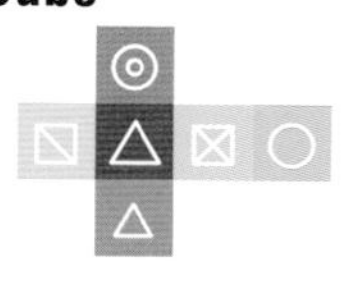

226. Coloring Time

227. Diamond Numbering

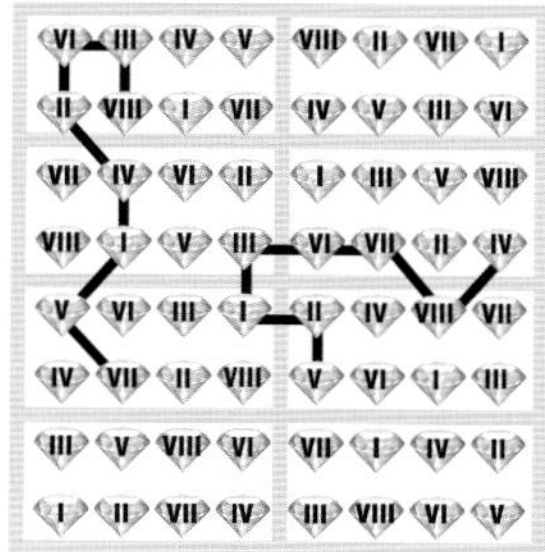

228. Help the Postman

Answer: 9

41 ➔ 4+1=5; $5^2=25$

25 ➔ 2+5=7; $7^2=49$

12 ➔ 1+2=3; $3^2=9$

33 ➔ 3+3=6; $6^2=36$

229. Tennis Game

Answer:

$(8+5) \times (2+3) \times (6+6) = 780$

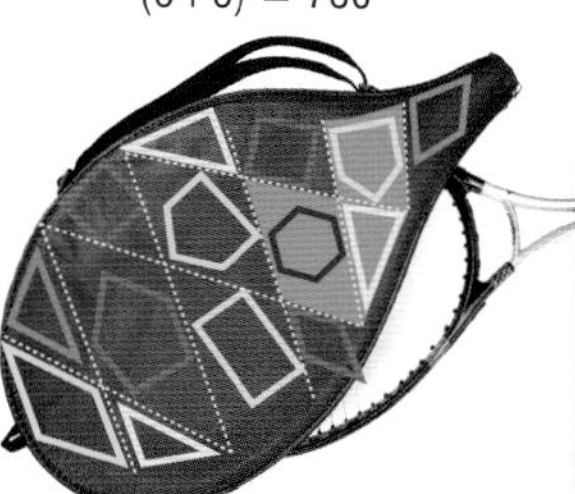

230. Fit the Kite

Answer: B and D

231. Puzzling Letters

D	H	G	I	F	B	A	C	E
C	B	E	H	A	D	F	G	I
F	I	A	E	G	C	B	H	D
E	D	B	F	C	I	H	A	G
A	F	H	G	D	E	I	B	C
G	C	I	A	B	H	D	E	F
B	A	F	C	I	G	E	D	H
I	E	C	D	H	A	G	F	B
H	G	D	B	E	F	C	I	A

232. Rings of Fire

Answer:

$(40/2)+16=36$

233. Baby Toys

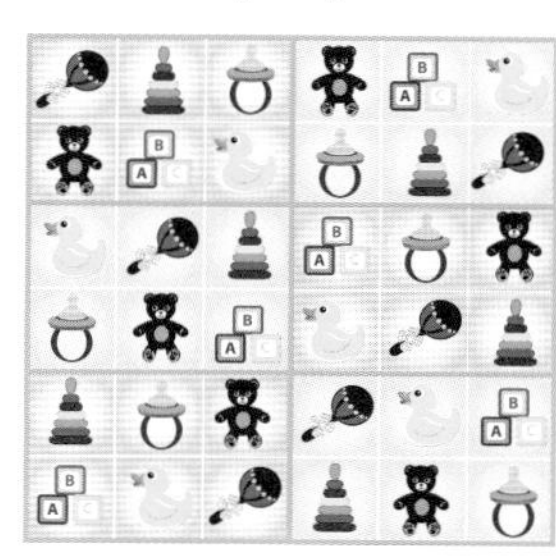

234. Picture Maze

235. Fumbled Fan

Answer: 32

Logic:

46–5=41 or
32+2=34

41–4=37 or
34+3=37

37–3=34 or
37+4=41

34–2=32 or
41+5=46

236. Missing Letters

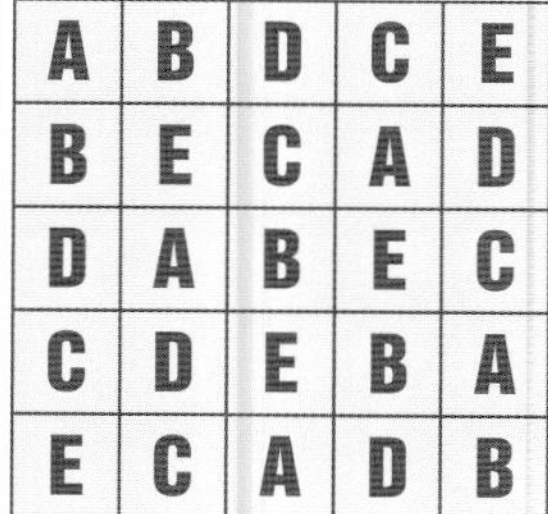

A	B	D	C	E
B	E	C	A	D
D	A	B	E	C
C	D	E	B	A
E	C	A	D	B

237. Match the Designs

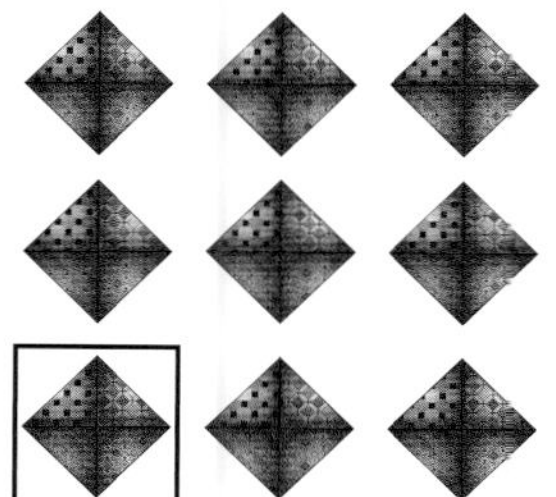

238. Number Jumble

(26/13)+3	$(1+1)^2$	6	1/1	9	$(4^2-10)+2$	7	2	3
3	2	8	6	7	$(2^2+2^2)-28/7$	$\sqrt{81}$	5	1
$13^2-(8x2x10)$	1	7	2	3	5	(7x3)-(5x3)	4	8
$(14x3)-(10x2^2)$	(42/14)+2	1	9	8	49/7	4	3	6
4	8	3	5	[(48/16)-1]+(51/17)	2^2-2	1	59-52	9
2	6	9	3	$(2^2/2)+(2^2/2)$	1	5	8	2
6	5^2-22	4	7	(32.5x2)-(15.75x4)	9	8	(23x2)-45	5
1	(36/12)+4	$(2^2/2)$	$8^2-(14x4)$	5	6	3	36/4	8/2
8	9	5	3^2-5	1	3	2	$\sqrt{36}$	7

239. Envelope Numbering

SOLUTIONS

240. Tent House

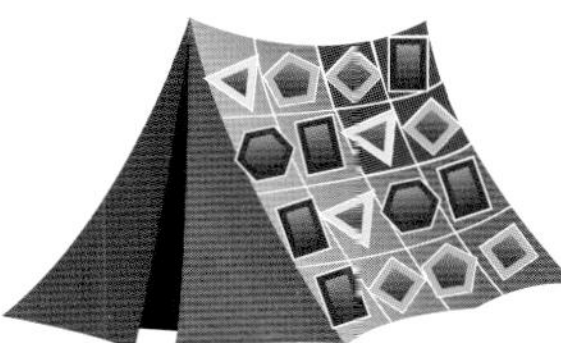

Answer: (20+10+10+16)/4=14

241. Rainy Day

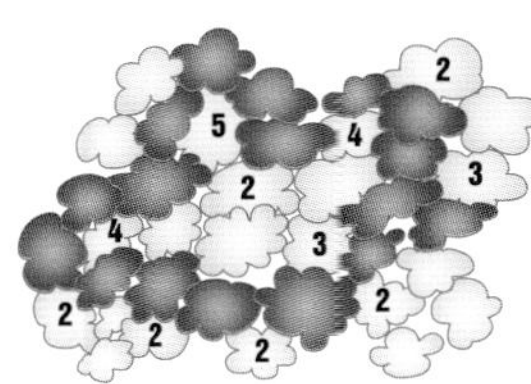

242. Gaming Time

Answer: A and D

243. Number the Mitten

C >	B	A	D
A	D	B	C
B	C <	D	A
D	A	C >	B

244. Arrange the Glasses

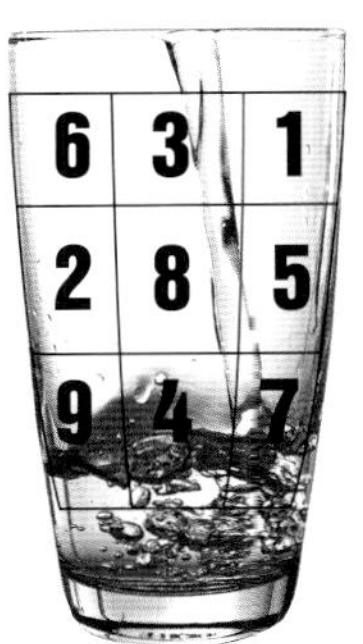

245. Hide and Seek

246. Diamond View

Answer: A

247. Double your Money

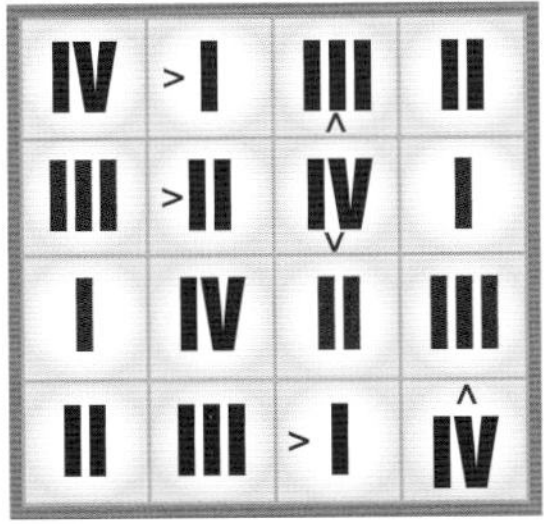

IV > I III II
III > II IV I
I IV II III
II III > I IV

248. Something Fishy!

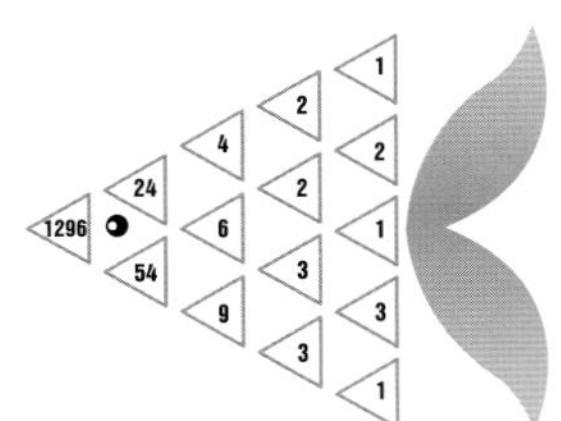

249. Santa Caps

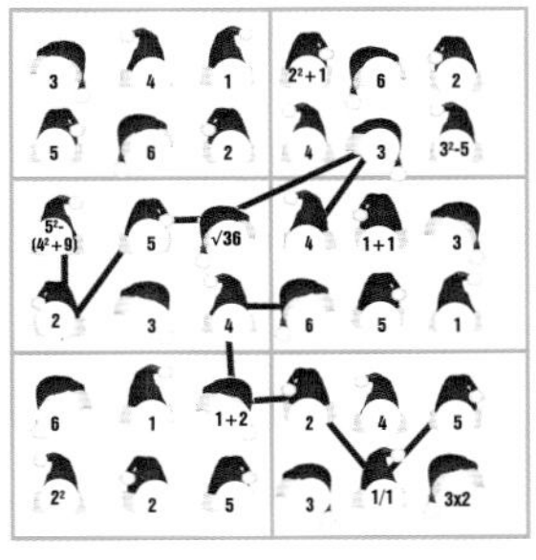

250. Arrange Sally's Wardrobe

1	4	13	11	23
10	24	21	30	28
16	41	26	40	39
43	45	48	50	47
29	7	17	46	27
34	42	14	31	19
37	20	35	8	44
32	3	25	6	18
36	49	38	15	22
33	12	9	5	2

251. Puzzling Necklace

Answer: E, R, A, S, T

252. Show the Shapes

Answer: Circle, Triangle, Hexagon, Rectangle, Square

253. Number Sorting

3	< 8	2	7	< 9	5	< 6	4	1
9	4	6	8	1	2	3	5	7
1	7	5	6	4 >	3	8	9	2
5	9	8	2	7	4	1	3 <	6
7	2	3	1	6	9	4	8	5
4	6	1	5 >	3	8 >	7	2	9
6 >	5	9	3	< 8	7	2 >	1	4
2	3	7	> 4	5	1	9	6	8
8	1	4	9	> 2	6	5	7	3

254. Look Out!

Answer: (178–94)+5=89

255. Flowchart Symbols

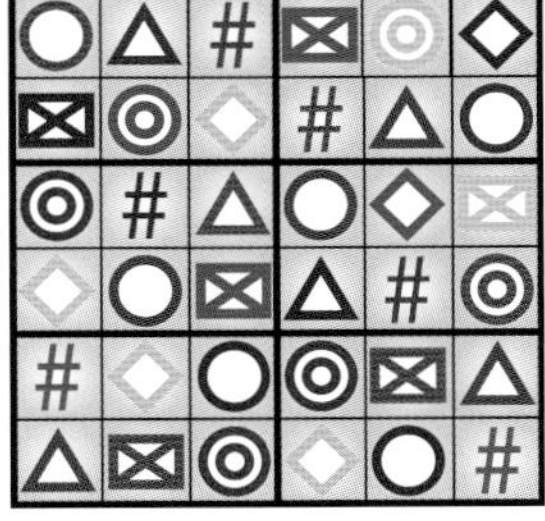

256. Picture Perfect

257. Object Maze

258. Puzzling Letters

B	A	D	C
C	D	B	A
D	C	A	B
A	B	C	D

SOLUTIONS

259. Filling Squares

2	1^2	$(3\times2)-2$ ∨	3
$\sqrt{4+1}$ <	4	2	$2-1$ ∧
$(4\times3)-8$ ∨	3 >	1	2
1 <	2	3 <	4

260. Confusing Circles

Answer: B

Every alternate piece of the pie chart has a colored tip.

261. Puzzling Square

XVI	XXV	XLVIII	XXXVI
IX	LXXII	VIII	XXXV
LVI	XX	LXX	XXVII
LXV	XXI	XLVIII	XXVIII
XXXII	L	XLVIII	XVIII

Answer: $12+5+7=24$

262. Number the Balloons

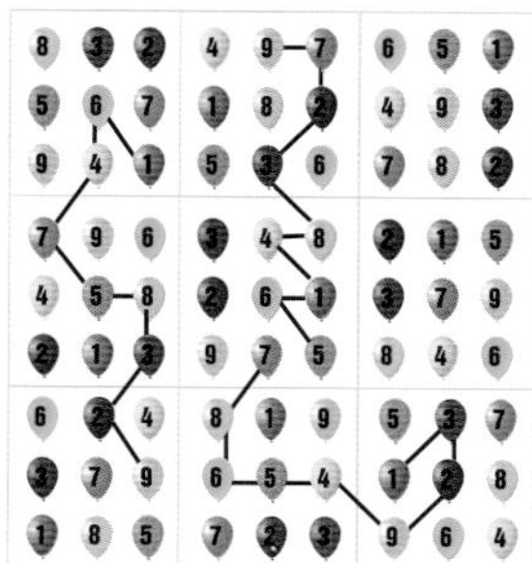

263. Color and Multiply

Answer:
Red=17.6
Green=15.2
Cream=67.2

264. Mystifying Mouse Pad

Answer: B

265. Pie Chart

Answer: 38

Logic: $4\times2=8$

$9\times2=18$

$19\times2=38$

$39\times2=78$

266. Time Setting

Answer: $(3+6)\times8=72$

267. Game Time

A	D	C	B	E	F
B	E	F	D	A	C
D	F	E	A	C	B
C	A	B	E	F	D
E	C	D	F	B	A
F	B	A	C	D	E

268. Number the Letters

Logic: E=5, C=3, A=1

$5+3+3+1=12$

and $12^2=144$

269. Number Game

270. Spider Web

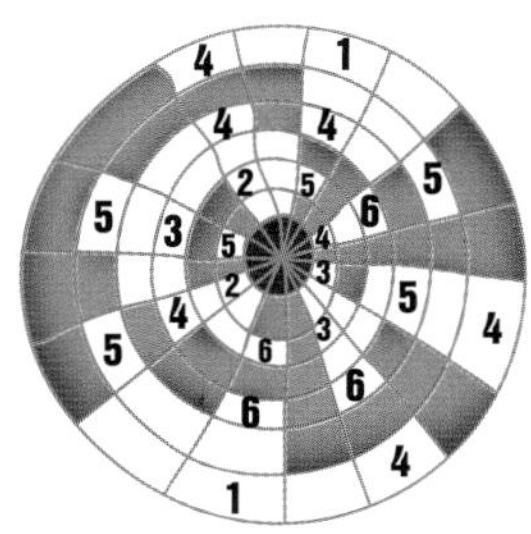

271. Colorful Wall

Answer:
Red=20%
Blue=11.11%
Green=11.11%
Cream=57.78%

272. Equation Time

Answer:

$(26+34)/5=12$

273. Looking from the Top

Answer: F

274. Dance Dance!

275. Number the Duckling

Answer: 43

Logic: $47-6=41$

$41+2=43$

$43-6=37$

$37+2=39$

276. Number the Dart Board

Answer: Outer circle: 4; Inner circle: 3

Logic: $9-4=5$

$7-4=3$

277. Show me the Honey!

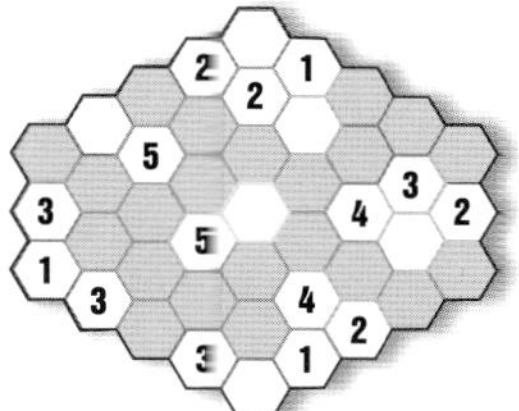

278. Mug Maze

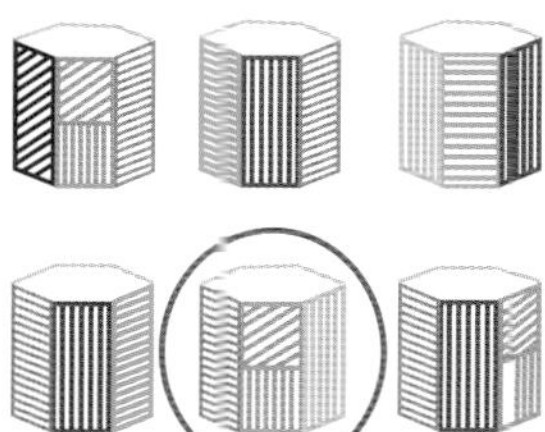

279. Fall Leaves

280. Fruit Frolic

3	7	5	2	4	21
4	4	2	3	3	16
7	7	2	2	5	23
5	7	2	7	7	28
3	2	7	3	5	20
22	27	18	17	24	

SOLUTIONS

281. Color the Ball

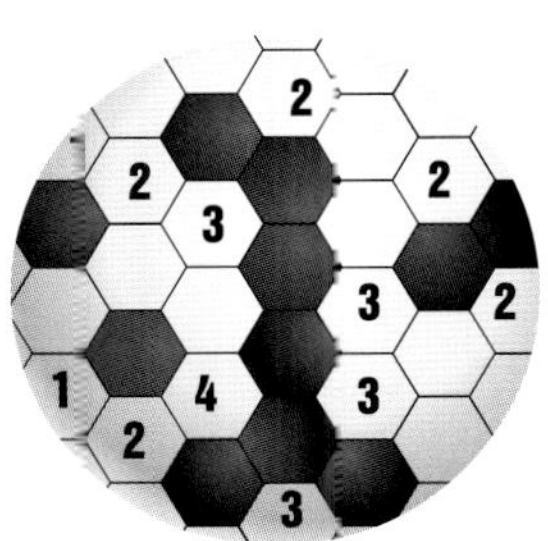

282. Counting Money

5^2-4^2-1	2	30/6	4 >	3
4	1 <	2	3 <	5
$(2\times2)-1$ <	4	3	$\sqrt{36}-1$	1 ∧
5 ∨	27–24	4	1	1^2+1^2
3	∧ 5	1 <	2 <	$(1+1)^2$

283. Number Juggler

Answer:
(7×6)+(3×4)=54

284. Tea Cup Set

Answer: B

Logic: The cups are three patterns. Each row has one cup of each pattern in it. In the third row the cup with the same pattern as cup B is missing

285. Helping Hands

286. Fix the Screen

287. Puzzling Patterns

288. Money, Money, Money

289. Pyramid Puzzle

290. Gem Search

Answer:
8×4=32
4×4=16
12×5=60
Avg of 32, 16, and 60 is 36.

291. Flower Placement

Answer: A

292. Mysterious Board

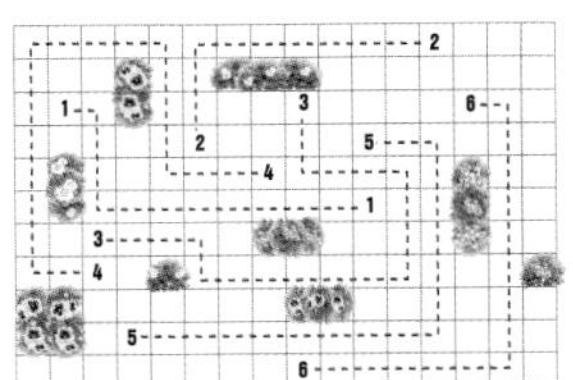

293. Horse Race

Answer:
(49/7) + 13 = 20

294. Unfold the Numbers

1	6	3	6	16
1	1	6	1	9
3	6	6	3	18
3	6	9	3	21
8	19	24	13	

295. Boggling Boxes

Answer: D

Logic: Total of first two numbers in a row is displayed as the third number. Also, all total values are odd numbers.

296. Sharing Happiness

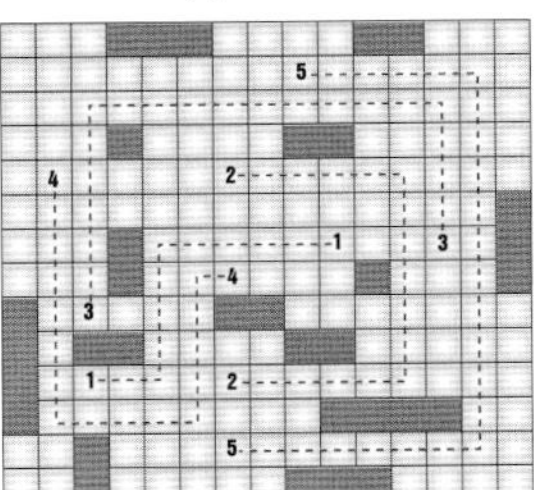

297. Missing Books

SOLUTIONS

298. Tricky Triangles

Answer: B

299. Tire Numbers

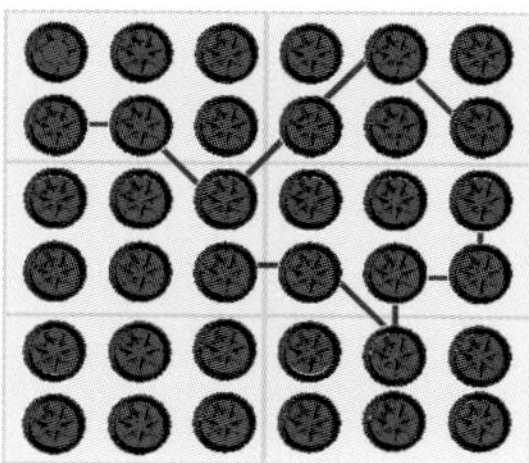

300. Flower Pot Mystery

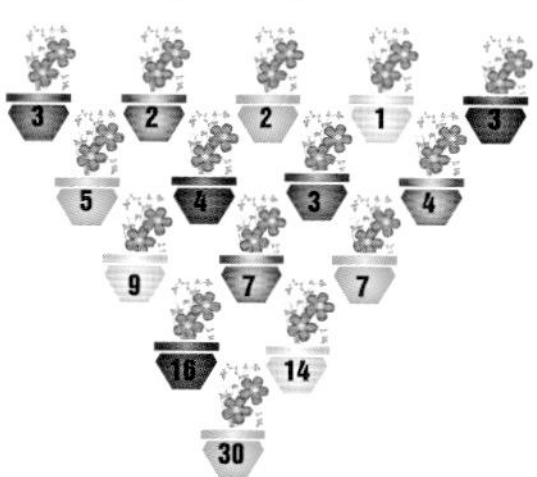

301. Tricky Truck

Answer:
[(3×4)+4] +
[(3×2)+4] +
[(6×2)+4] +
[(5×1)+5] +
[(2×6)+4] = 68

302. Free Coffee

303. Number Stumper

1	5 >	4	2	3 ^	6
2 ^	6	3 <	5	4	1
4	1	2	3 <	6	5 v
5	> 3	6 v	4	> 1	2
6	4	5 v	1	2	3
3	> 2	1	6	^ 5	> 4

304. Tulip Teaser

Answer:
(92–7)+43=128

305. Hexagon Maze

Answer: D

Logic: The blue hexagon is placed in hexagon in the same location for all the boxes. Also, the background is blue for the box to the right of the purple hexagon.

306. Number Relation

307. Zoo Entry Discount

F	C	E	B	D	A
A	B	D	F	C	E
B	E	F	D	A	C
D	A	C	E	F	B
E	D	A	C	B	F
C	F	B	A	E	D

308. Find the Flag!

309. Whistle Blowing

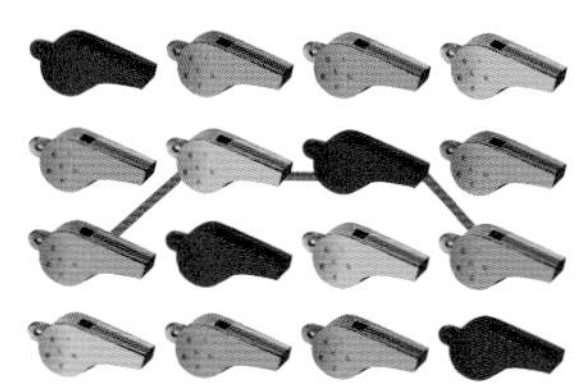

310. Shade the Blocks

Logic: 3+5=8
5+4=9
2+3=5
8+9+5=22

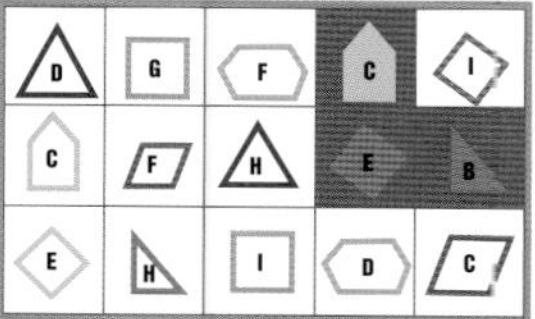

311. Shading Time

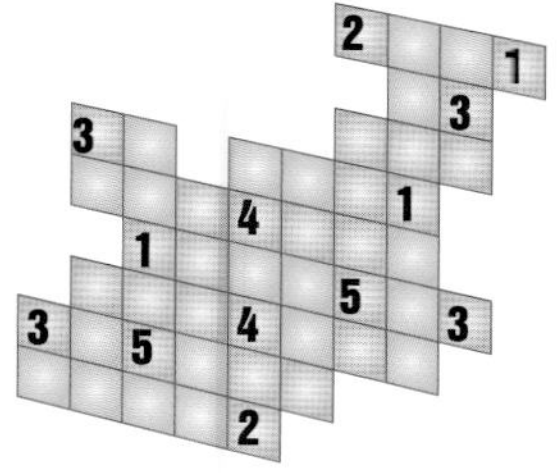

312. Sudoku Stumper

VI	VIII	V	II	III	I	IV v	VII
VII	IV >	III	I	V	< VI	II	VIII
III	I	VII >	IV	VIII	II ^	V v	VI
II	V	VIII	VI <	VII	IV	III	I
I	III	< IV	V	VI	VII <	VIII	II
VIII	VI ^	II	VII	IV	< V	I	III
IV	VII	I	III	II	VIII	VI >	^ V
V >	II	VI	VIII	I	III	VII	> IV

313. The Drugstore

SOLUTIONS

314. Leaves and Numbers

Answer: $5+6-7=4$ and $4^2=16$

315. Missing Stationery

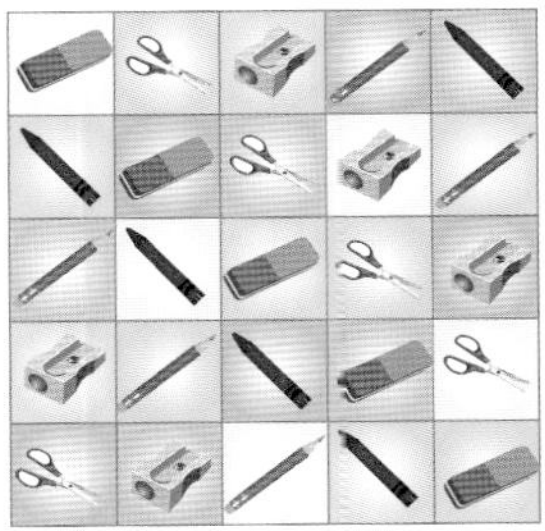

316. Brain Boggle

Answer: C
Logic: All numbers belong to Fibonacci series.

317. Flower Power

Answer: 32

Logic: $3^2+3=12$
$5^2+7=32$
$7^2+11=60$

318. Roaring Races

C	B	D	A	E	F
E	A	F	B	D	C
D	E	C	F	A	B
A	F	B	E	C	D
B	C	A	D	F	E
F	D	E	C	B	A

319. Bird Watching

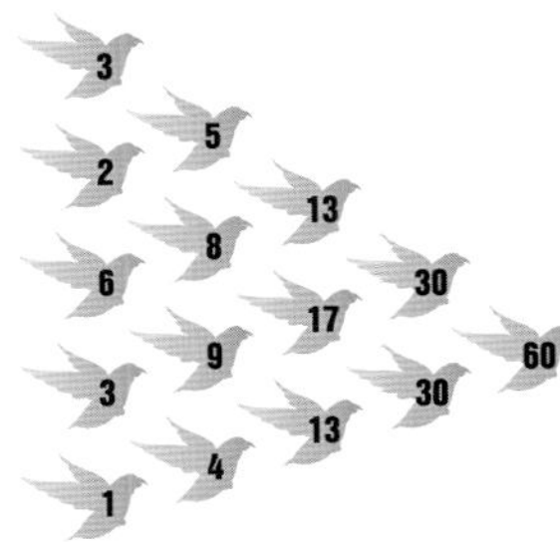

320. Boat Logic

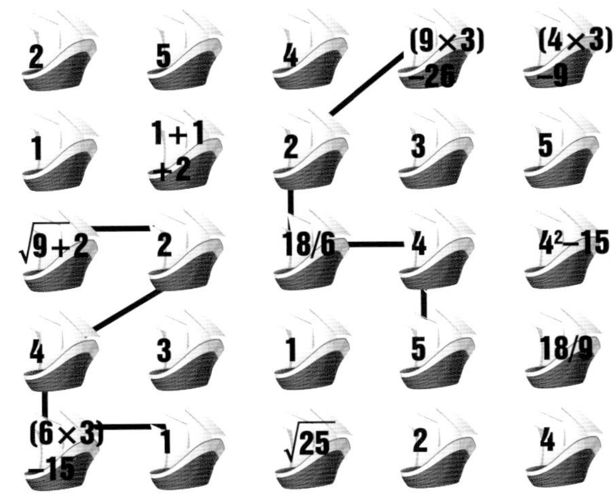

321. Equation Time

Answer: $(12\times4)/3=16$

322. All Packed Up

Logic: $6+3=9$
$7+4=11$; $6+4=10$
$3+4=7$; $5+3=8$
$9+11+10+7+8=45$

323. Coloring Fun

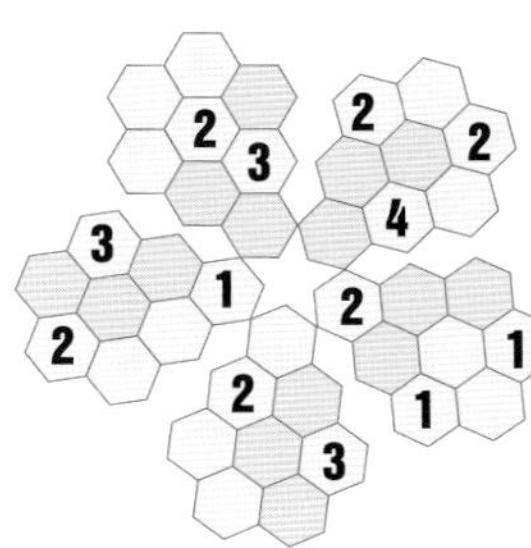

324. Dolphin Frolic

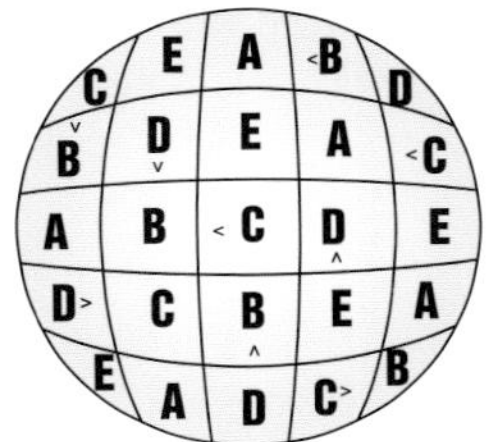

325. Remote Equation

Answer: $7\times(5+3)=56$

326. Skyscraper Teaser

Answer: $6+3=9$
$1+5=6$
$7+4=11$
$9+6+11=26$

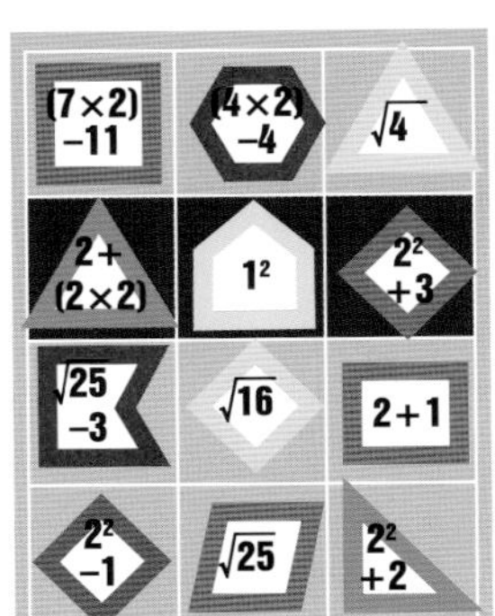

327. Dog House

328. Fruit Confusion

F	B	E	G	A	H	C	D
D	H	A	C	F	B	G	E
A	C	D	H	G	E	F	B
G	E	F	B	H	C	D	A
H	G	B	D	C	A	E	F
E	A	C	F	B	D	H	G
C	D	G	A	E	F	B	H
B	F	H	E	D	G	A	C

329. Shape Shuffle

330. Action!

II	IV	V	III	I	VII	VI	IX	VIII
VIII	VI	IX	VI	II	V	VII	I	III
III	I	VII	VIII	VI	IX	IV	II	V
I	V	VI	VII	IV	III	II	VIII	IV
IV	IX	II	V	VIII	I	III	VII	VI
VII	III	VIII	VI	IX	II	V	IV	I
IX	VII	IV	I	V	VI	VIII	III	II
VI	VIII	I	II	III	IV	IX	V	VII
V	II	III	IX	VII	VIII	I	VI	IV

SOLUTIONS

331. Plate Jumble

Logic:
(4+6) + (5+4) + (4+3) + (2+4) + (2+4) + (7+3) = 48
Average = 48/6 = 8

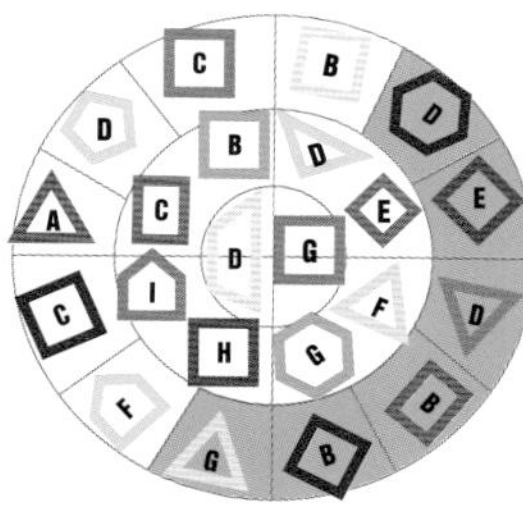

332. Find the Crack

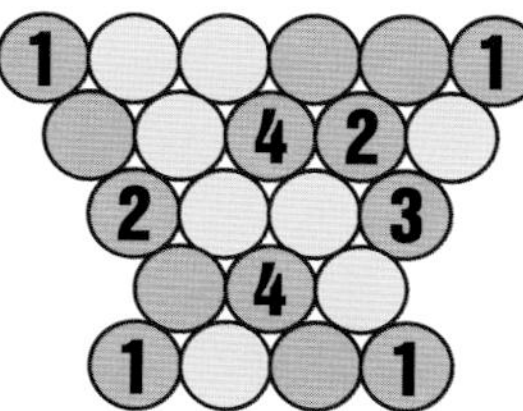

333. Grape Count

Answer:
18×(42–30)=216

334. Spot the Difference

335. Discount Delights!

Answer: 3125
$2^2=4$
$3^3=27$
$5^5=3125$

336. Circle Dilemma

Answer: D

337. Can Craze

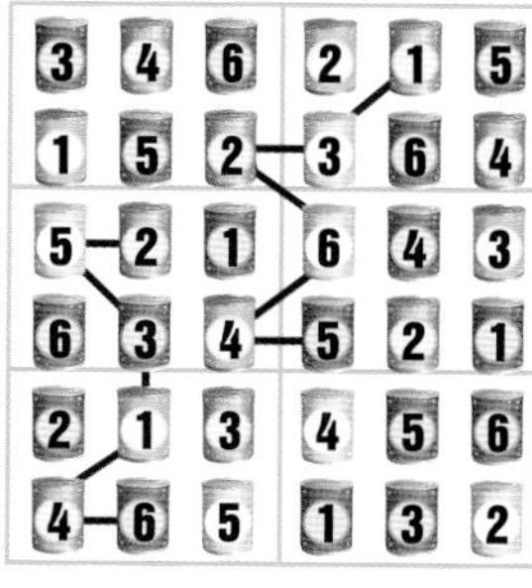

338. Heart Search

339. Totaling Shapes

Answer:
(24/4) + (18/6) + (8/4) + (20/4) = 16

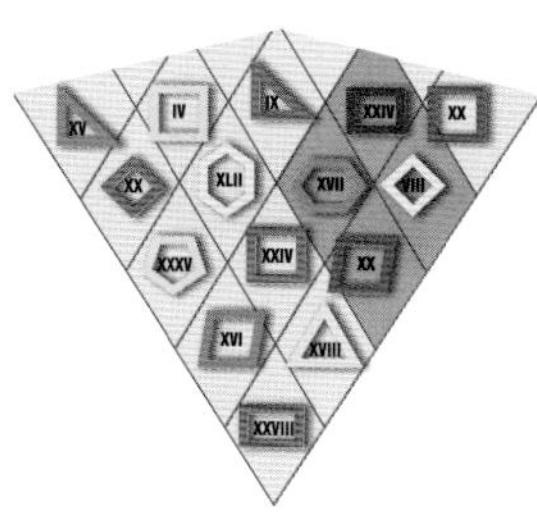

340. Free the Giraffe

Answer:
(27–5)×(13–2)=242

341. Baffling Boxes

Answer: 7

Logic: For the last box: 9+2+1+4=16 and 1+6=7

342. Four by Four

1	2	3	4
3	4	(5×2)–9	√4
2	√16–1	4	1
4	1	(8×2)–14	3

343. Shining Star

344. Beaker Seeker

Answer: (3×5) + (4×4) + (1×4) = 35

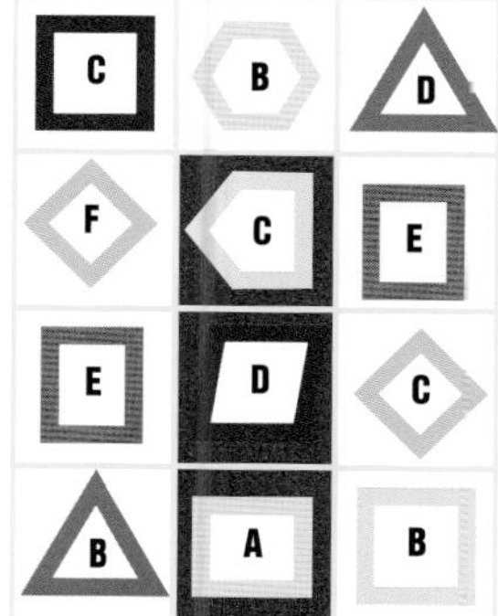

345. Elephant Equation

Answer:
(54–23)×6=186

346. Unfold the Picture

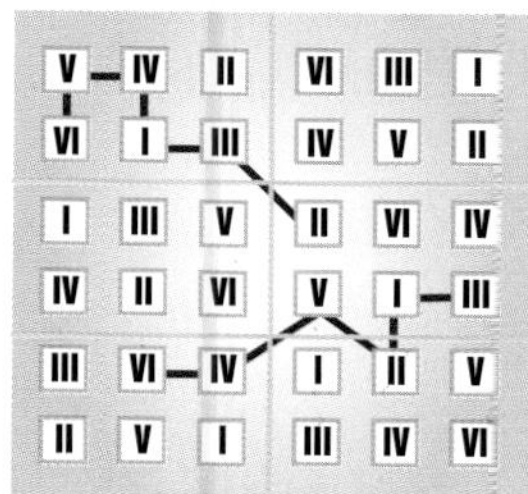

347. Compound Clouds

SOLUTIONS

348. Color the Pattern

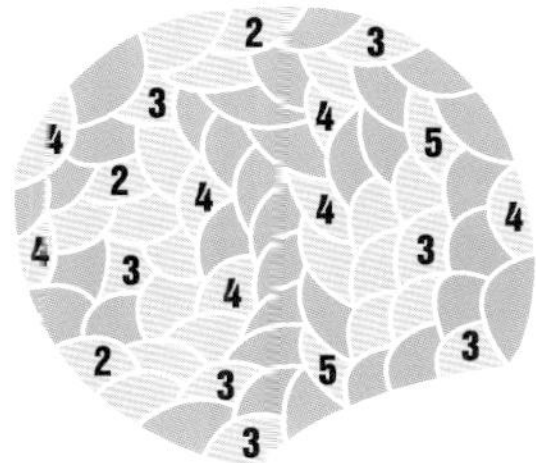

349. Art Decor

Answer: If we look at every alternate circle from left to right, these are in descending order. Starting from second circle 6; every alternate circle is - 6, 5, 4. So starting from circle one -10, every alternate number should be 10, 9, 8. So the missing number is 8.

350. Addition and Subtraction

Answer:
5–3=2
7–4=3
2+3=5

351. Number Game

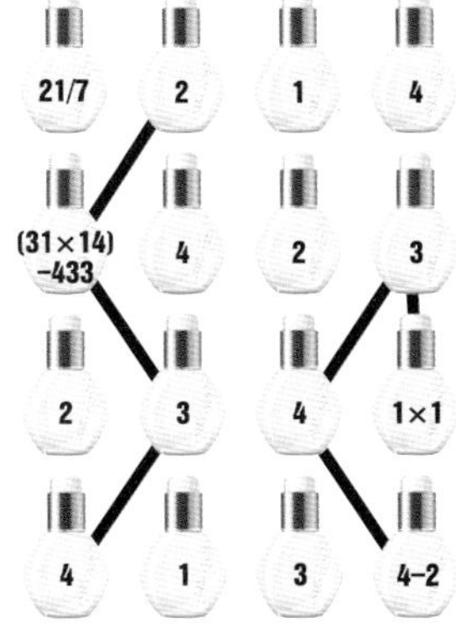

352. Number Calculations

Answer:
(5/0)+[(4–3)×(2+1)]–(9–7)=1

353. Picture Comparison

354. Unfold the Sum

Answer:
3+4=7
4+6=10
5+3=8
6+4=10
7+10+8+10=35

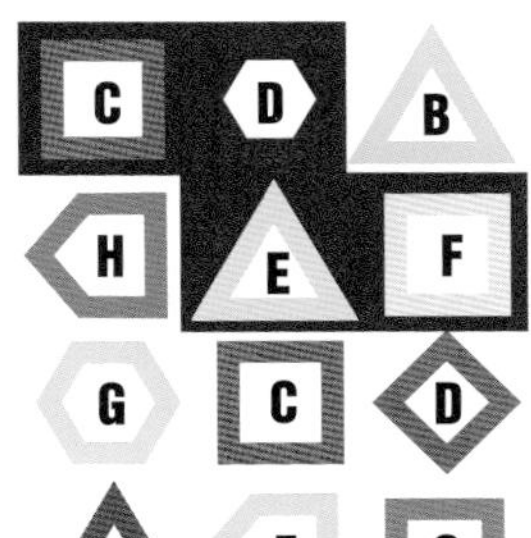

355. Number the Tomatoes

SOLUTIONS

356. Fix It!

					3
	4		5		
					2
3		5			
				6	
2		6			
					4
3		4		2	

357. Mind Twister

Answer: D

Logic: Division of all opposite corners and opposite middle squares results in the center number.
Example for first cube:
36/4=9
81/9=9
45/5=9
27/3=9

358. Television Game

Answer:
(12×5×16)–906=54

359. Strawberry Teaser

3 >	9–7	4 v	4^2–15
1 ^	9–5	3	2
4	1	< 2	^ 24/8
2^2–2 <	3	1	4

360. Parking Conundrum

4	2	5	1	3
3	1	4	2	5
1	5	3	4	2
2	3	1	5	4
5	4	2	3	1

361. On the Bus

	2		3	
3		4		
				2
3		6		
				3
4		5		

362. Sandra's Shoe Challenge

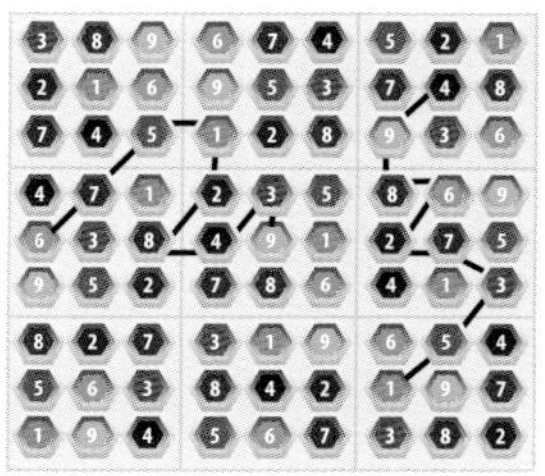

363. Fruit Placement

364. Letter Hunt

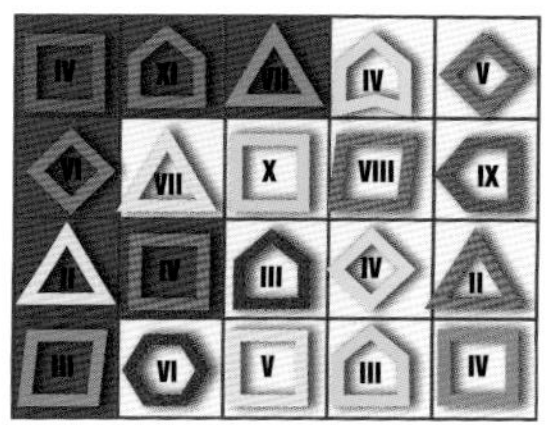

Hidden letter F

Logic:
4×4=16
11×5=55
7×3=21
6×4=24
2×3=6
4×4=16
3×4=12

365. Wildlife Differences